D = Desert District
C = Coastal District
R = River District
S = Salton District

D0883759

NEVADA

INYO

Inyo Mtns.

Panamint Mtns.

SAN

BERNARDINO

Kingston Mtns.

Clark Mtn.

New York Mtns.

Providence Mtns.

Granite Mtns.

ARIZONA

Colorado

San Bernardino Mtns.

Little San Bernardino Mtns.

San Jacinto Mtns.

Santa Rosa Mtns.

Eagle Mtns.

RIVERSIDE

Salton Sea

Mt. Palomar

Cuyamaca Mtns.

SAN

DIEGO

SAN DIEGO

Laguna Mtns.

IMPERIAL

R.

MEXICO

114°

Birds of Southern California
Status and Distribution

Birds of Southern California
Status and Distribution

by Kimball Garrett
and
Jon Dunn

Illustrations by Lee Jones

Los Angeles Audubon Society

Aerial maps by Aerial Information Systems, Crestline, California

To JEAN BRANDT, who, as President of the
Los Angeles Audubon Society,
helped turn an abstract dream into a real book

TABLE OF CONTENTS

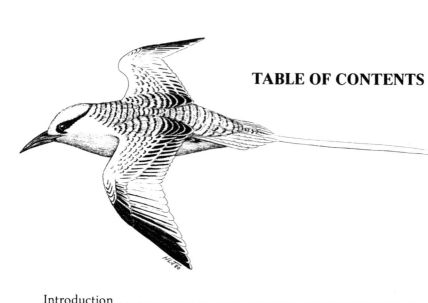

LIST OF ILLUSTRATIONS

INTRODUCTION

This book is intended to give the reader a concise summary of the distribution, abundance, and seasonal status of southern California's 500+ bird species. Simplified bar graphs of seasonal abundance indicate where and when a species may be expected. A text account for each species treats geographical and seasonal status in detail and contains information on ecological requirements, the status of selected subspecies, and specific unusual records. Accounts for introduced species, species of hypothetical occurrence, and species recorded from California only outside of the southern California region follow the main text.

We have placed much emphasis on *patterns* of occurrence in space and time, with less attention paid to minute geographical detail and exhaustive lists of records for each species and subspecies. *Birds of Southern California* is a "field guide" only by way of the distributional data it offers; we firmly believe that a knowledge of the geographical and seasonal distribution of bird species is a necessity for the development of proper identification skills. It is beyond the scope of this book to discuss morphological and behavioral characters aiding in field identification. In cases where frequent confusion has existed and past reports often pertain to misidentifications the problems of field identification are briefly stated. We discount, for example, numerous winter records of Black-chinned Hummingbirds and Swainson's Thrush (species known, in fact, to be accidental in southern California at this season) and mention the likely basis for such frequent misidentifications. This book is also not a bird-finding guide *per se*. We generally do not attempt to give detailed instructions for finding particular species. It is our belief that, armed with a knowledge of the distribution, seasonal status, and ecological requirements of a bird species, the diligent observer will usually be successful in locating that species. Bird-finding guides which offer only meticulous instructions for reaching sites where a species is known to occur are counterproductive because they do not encourage the filling of gaps in our knowledge of bird distribution. We have pointed out such gaps where we feel they exist, making occasional calls through the text for additional study.

The information provided will assist the birdwatcher in determining how his or her observations are significant. Readers are encouraged to carefully record and document their observations so that our information on the region's birdlife may be supplemented and, when necessary, corrected. The format adopted here will hopefully prove useful not only to the birder, but to students and enthusiasts of the natural world in general, including biologists who may work with wild birds, environmental consultants, and teachers wishing to acquaint students with the diversity and beauty of California's natural world.

Abbreviations Used In The Text

Abbreviations have generally been kept at a minimum, but the following ones have been employed throughout the text:

County names:
  IMP = Imperial
  INY = Inyo
  KRN = Kern
  LA = Los Angeles
  MNO = Mono
  ORA = Orange
  RIV = Riverside

SBA = Santa Barbara
SBE = San Bernardino
SD = San Diego
SLO = San Luis Obispo
VEN = Ventura
Other abbreviations:
ad. = adult
AB = American Birds
AFB = Air Force Base
AFN = Audubon Field Notes
AZ = Arizona
CBRC = California Bird Records Committee
ck. = creek
Co(s) = county(ies)
e. = east(ern)
I(s). = island(s)
imm. = immature
juv. = juvenile
L. = lake
Mtn(s). = mountain(s)
n. = north(ern)
ne = northeast(ern)
NESS = north end of the Salton Sea
nr. = near
NV = Nevada
nw = northwest(ern)
NWR = National Wildlife Refuge
R. = river
Res. = reservoir
s. = south(ern)
se = southeast(ern)
SESS = south end of the Salton Sea
sw = southwest(ern)
vic. = vicinity
w. = west(ern)

Virtually all place names mentioned in the text may be located on standard road maps of the southern California region. For this reason, we have not provided a gazetteer. We have, however, given the county name (using standard abbreviations) for each locality upon its first mention in each species account.

3

GEOGRAPHICAL SCOPE

The region encompassed by *Birds of Southern California* is southern California south of the Central (San Joaquin) Valley and the Sierra Nevada, and inclusive of the Owens Valley and the White Mountains east of the Sierra Nevada. This essentially corresponds to the Southern Pacific Coast Region as defined in the National Audubon Society publication *American Birds*.

All of the following counties lie totally within the region: Coastal — San Luis Obispo, Santa Barbara, Ventura, Los Angeles, Orange, and San Diego; Interior — San Bernardino, Riverside, and Imperial.

Portions of Kern, Inyo, and Mono Counties are also included. The areas covered for each are as follows: **Kern** — The eastern and southern portions of the county (biologically related to the Mohave Desert), the Tehachapi and Piute Mtns. and Mt. Pinos and its surrounding peaks (but not the Greenhorn Mtns. which are adjacent to the Sierra Nevada, with a related biota), and the saltbush desert areas which comprise the western part of the county. Excluded is the floor of the San Joaquin Valley (largely converted to agriculture) lying east of California Highway 33 and north of the 35th parallel. Also excluded is the Kern River basin and, in the northeastern part of the county, the southern flank of the Sierra Nevada (above the 1500m contour). **Inyo** — Only the eastern escarpment of the Sierra Nevada (above the 1500m contour) in the extreme western part of the county is excluded. **Mono** — The White Mtns., and, at their eastern base, the Fish Lake Valley. Thus, only that portion of the county east of U.S. Highway 6 is included.

The northern boundary outlined above essentially corresponds to the southern boundary adopted by McCaskie *et al* in *Birds of Northern California* (see literature section). However, large portions of Kern County are excluded from that work and the present one. We have, therefore, mentioned a number of significant records from that area within this text.

The maps located on the inside cover and on pages 32-36 show the boundaries of the region, as well as localities and geographical features frequently mentioned in the text.

METHODS

The distributional data in this work is largely drawn from the Southern Pacific Coast Region report in *American Birds*, edited since 1963 by Guy McCaskie, and from the unpublished field notes of the authors and those generously supplied by numerous other field ornithologists. The framework upon which we have based our endeavor is the classic *Distribution of the Birds of California* by Joseph Grinnell and Alden H. Miller, published in 1944. All pertinent ornithological literature since the publication of that work has been examined. In addition, we have examined the collections in the following museums: University of California at Los Angeles; Los Angeles County Museum of Natural History; San Diego Natural History Museum; San Bernardino County Museum; and Western Foundation of Vertebrate Zoology.

The bulk of our knowledge of the status of vagrants and rarer migrants has been generated since the early 1960s by both amateur and professional field ornithologists. Most of these records are not supported by specimens or published details, but to ignore them would be to paint a very incomplete picture of California ornithology today. Details of many of these records are on file with the California Bird Records Committee of the Western Field Ornithologists. In virtually every case details of records have been examined either by the authors, or by the *American Birds* regional editor. In many cases we have elected not to include records published in *American Birds* or its predecessor, *Audubon Field Notes*, or elsewhere because doubts as to their validity have arisen after their publication. It should be noted that reliability in *American Birds/Audubon Field Notes* has greatly increased over the years. The authors are, of course, responsible for the acceptance or rejection of published records; we have undoubtedly overlooked or wrongly rejected valid records but feel that, by this caution, suspicious or invalid records have not been perpetuated.

It is unfortunate that the fervor with which vagrants and rarer migrants are sought has not been vented equally on our breeding species and regular passage migrants. While Grinnell and Miller's 1944 book evinced a near-complete ignorance of the occurrence of vagrants in California, nevertheless it contained nearly the total of our present-day knowledge of the distribution and habitat preferences of our commoner species and their component subspecies. Further advances have come partly from material published in *American Birds* and elsewhere in the ornithological literature, but also largely from individual workers who have devoted considerable energy to the assessment of bird distributions and populations in specific sectors of the region. Mentioned in the acknowledgements are some of these individuals and their areas of expertise. Countless others have supplied much information by personal communication.

We have elected to follow one departure from standard distributional methodology: literature citations for specific records have been omitted. Inclusion of citations would prohibitively expand the length of this work and seriously detract from its readibility. We have occasionally included references to expanded accounts of noteworthy records, to distributional summaries for particular species, and to taxonomic works of particular relevance. Virtually all records included since 1960 have been published in *American Birds/Audubon Field Notes* and can be referenced from the date given. Researchers interested in specific citations for records not published in *American Birds/Audubon Field Notes* will be supplied, upon request to the authors through the Los Angeles Audubon Society, a mimeographed listing of such citations.

Records through August 1980 are included in the main text. An addendum, page 387, lists later records of special significance up to press time.

There is no "senior" author of this work; the roles of each author were somewhat different, but certainly equal. Dunn took primary responsibility for researching and synthesis of records, while the introductory material and writing was primarily Garrett's responsibility.

ACKNOWLEDGEMENTS

Virtually every active field ornithologist in California has contributed data, suggestions, or criticism during the evolution of this book. The authors express their gratitude to those who unearthed dates, breeding localities, rarity descriptions, or other important information to ensure some semblance of completeness of the work. Our foremost thanks surely go to the reviewers who labored endlessly over an early draft of the manuscript. Guy McCaskie's extensive knowledge of southern California's birds, and his generosity in sharing his treasury of records, made the writing of a book of this scope possible; our sincerest thanks go to this important figure of California field ornithology. Richard Erickson and Richard Webster attacked a review draft of the manuscript with fine-toothed comb, high-powered binoculars, and a gifted outlook on the science of ornithology and the art of birdwatching. The evolution of the text owes much to these two reviewers. Webster additionally agreed to undertake the arduous task of editing an entire late draft of the manuscript, and is largely responsible for pulling together an often untidy collection of thoughts and facts. The invaluable assistance of the following reviewers is also deeply appreciated: Louis Bevier, Lee Jones, Paul Lehman, Van Remsen, Kenneth Rosenberg, Rich Stallcup, and Philip Unitt. Unitt provided important information from San Diego County and added suggestions and cautions concerning taxonomy, subspecies treatment, and racial migratory patterns. Jones kindly made available his extensive notes on the birds of the California Channel Islands. Lehman and Bevier, along with Richard Webster, brought the authors up to date on bird distribution in the northern coastal part of the region. Remsen, along with Steve Cardiff, shared an extensive knowledge of the California deserts, particularly the eastern Mohave Desert. Stallcup was his customary brilliant and helpful self. Kenneth Rosenberg, along with Gary Rosenberg, Scott Terrill, and others, was invaluable in the development of our treatment of the Colorado River Valley.

Our thanks also go to the following individuals for supplying information and conversation: Jon Atwood, Elizabeth Copper, Robert Copper, Eugene Cardiff, Eugene Eisenmann, Gilbert Grant, Phil Henderson, Alton Higgons, Thomas Howell, Kenn Kaufman, Paul Kelly, Lloyd Kiff, John Luther, Gary Page, Will Russell, Chuck Sexton, Hal and Nancy Spear, Lynne Stenzel, and Glenn Walsberg.

The idea for this book grew out of early discussions with Sandy Wohlgemuth, Jerry Maisel, Jean Brandt, Jim Clements, and, especially, Barry and Terry Clark. As President of the Los Angeles Audubon Society, Jean Brandt was particularly helpful and supportive in seeing this project through to completion.

We are very grateful to Fred Heath, who worked hard to oversee virtually every phase of the production of the book. Our hearty thanks also go to Bob and Roberta Shanman, who proofread and indexed the manuscript and helped in countless other ways. The cooperation and hard work of John Parque (The Artisan Press), Fran Jessee and Shellie Fletcher turned the manuscript into a book. Virtually the entire board of the Los Angeles Audubon Society became involved in various aspects of planning and production of the book; our thanks go to each of these persons.

The cover photograph was kindly offered by one of the West's foremost bird photographers, Herb Clarke. The attractive line drawings and the maps on the inside covers are the work of Lee Jones, whose many talents have embraced nearly every aspect of this book (including the dust jacket design). The final species range maps are the work of Tom Frillman, to whom we are grateful. We also are grateful to John Menke and Alan Kilgore of Aerial Information Systems for providing the detailed map of the region found early in the text.

Special thanks go to the following persons who provided support, food, drink, shelter, company, and/or sanity to the authors during the long production of this book: Elizabeth Copper, Lloyd and Priscilla Dunn, Lewis and Jean Garrett, Patricia Glatt, Thomas Howell, and Scarlette Oshima.

LITERATURE

Growing regiments of birdwatchers and ornithologists have greatly enhanced our knowledge of southern California's birds since Robert L. Pyle's *Annotated Field List: Birds of Southern California* (published by the Los Angeles Audubon Society in 1953) was revised in 1961 by Arnold Small. An alarming rate of habitat loss and alteration has affected many bird species, further rendering this older publication out-of-date. Small's *The Birds of California* (1974; paperbound edition with revisions in 1975) has incorporated considerable recent information and today constitutes the best popular single-volume reference dealing with the state's avifauna; its sections on California's habitats for birds will be very useful to readers of the present work. It remains, however, that Grinnell and Miller's *Distribution of the Birds of California* (1944) provides the best detailed analysis of the distribution and habitat preferences of California's birds. This publication is out of print and thus not readily available to the amateur ornithologist, but a perusal of its pages will reveal to the reader just how accurate and complete was the authors' assessment of the distributional ecology of California's avifauna. An important adjunct is Miller's 1951 paper "The analysis of the distribution of the birds of California"; it contains a classification of habitats and bird communities and is a valuable extension of Grinnell and Miller's monumental work.

Grinnell and Miller incorporated published works prior to the 1940s. Worthy of mention in itself, however, is George Willett's 1933 work, "A revised list of the birds of southwestern California" and its progenitor, "Birds of the Pacific slope of southern California" (Willett 1912). Seriously out of date, these works are still informative and well-written, and constitute the most ambitious earlier treatment of the birds of southern California. We have relied heavily on the works of Willett, Grinnell, and Miller in assessing historical changes in the region's avifauna.

Since the publication of *The Distribution of the Birds of California*, work on the distribution and taxonomy of southern California birds has been scattered in the ornithological literature, notably in *The Condor* (the journal of the Cooper Ornithological Society) and the publications of other ornithological societies, natural history museums, and universities. It is beyond the scope of the present work to provide a bibliography of such works. Of note, however, are two journals which regularly contain valuable information on southern California birds. *Western Birds* (the journal of the Western Field Ornithologists) publishes a variety of papers based on field studies of California birds; additionally, it regularly publishes reports of the Western Field Ornithologists' California Bird Records Committee, a body charged with reviewing records of species unusual within the state. Summaries and details of the occurrence of vagrants and rare migrants are regularly published, providing an alternative to the often-unfeasible specimen supported documentation of unusual records. The Southern Pacific Coast Region report in *American Birds* (formerly *Audubon Field Notes*) reports distributional data, seasonal status, and population trends in southern California's resident species, transients, and vagrants. The regional reports in *American Birds* are the primary vehicle by which the observations of thousands of amateur field ornithologists are available as scientific record. The Los Angeles Audubon Society's publication, *The Western Tanager*, has regular reports on bird sightings in the region, as do the publications of numerous other local ornithological clubs.

Several recent and forthcoming works are particularly relevant to the student of southern California birdlife. *The Waterbirds of California* by Howard Cogswell (University of California Press, 1977) is a detailed treatment, largely in graphical and coded form, of waterbird distribution and habitat requirements throughout the state. A landbird companion volume is anticipated. *The Birds of Northern California, An Annotated Field List* by Guy McCaskie, Paul DeBenidictis, Richard Erickson, and Joseph Morlan (revised edition, 1979; published by the Golden Gate Audubon Society) can be regarded as complementing the present work, as it deals with most of the state of California not covered here. *The Birds of the Santa Barbara Region* by T. Nelson Metcalf has been updated and revised by Richard Webster, Paul Lehman, and Louis Bevier and retitled *The Birds of Santa Barbara and Ventura Counties* (1980; Santa Barbara

Museum of Natural History, Occasional Paper No. 10). This detailed treatment of an important center of southern California ornithology is a valuable adjunct to the present work. The occurrence and identification of vagrants is discussed in detail in *Rare Birds of the West Coast* by Don Roberson (1980; Woodcock Publications).

Numerous checklists exist at the regional or local level; they vary greatly in accuracy, but many are excellent and up to date. Exemplary are the *Field Checklist of the Birds of San Diego County* compiled by Guy McCaskie and the *L.A.A.S. Field List of the Birds of Los Angeles County* compiled by Jon Dunn and Lee Jones. Also compiled by Guy McCaskie is the *L.A.A.S. Field List of the Birds of California* (latest revision January 1978). Many refuges, sanctuaries, and parks provide checklists of birds recorded within their boundaries.

Bird-finding guides are particularly useful to beginning and visiting birdwatchers. Jim Lane's *Birders' Guide to Southern California* (latest revision 1979) contains well-planned loop trips for finding the more unusual or localized species. A quick summary of the status of each species is given. Regular articles on birding locations in southern California appear in the *Western Tanager*.

HLJ°0

TAXONOMY
AND
NOMENCLATURE

The American Ornithologists' Union (hereafter AOU) *Check-List of North American Birds* has been the standard North American taxonomic work upon which works such as *Birds of Southern California* are based. The Fifth Edition of the Check-List was published in 1957, with supplements appearing in 1973 and 1976 in *The Auk*. At this writing, work has been largely completed on a Sixth Edition (with publication anticipated in 1983). The Sixth Edition will incorporate some changes at the species level, numerous revisions at the generic level, and a highly altered sequence of families and of species within families to reflect current taxonomic thinking. Because of the extent of revision to be found in the Sixth Edition of the Check-List, the authors have elected to depart from the Fifth Edition taxonomic treatment in an attempt to produce a list which reflects current thinking and closely approaches the forthcoming AOU list. Our treatment of loons, grebes, tubenoses, pelicans and allies, herons, storks, waterfowl, and raptors is based partly on the Second Edition of Peters' *Check-List of Birds of the World, Volume One* (1979), edited by E. Mayr and G.W. Cottrell. Treatment of the Tyrannidae (tyrant flycatchers) is basically that of the other recently published volume of the Peters' Check-List (Volume Eight, 1979, edited by M.A. Traylor, Jr.). Treatment of the remaining families has been based partly on the *Reference List of the Birds of the World* by Morony, Bock, and Farrand (American Museum of Natural History, 1975). We are very grateful to T.R. Howell of the AOU Check-List Committee for advice on our taxonomic treatment.

Our aim is not to complicate the work with novel taxonomic treatments, but rather to stress to the reader that divergent taxonomic opinions exist and that ideas on avian systematics are constantly in flux. Brief notes concerning taxonomic matters will be found at the end of the species account when relevant.

English names employed conform, with minor changes, to those of the *American Birding Association Checklist: Birds of Continental United States and Canada* (1975, with supplements). Alternative English names are given in parentheses if they currently enjoy widespread and popular usage.

We have elected to deal selectively with subspecies, with subspecific treatment generally limited to forms which are sufficiently distinct morphologically for a body of distributional data based on sight records to have developed. Published treatments based on extensive analysis of specimens (notably Grinnell and Miller 1944) have been invaluable in supplementing and setting a foundation for field observations. The choice of forms treated largely reflects the authors' sphere of competence. Regrettably, we can shed little new light on the status of such fascinating polytypic species as the Horned Lark, Hermit Thrush, and Song Sparrow. We again stress that our subspecies treatment has been highly selective; *Birds of Southern California* is by no means a complete list of all subspecies occurring in the region. In many cases subspecies are considerably easier to identify in the field than forms which are indisputably considered "good" species. Birdwatchers should be aware of the magnitude of intraspecific variation and the forms it may take. Casual reporting of out-of-range forms based on average differences noted in the field cannot be encouraged.

SEASONAL MOVEMENTS IN SOUTHERN CALIFORNIA

Southern California's complex topography and varied habitats, combined with its latitudinal position between the tropics and the seasonally teeming arctic and boreal expanses, promote a complicated array of strategies of seasonal movements through and within the region. Some brief generalizations can be made concerning the complex patterns of bird migration through the region. The total magnitude of landbird migration is less than that experienced in the eastern part of the continent; migration is a protracted affair in the region, with some sort of migration taking place virtually throughout the year.

The earliest spring migrant landbirds (e.g Allen's Hummingbird and Rough-winged Swallow) may begin passing through the region in January. On the other hand, such typically late migrants as Willow Flycatcher and Swainson's Thrush are still moving northward through the region in early to mid-June, barely before such early fall migrants as Allen's and Rufous Hummingbirds begin to push southward through our area.

The spring migration of shorebirds is lengthy, but the peak period is April through mid-May (slightly later at the Salton Sea; these late birds may represent individuals of more southerly wintering origin). Non-breeding shorebirds of many species typically remain through the summer, and fall migration of shorebirds begins quite early (in late June for the earliest species, and by mid-to-late July for most of the rest. Waterfowl migration is not as marked as that of many other bird groups because many of the waterfowl species do not have large populations wintering to the south of the region. Most seabirds have marked migration peaks. In general, the northward spring migration of brant, scoters, loons, etc. takes place closer to shore and in a briefer time span than the fall migration, especially south of San Luis Obispo Co. Late March to mid-May is an excellent period to watch these seabirds migrating past coastal promontories, especially from Los Angeles Co. north. At this time, and into summer, flocks of Sooty Shearwaters numbering up to several hundred thousand individuals are routinely found off the coast.

Spring landbird migration is most pronounced at lower elevations, with the deserts and coastal woodlands being especially productive. Migration typically proceeds as a series of small "waves;" the largest waves of passerine migrants occur from late April through mid-May. Migration is skewed somewhat later in spring on the northern deserts, with large numbers of passerine migrants often present into early June. Arrivals of a given species will often be noted considerably later on the northern deserts than on the southern deserts.

In fall large numbers of hummingbirds and passerines migrate through the mountains, commencing in mid-July (or as early as mid-June in some hummingbirds). Again in fall, the coast and deserts are productive, although waves are generally of a smaller magnitude than in spring. Isolated desert oases, the immediate coast, and the Channel Islands are particularly favored areas for searching for fall migrants and vagrants (see below). Late fall migrants and stragglers sometimes occur through December (and even well into January); care should be taken in differentiating between these stragglers and truly wintering birds. For example, Warbling Vireos are frequently noted well into December, but there are very few records of birds spending the entire winter in the region.

Vagrants (lost individuals well outside their normal areas of residence and migration) are most frequently encountered late in the migration periods for the species involved, but may turn up at practically any time and place. In many ways, the pattern of occurence of vagrants is quite predictable; such patterns are discussed in the text for each vagrant species. Certain "vagrant traps" have come to be recognized, and bird-watchers devote an inordinate amount of attention to these areas. Such areas receive almost daily coverage during peak vagrant periods (mid-May to mid-June, and early September through early November) but are often ignored at other seasons. This type of observer bias should be kept in mind when the temporal span of records of a vagrant species is examined.

In the desert regions "oasis" situations are most productive for vagrants (and migrants in general). Patches of taller, denser vegetation, especially when water is present, can harbor large numbers of migrants. The northern desert oases generally tend to produce greater quantities of vagrants than the southern ones. Well-worked oases include Oasis, Mono Co.; Deep Springs, Scotty's Castle, Mesquite Springs, Stovepipe Wells, and Furnace Creek Ranch, Inyo Co.; Kelso, Ft. Piute, and Morongo Valley, San Bernardino Co.; Desert Center, Riverside Co.; and Brock Ranch, Imperial Co.

Coastal vagrant and migrant traps generally consist of isolated clumps of vegetation on coastal promontories or coastal plains. Such areas include: Morro Bay, San Luis Obispo Co.; Goleta and Carpinteria, Santa Barbara Co.; Oxnard Plain and Big Sycamore Canyon, Ventura Co.; Palos Verdes Peninsula, Los Angeles Co.; and Pt. Loma and the Tijuana River Valley, San Diego Co. The Channel Islands have also proved to consistently concentrate vagrants; the smaller, more barren islands (San Nicolas, Santa Barbara Is.) are especially good.

Migration patterns through the localities mentioned above are especially well-studied. Once again it is emphasized that the reader must bear in mind the forms of observer bias when examining records of migrants and vagrants. For example, the fact that two of the four regional records for the Dusky-capped (Olivaceous) Flycatcher come from Furnace Creek Ranch on Thanksgiving weekend does not necessarily mean that this species is particularly partial to either that locality or that holiday; rather, it reflects a general geographical and seasonal pattern of vagrancy, and also the intensive coverage that this favorite birdwatching locality receives during a "traditional" birding weekend.

Bird movements in the region are not limited to simple "north in spring, south in fall" patterns. Several types of post-breeding dispersal occur; these are elaborated upon in the species accounts. It is common for many lowland and foothill species to undertake a marked upslope movement in summer or early fall after breeding. Even such sedentary species as the Wrentit have been recorded well above their normal altitudinal range at this season. Another type of post-breeding dispersal involves the movement of subtropical waterbirds northward into our region in summer and fall. The Elegant Tern, for example, moves northward in large numbers from its breeding grounds in July, remaining along our coast at least through October (when the species withdraws to its wintering grounds off South America). Brown Pelicans and Heermann's Gulls perform a similar post-breeding immigration, but remain until just before the following breeding season. Other subtropical waterbirds undergo post-breeding movements into the region only rarely or irregularly (with immatures greatly predominating). Examples are Blue-footed and Brown Booby, Magnificent Frigatebird, Roseate Spoonbill, and Black-bellied Whistling-Duck.

Wintertime movements of birds in the region are poorly understood. Irregularly, such species as Purple Finch, Pine Siskin, Red-breasted Nuthatch, and Mountain Chickadee may be numerous in the lowlands in fall and winter; however, much needs to be learned of the origins of these birds. It is likely that the majority do not represent individuals which have simply moved downslope from montane breeding habitats within the region. This is certainly the case with polytypic species which have been studied in this regard (e.g. Fox Sparrow, where our most wide-spread breeding race *stephensi* winters almost exclusively to the south of the region and our wintering races come from well to the north of the region).

For further peculiarities in the fascinating subject of bird movements in southern California see text comments under the individual species.

POPULATION TRENDS

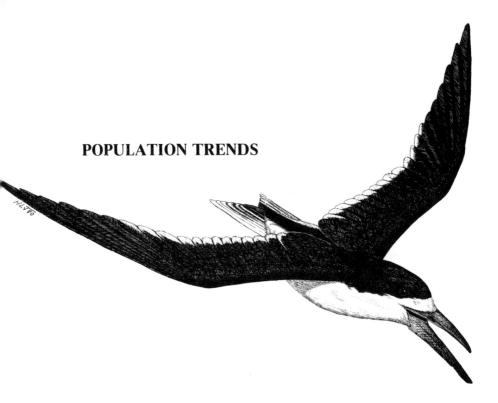

No habitat type in southern California has been free from modification at the hands of man. Certain habitats, such as coastal salt marshes and the Colorado River floodplain forests have been severely reduced in extent. Others have been wholly created during the present century, such as the Salton Sea and the numerous freshwater reservoirs. Ever-increasing human settlement and urbanization throughout the coastal slope has had pronounced effects on the population of many bird species, as have changing agricultural and grazing practices on the deserts and forestry practices in the mountains. The following section briefly details trends of increase or decrease in the southern California avifauna. In most cases additional details will be found under the appropriate species accounts.

Decreasing Species

Declines of bird species in southern California can generally be attributed to one or more of the following categories: (1) habitat loss or alteration; (2) competition, predation, or brood-parasitism effects of species which have become established or increased due to man (e.g. Brown-headed Cowbird, European Starling); (3) pesticides; and (4) direct human persecution. The reasons for the decline of many species are unknown or poorly understood. The following species or subspecies have suffered marked declines in the region since the publication of Willett (1933): Fork-tailed Storm-Petrel (for reasons operating outside of the region?), Brown Pelican, White-faced Ibis, California Condor, Cooper's Hawk, Swainson's Hawk, Bald Eagle, Northern Harrier, Peregrine Falcon, Clapper Rail (except *yumanensis*), Black Rail (coastal populations), Snowy Plover (coastal populations), Least Tern, Tufted Puffin, Yellow-billed Cuckoo, Elf Owl, Long-eared Owl, Willow Flycatcher, Vermilion Flycatcher, Tree Swallow, Bank Swallow, Purple Martin, Swainson's Thrush, Black-tailed Gnatcatcher (*californica*), Ruby-crowned Kinglet (breeding), Bell's Vireo, Gray Vireo, Warbling Vireo (southern breeding range), Yellow Warbler (Colorado River and southern coast), Wilson's Warbler (breeding), Grasshopper Sparrow, and Savannah Sparrow (*beldingi* and *rostratus*).

For further information on declining bird species in southern California, see the list of "Species of Special Concern" by Remsen (1979). Official designations as rare, threatened, or endangered species or subspecies have been applied by the State of California and the United States Department of the Interior to the following: California Brown Pelican (State and Federal Endangered), Aleutian Canada Goose (Federal Endangered), Southern Bald Eagle (State and Federal Endangered), American Peregrine Falcon (State and Federal Endangered), California Condor (State and Federal Endangered), Clapper Rail (all local races State and Federal Endangered), California Black Rail (State Rare), California Least Tern (State and Federal Endangered), California Yellow-billed Cuckoo (State Rare), Least Bell's Vireo (State Endangered), and Belding's Savannah Sparrow (State Endangered).

Increasing Species

Many bird species have colonized or increased within urban, suburban, agricultural, or altered wetland habitats since the publication of Willett (1933). A very few other species have increased within more or less natural habitats, often with no apparent explanation. The increase of some species (e.g. Cattle Egret) represents part of a widespread expansion. Very local or short-term increases are not considered in the following list. Markedly increasing species in the region include: Cattle Egret, Yellow-footed Gull, Elegant Tern, Band-tailed Pigeon (lowland breeding), Inca Dove, Chestnut-backed Chickadee, European Starling, Hooded Oriole, Great-tailed Grackle, and Brown-headed Cowbird.

DISTRICTS AND HABITATS

The southern California region has been divided into five districts (see p. 32). These follow, with some modifications, the schemes employed by Pyle and Small (1961) and McCaskie, DeBenidictis, Morlan, and Erickson (1979). Some of these districts are relatively easily defined; others are considerably more complex and merge into one another in complicated ways. District designations are intended to give the reader a quick indication of the geographical patterns of occurrence of each species. An elaboration of these distributional patterns is found in the text for each species, and on breeding range maps for selected species. The district codes are repeated here:

     C = coast and ocean
     M = mountains
     D = desert
     S = Salton Sea
     R = Colorado River

The Channel Islands are not given district status in this book. Species breeding on the Channel Islands are so noted in the text; non-breeding visitants to the islands are likewise annotated. Many species occur commonly in District C but have rarely, or never, been recorded on the

20

Channel Islands (due either to their extremely sedentary nature — e.g. Wrentit or Brown Towhee — or to their "psychological" indisposition to cross large water gaps — e.g. Common Crow). These interesting situations are also pointed out in the text. Channel Islands status is graphed under District C, or explained separately in the text. Distributional information from the Channel Islands comes primarily from the work of H.L. Jones (1976 and unpublished notes).

For a general overview of the district scheme employed in this book, consult the maps on pages 32 - 35. The following section defines more clearly the districts used, their boundaries, habitats, and characteristics of their avifaunas.

DISTRICT C

The marine portion of District C includes the Pacific Ocean within 100 miles (160km) of the mainland as well as inshore waters, including protected bays, harbors, and marinas. The 100 mile limit is somewhat arbitrary, but roughly defines the limits of seabird surveys and pelagic bird-watching trips from which most of our distributional data is derived. Our knowledge of pelagic bird distribution is best for the frequently birded channels between Santa Barbara, Ventura, Oxnard, San Pedro, and San Diego, and their respective offshore islands. Also relatively well-covered (at least recently) are certain submerged banks, ridges, and seamounts well off San Diego and Morro Bay.

Subtle factors of water temperature, current patterns, and submarine topography are important determinants of marine bird distribution. It is generally beyond the scope of this work, however, to discuss the particular environmental requisites of such birds other than noting, for example, which species are partial to warmer water, which are regularly observable from shore, and so on.

We have made a habitat distinction between offshore waters (**HABITAT "o"**) and inshore waters (**HABITAT "i"**). Habitat "o" species are not regularly seen from shore, although sightings from shore may occur under certain weather conditions; these constitute our truly "pelagic" bird species. Habitat "i" encompasses species which are habitually seen from shore, and which may occur in protected bays, harbors, and lagoons. The distinction between the two habitats is obviously not a sharp one, and details in the text should be consulted.

Seashore habitats can be grossly divided into two major types: rocky shore and sandy beach (both of which are included within **HABITAT "b"**). Artificial jetties and breakwaters form "islands" of rocky shore habitat at intervals along the entire coastline. Natural rocky coastline occurs widely, but interrruptedly, around the Channel Islands, the San Luis Obispo Co. coastline, and various parts of the remaining coastal counties. Typical birds of rocky coasts include Pigeon Guillemot (northern islands and San Luis Obispo Co. only), Brandt's and Pelagic Cormorants, Black Oystercatcher (primarily San Luis Obispo Co. and some Channel

21

Islands), Black Turnstone, Wandering Tattler, and Surfbird. Most of the remaining shoreline is sandy, often with heavy human impact during the warmer months. Typical sandy shore birds are Snowy Plover, Marbled Godwit, Sanderling, and (locally, in summer) Least Tern. Breeding species of sandy shores (Snowy Plover, Least Tern) have declined greatly because of human disturbance.

Estuary and salt marsh habitats today represent only pitiful remnants of their former state. Many estuaries (**HABITAT "e"**) have been completely "improved" by conversion to yacht harbors, housing developments, and so on; others have been altered to varying degrees or are immediately threatened. Estuaries still form critical and valuable wildlife habitats in San Luis Obispo Co. (Morro Bay, Santa Maria River mouth); Santa Barbara Co. (Santa Maria River mouth in part, Santa Ynez River mouth, Devereux Slough, Goleta Slough, Sandyland Slough); Ventura Co. (Santa Clara River estuary, Mugu Lagoon); Los Angeles Co. (Malibu Lagoon, Ballona wetlands); Orange Co. (Seal Beach marshes, Bolsa Chica Lagoon, Upper Newport Bay); and San Diego Co. (Santa Margarita River mouth, Buena Vista Lagoon, San Elijo Lagoon, San Diego River mouth, Tijuana river estuary, etc.) Estuaries and their shores and mudflats support teeming shorebird populations (outside of early summer) and are important foraging areas for herons, waterfowl, etc. Salt marshes (part of **HABITAT "m"**, but merging gradually into habitat "e") have suffered greatly from dredging and landfill but, where preserved, support diverse and abundant bird populations; perhaps most characteristic of this habitat is the Clapper Rail, whose coastal races are considered endangered to the region.

Inland, the coastal region comprises lowland, valley, and foothill habitats on the coastal side of the mountains which comprise District M. Somewhat arbitrarily, all of San Luis Obispo Co., and virtually all of Santa Barbara Co. are included within District C, even though these counties have well-wooded mountains and very arid portions of their interior. In Santa Barbara Co., only the immediate vicinity of Figueroa Mtn. and Big Pine Mtn. is sufficiently forested to be considered marginally part of Distrct M. The distinctly arid eastern border of San Luis Obispo Co. and adjacent portions of Kern Co. do not conveniently fit within the district scheme and, although nominally considered a part of District C, their avifauna is often treated primarily in the individual species accounts.

With well over ninety percent of the region's human population living within District C, habitat alterations have been especially severe here. Native grassland and cienega (poorly-drained bottomland) habitats have been virtually eliminated. Most river and stream courses in lowland areas have been channelized, and riparian woodlands have been decimated. Large tracts of chaparral and coastal sage scrub remain undeveloped, although modern fire management practices have altered the original state of such habitats. Numerous canyons in the low coastal mountain ranges and the foothills below District M remain in more or less natural condition. Agriculture is extensive in the inland valleys and, coastally, in some of the broader river valleys.

Much of District C, especially the sprawling Los Angeles Basin, is heavily urbanized. A variety of trees and shrubs, mostly introduced and largely evergreen, harbor a typical complement of urban birds such as Rock Dove, European Starling, House Sparrow, Scrub Jay, Common Crow (not in the San Diego area), Northern Mockingbird, Brewer's Blackbird, and House Finch. No habitat designation is given for urban areas and no native species is restricted to such areas. Many residential and park areas are heavily planted and can be considered woodland habitats in terms of vegetation structure, even though many of the component plant species are exotic. Residential and park woodlands are considered part of **HABITAT "w"**.

Deciduous riparian woodlands, **HABITAT "r"**, are dominated in District C by cottonwoods (*Populus fremontii*) and various species of willows (*Salix*); in canyons, dominant trees are often sycamores (*Plantanus racemosa*) and alders (*Alnus rhombifolia*). Some bird species typical of riparian woodlands have been virtually eliminated from District C (e.g. Yellow-billed Cuckoo, Willow Flycatcher). Some representative species still occurring are: Downy Woodpecker (north of San Diego Co.), Black-chinned Hummingbird (summer), Bell's Vireo (now rather rare, summer), Yellow Warbler (declining, summer), and Song Sparrow.

Much of District C is covered by chaparral, a low, dense, stiff-twigged vegetation type unique to Mediterranean climates. "Soft" chaparral, or coastal sage scrub, occurs at lower elevations, especially near the coast; dominant plants include sagebrush (*Artemisia californica*) and buckwheat (*Eriogonum* spp.). Typical, or "hard" chaparral occurs at slightly higher elevations and is almost always dominated by chamise (*Adenostoma fasciculatum*). Taken together, these chaparral types, along with miscellaneous brushy habitats, comprise **HABITAT "c"**. California Quail, Anna's Hummingbird, Wrentit, California Thrasher, Brown Towhee, and many other species are common and widespread in chaparral habitats; scarcer and more localized are, for example, the Black-tailed Gnatcatcher (*californica* race, Rufous-crowned Sparrow, and Sage Sparrow (*belli* race).

Various types of woodlands (all part of **HABITAT "w"**) occur in District C. Live oak woodland (generally dominated by *Quercus agrifolia*) is an important habitat above or within the chaparral zone; Blue Oak (*Quercus douglasii*) woodland, often mixed with Digger Pine (*Pinus sabiniana*), is important from central Santa Barbara Co. northward. Open woodlands of Valley Oak (*Quercus lobata*) occur in interior valleys north and west from Los Angeles Co. Oaks form the dominant woodland type on the Channel Islands. Typical oak woodland birds include Acorn Woodpecker, Scrub Jay, Plain Titmouse, Western Bluebird, Hutton's Vireo, and Lark Sparrow. Coastal closed-cone pine woodlands, composed of Bishop Pine (*Pinus muricata*) and Monterey Pine (*P. radiata*), occur in San Luis Obispo Co., and support a few species more typical of montane coniferous forests (e.g. Steller's Jay and Pygmy Nuthatch). Coastal redwood forests reach their southern limit just north of the region.

HABITAT "g" consists of grasslands (largely composed now of non-native species), agricultural regions, and other open field habitats. Grasslands occur on the immediate coastal plain, in the interior valleys (where generally interspersed with oaks), and in other scattered areas throughout the district. Agriculture is declining in coastal southern California, but croplands still form much of the landscape within the district. Typical birds of habitat "g" within the district are White-tailed Kite, Western Kingbird (summer), Water Pipit (winter), Horned Lark, Western Meadowlark, Tricolored Blackbird, and Savannah Sparrow (winter).

Small lakes and reservoirs are scattered through District C, and comprise part of **HABITAT "l"**. Among the more important bodies of water are: Nacimiento and Twitchell Reservoirs SLO; Lake Cachuma SBA; Lake Casitas, Lake Piru, and Lake Sherwood VEN; Pyramid Lake, Elizabeth Lake, Bouquet Reservoir, and Puddingstone Reservoir LA; Santiago Reservoir ORA; Lake Hodges, Sweetwater Reservoir, and Otay Reservoir SD; and Lake Mathews and Lake Elsinore RIV. Most lakes and reservoirs support transient and wintering waterfowl, and a few have good populations of breeding birds. Marshes of cattails and rushes border many lakes, rivers, and flood control basins in District C; these form part of **HABITAT "m"**.

In general the higher mountains form a barrier between District C and District D. In a few areas, the two districts meet to form blending zones, e.g. the western Antelope Valley LA, San Gorgonio Pass RIV, and various portions of east-central San Diego Co. These areas are interesting ornithologically because of the contact or proximity of desert/coastal species pairs such as Gambel's and California Quail, Ladder-backed and Nuttall's Woodpeckers, and Crissal and California Thrashers.

As District C spans the latitudinal length of the region, it is far from uniform. It should be noted that there is a distinct gradient in precipitation from the relatively wet northwestern portion of the district to the rather arid southeastern portion. Bird distributions within District C are often elaborated upon in the text. Some, such as the Chestnut-backed Chickadee, are restricted to the northern part of the district; others, e.g. Verdin and Common Ground-Dove are (or were) restricted to the drier southern part. The term "northern coastal counties" generally refers to Santa Barbara and San Luis Obispo Counties; the "southern coastal counties" are San Diego, Orange, and (often) Los Angeles Counties.

DISTRICT M

The mountain district includes only those ranges which are high enough to support well-developed coniferous forests (generally exclusive of pinyon-juniper and coastal closed-cone pine associations). The major mountain ranges encompassed by this district are the following:

1. Coast Ranges
    Figueroa Mtn. SBA (1393m)
    Big Pine Mtn. SBA (2101m)
    Reyes Peak VEN (2311m)
2. Mt. Pinos/Tehachapi Mtns. region
    Mt. Pinos region KRN/VEN (to 2717m)
    Tehachapi Mtns. KRN (to 2456m)
    Piute Mtns. KRN (to 2595m)
3. Transverse Ranges
    San Gabriel Mtns. LA/SBE (to 3097m)
    San Bernardino Mtns. SBE (to 3539m)
4. Peninsular Ranges
    San Jacinto Mtns. RIV (to 3324m)
    Santa Rosa Mtns. RIV (to 2682m)
    Santa Ana Mtns. ORA/RIV (to 1750m)
    Palomar Mtn. region SD (to 1889m)
    Cuyamaca and Laguna Mtns. SD (to 2004m)
5. Great Basin and East Mohave Ranges:
    White Mtns. INY/MNO (to 4383m)
    Inyo Mtns. INY (to 3423m)
    Panamint Mtns. INY (to 3400m)
    Grapevine Mtns. INY (to about 2455m)
    Coso Mtns. INY (to 2511m)
    Argus Mtns. INY (to 2723m)
    Kingston Mtns. SBE (to 2253m)
    Clark Mtn. SBE (2440m)
    New York Mtns./Mid Hills region SBE (to 1900m)
    Providence Mtns. SBE (to 1845m)
    Granite Mtns. SBE (to 2070m)

County names are generally not given in the main text for the ranges noted above.

The mountain ranges listed above are by no means uniform in their vegetation. The Great Basin and east Mohave ranges are quite arid, and are largely cloaked in pinyon and juniper woodland with little understory; large tracts of the Great Basin ranges are covered with sagebrush (*Artemisia*). The higher ranges west of the deserts support a more varied set of habitats.

The most important habitat type in District M is **HABITAT "f"**, or forests. We restrict this designation to conifer-dominated montane associations, exclusive of pinyon-juniper woodland. Yellow Pine (*Pinus ponderosa*) and Jeffrey Pine (*P. jeffreyi*) generally dominate, except at high elevations and in the Great Basin and Mohave Desert ranges. Other important forest trees include White Fir (*Abies concolor*), Incense-Cedar (*Libocedrus decurrens*), Sugar Pine (*Pinus lambertiana*), Coulter Pine (*P. coulteri*), and California Black Oak (*Quercus kelloggii*). High elevation forests (above about 2000-2500m) are often dominated by White Fir, Lodgepole Pine (*P. contorta*), or Limber Pine (*P. flexilis*). White Fir, Limber Pine, and Bristlecone Pine (*P. aristata*) are locally dominant in the desert ranges.

In District M, woodland habitat (**HABITAT "w"**) is dominated by oaks, pinyons, junipers, or, when sparse or stunted as near timberline or in very arid areas, the various conifer species mentioned above. Woodland habitats of pinyon, juniper, and/or Joshua Tree *(Yucca brevifolia)* merge gradually into desert scrub habitats at lower elevations, and can be considered transitional between Districts D and M.

Riparian woodlands in District M (**HABITAT "r"**) are variously dominated by alders (*Alnus rhombifolia*), willows, cottonwoods (*Populus fremontii* and *P. trichocarpa*), and brushy thickets of many species. Montane riparian woodland is not very extensive; however, it has been freer from human modification than lowland riparian habitats, and its bird populations have suffered less impact from Brown-headed Cowbird parasitism.

Montane chaparral (**HABITAT "c"**) is dominated by manzanita, mountain mahogany, ceanothus, and other shrubs; it is often interspersed with woodland and forest habitats, and may have many breeding species (e.g. Green-tailed Towhee and Fox Sparrow) which do not breed in lowland chaparral habitats. The Great Basin and eastern Mohave Desert mountain ranges generally lack extensive chaparral.

Grasslands (**HABITAT "g"**) occur locally in the lower portions of District M, especially around Baldwin Lake in the San Bernardino Mtns. and near Lake Henshaw on the flank of Mt. Palomar. Alpine habitat (above timberline) is quite restricted in the region, limited mainly to the highest portions of the White Mtns., and to the summit of Mt. San Gorgonio in the San Bernardino Mtns.

Large areas of sagebrush (primarily *Artemisia tridentata*) cloak the Great Basin ranges and parts of the ranges west of the deserts (such as in the Mt. Pinos region and in the eastern San Bernardino Mtns.). This habitat supports a rather different avifauna than chaparral and other brushland habitats, and is considered separately as **HABITAT "s"**.

Important lakes (**HABITAT "l"**) in District M include: Silverwood Lake, Lake Arrowhead, Big Bear Lake, and Baldwin Lake in the San Bernardino Mtns., Lake Hemet in the San Jacinto Mtns., and Lake Henshaw (on the border of District C) and Cuyamaca Reservoir in the mountains of San Diego Co.

Note that District M merges quite gradually in some areas with both District C and District D. Conifer groves extend down many coastal canyons into elevations normally considered District C. Big-cone Douglas

Fir (*Pseudotsuga macrocarpa*) and Coulter Pine are especially frequent at these lower elevations. Numerous small ranges within District C have some conifer growth, but lack the extensive forests which characterize District M. As noted above, woodlands on the desert slopes of District M merge gradually into woodlands and scrub of District D. Many ranges on the deserts have extensive pinyon and juniper growth, but are not here considered part of District M. Some of these may have some birds characteristic of montane forests (for example, the Little San Bernardino Mtns. RIV/SBE have Mountain Quail, Pinyon Jays, etc.).

Human impact on District M habitats has come mainly through timber harvesting, fire management, grazing, and resort development; the magnitude of human disturbance has been less in montane areas than in most lowland areas.

DISTRICT D

The vast interior of the southern California region is primarily desert, a term which encompasses a variety of habitat types and a surprisingly rich birdlife. A number of forested mountain ranges dotting the deserts are discussed under District M. The Salton Sea and the adjacent Coachella and Imperial Valleys are considered separately under District S, and the Colorado River Valley is considered District R. The remainder of the arid interior is District D.

Several major sub-divisions of District D may be made. The southern deserts (Colorado Desert), roughly from southern San Bernardino Co. and Riverside Co. south through portions of Imperial and San Diego Co., are generally low-lying and without frequent winter frosts. Dominant plants include ocotillo, cholla, creosote, and a variety of taller shrubs and low trees in washes. The Mohave Desert covers much of San Bernardino Co., and extends west and north into Los Angeles Co., Kern Co., and Inyo Co. It is generally higher in elevation than the southern (Colorado) desert, and experiences regular winter frosts and snows. Creosote is again a dominant shrub on the Mohave Desert, and the Joshua Tree *(Yucca brevifolia)* is typical of large areas. A series of desert valleys in the rain shadow of the Sierra Nevada, in the northern part of the region, comprises part of the Great Basin. Great Basin deserts are relatively high and cool, with winters that may be severely cold. The Owens Valley, Deep Springs Valley, and Fish Lake Valley are typical of the Great Basin; dominant shrubs include sagebrush (*Artemisia tridentata*), and saltbush (*Atriplex* spp.). The Death Valley region, geographically transitional between the Mohave and Great Basin Deserts, is also quite distinct from either. Desert-like areas exist west of District D, as in extreme western Kern Co. and eastern San Luis Obispo Co. The text accounts for each desert species will discuss their distribution in more detail.

The dominant habitat type in District D is **HABITAT "d"**, or desert

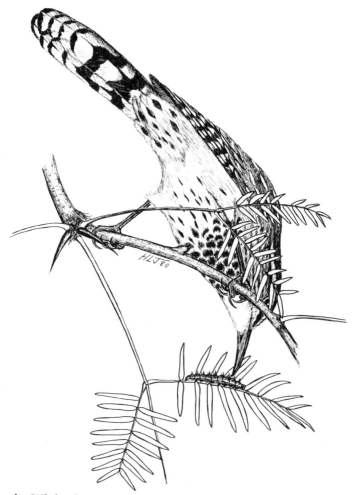

scrub. While the component plant species vary (as briefly discussed above), the general structure of this habitat is sparse, low shrub growth with varying amounts of herbaceous growth. Much of this habitat has been severely affected by grazing and off-road vehicle activity, but large tracts remain in a relatively unaltered state. Shrub growth is often taller and denser near desert watercourses. Where sufficient ground water is available, ironwoods, willows, cottonwoods, mesquites, California Fan Palms, and other trees may grow. This riparian growth comprises part of **HABITAT "r"**. Habitat "r" is also considered to include artificially-watered desert "oases", which may be planted with cottonwoods, elms, tamarisks, and other tall trees which are very attractive to birds.

Desert grasslands, **HABITAT "g"**, are limited in extent in the region, and have been adversely affected by decades of grazing activity. Grassy growth is more lush and extensive after years of relatively high rainfall. Habitat "g" also includes agricultural fields; large sections of District D have been converted to agricultural uses, with alfalfa being the most important crop.

Desert woodland habitats, **HABITAT "w"**, are usually transitional toward District M, with Joshua Trees, pinyons, and junipers dominating. **HABITAT "s"** (sagebrush) occurs in the higher northern desert valleys, and is also transitional toward District M.

A number of lakes and reservoirs, **HABITAT "l"**, are scattered through the deserts. Among them are: Deep Springs Lake INY, Tinnemaha Res. INY, Haiwee Res. INY, Little Lake INY, Owens Lake INY (mostly dry), and Lake Palmdale LA. After heavy rains, many other normally dry desert sinks, such as Harper Dry Lake SBE, may fill.

The diverse nature of southern California's deserts makes it difficult to generalize bird distributions. Several species are limited on the deserts only to the western fringes; these species, such as California Quail, are more typical of coastal regions. A few species are primarily restricted on the deserts to the relatively mesic, high Owens Valley (Downy Woodpecker, Common Crow, Black-billed Magpie, etc.). Many shorebirds and other waterbirds which are generally quite rare or even unknown as transients through the majority of District D are actually regular and in some cases rather common in the Antelope Valley of the western Mohave Desert. If the bar graph for a species in District D primarily reflects its status in the Antelope Valley or another specialized area, this is clearly noted in the text.

The timing of migration and breeding may differ greatly between the northern and the southern deserts. The arrival of some spring transients may be up to a month earlier in the southern deserts. Southern populations of Phainopepla, Costa's Hummingbird, and other species breed significantly earlier than northern populations.

DISTRICT S

This district consists of the Salton Sea and surrounding agricultural areas in the Coachella Valley of Riverside Co. and the Imperial Valley of Imperial Co. The native desert flora of these valleys has been largely replaced by commercial crops of cotton, alfalfa, carrots, etc. and by groves of citrus and date palms. Water edge thickets are now largely composed of introduced salt cedar (*Tamarix*). These habitat changes have greatly altered the composition of the area's avifauna.

The Salton Sea was created in 1905-1906 by floodwaters from the Colorado River. It is the largest inland body of water in the region, and has attracted waterbirds which are otherwise nearly or entirely unknown in the interior. Increasing agricultural runoff continues to raise the level of the sea, with habitats along a formerly stable shoreline suffering increasing flooding. The Salton Sea itself is considered as **HABITAT "l"**. Most of the shoreline is barren, being composed largely of crushed barnacle remains. Rock jetties have been constructed in a few areas. The Salton Sea shoreline is considered **HABITAT "b"**. Extensive marshes

(**HABITAT "m"**) occur in certain freshwater impoundments and at the mouths of freshwater rivers (the Whitewater River at the north end, the New and Alamo Rivers at the south end, and Salt Creek on the east shore). Much of this marshland is threatened by the rising level of the sea and by channelization of the Whitewater River.

Other bodies of water within District S include Ramer Lake and Finney Lake near the southeast corner of the sea. A network of irrigation canals, often with some marshy vegetation, occurs throughout the Imperial Valley.

Terrestrial habitats in District S include extensive agricultural fields (**HABITAT "g"**), thickets of salt cedar, mesquite, and willow (**HABITAT "r"**), and groves, windbreaks, and shade trees around towns and ranch-yards (**HABITAT "w"**). These habitats merge gradually into desert scrub regions which are considered part of District D; the boundary between Districts S and D is therefore not a sharp one. District S can best be defined by the limits of agricultural activity in the Coachella and Imperial Valleys. In the former area, the district extends north through and around the towns of Mecca, Thermal, Coachella, and Indio, but does not include the predominantly non-agricultural Palm Springs/Palm Desert area. All of the Imperial Valley, south to the Mexican Border, is included. The western and eastern borders of the district are generally formed by California Highways 86 and 111, respectively.

Of extreme interest to the birder is the Salton Sea's relationship to the Gulf of California. Lying only some 275 km north of the head of the gulf, the Salton Sea attracts several species of marine and shore birds which do not occur regularly at other inland localities in the region. Breeding species include Black Skimmer, Gull-billed Tern, and Laughing Gull (formerly). Other visitants (some quite irregular) include Magnificent Frigatebird, Blue-footed Booby, Brown Booby, Wood Stork, and Roseate Spoonbill. Even four species of Procellariiformes (Buller's Shearwater, Sooty Shearwater, Least Storm-Petrel, and Leach's Storm-Petrel) have been recorded on the Salton Sea. There appears to be a regular spring migration of many normally coastal species out of the Gulf of California, with the Salton Sea as a regular stopping ground (e.g. Brant, Surf Scoter, Red Knot).

DISTRICT R

The Colorado River Valley, from the Nevada border north of Needles SBE south to the Mexican boundary near Winterhaven IMP, comprises District R. While that portion of the river valley lying within the state of Arizona has been excluded, we do mention relevant Colorado River records from Arizona in many cases.

Because of an abundance of surface water, the habitats and birdlife along the Colorado River are distinct from those of the surrounding Colorado Desert. Nevertheless, Districts D and R merge in a complex way, with many bird species characteristic of Colorado River riparian woodland following wooded desert washes well away from the river valley. We restrict District R to include only aquatic habitats, riparian woodlands and brushlands of the river's floodplain, and agricultural areas, towns, and ranchyards. Note that birdlife of riparian oases on the southern deserts (District D) may closely resemble that of District R. Among the widespread woodland-nesting species of District R that also breed very locally in riparian oases or town woodlands within Districts D and S are Gila Woodpecker, Brown-Crested Flycatcher, Lucy's Warbler, and Summer Tanager.

The riparian forest of cottonwoods, willows, and mesquite which once dominated the Colorado River floodplain has now been virtually eliminated from the region; only very locally on the Arizona side of the river (e.g. the Bill Williams River delta) does such habitat remain to any extent. **HABITAT "r"** in District R now consists of highly disturbed and limited fragments of such riparian woodlands, along with cottonwood and other shade tree plantings around towns, ranchyards, and trailer parks. Salt cedar (*Tamarix*), occurring in dense, low thickets, now dominates much of the river's floodplain. Honey mesquite, screwbean mesquite, and willows are mixed in to varying degrees, along with other desert water-loving shrubs. As such, these floodplain habitats still harbor fair densities of breeding birds, including some sensitive riparian species (e.g. Yellow-billed Cuckoo, Common Screech-Owl, Brown-Crested Flycatcher, and Bell's Vireo). The Yellow Warbler (*D.p. sonorana*) has been eliminated from District R as a breeding bird, and the Elf Owl has now been reduced to a very few pairs.

Park-like woodlands around towns, ranches, and trailer parks derive most of their birdlife from riparian habitats, and are not considered as a separate habitat here. Some species, such as Inca Dove and Bronzed Cowbird, are virtually restricted to such "artificial" woodlands in the region.

Agricultural areas exist in the Palo Verde Valley from the vicinity of Blythe RIV south to Palo Verde IMP, and around Bard and Winterhaven IMP. Extensive agricultural areas also exist on the Arizona side of the river, especially around Parker. This comprises **HABITAT "g"**; no natural grassland habitat occurs in the Colorado River Valley.

The Colorado River itself has been tamed, channelized, and robbed of much of its water. Open freshwater (**HABITAT "l"**) is attractive to birds primarily at reservoirs formed by major dams, especially Lake Havasu, formed by Parker Dam and, to a lesser extent, Imperial Reservoir formed by Imperial Dam. Smaller backwater areas and ponds along the length of the river are also attractive to waterbirds. Fast-flowing water below Parker Dam is home in winter to large numbers of goldeneyes and mergansers. Extensive marshes (**HABITAT "m"**) occur at various points along the river, especially in the area between Needles SBE and Topock AZ, and above Imperial Dam IMP.

31

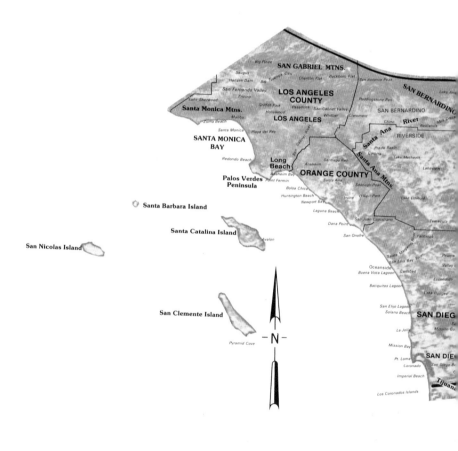

SAN GABRIEL MTNS.

Big Pines

Saugus
Tujunga City
Chanton Flat
Buckhorn Flat
San Antonio Peak
SAN BERNARDINO
Lake Arro

Hansen Dam
Big
San Fernando Valley
Encino
LOS ANGELES
COUNTY
Puddingstone Res

Lake Sherwood
Griffith Park
Pasadena
San Gabriel Valley
Claremont
SAN BERNARDINO

Santa Monica Mtns.
Hollywood
Whittier
Chino
River
Redlands
Mill Cree

Malibu
LOS ANGELES
Santa Ana
RIVERSIDE

Zuma Beach
Playa del Rey
Prado Basin

Santa Monica
Cucamonga

SANTA MONICA
BAY
Corona
Lake Mathews

Redondo Beach
Santiago Res.
Lakeview

Long
Beach
Anaheim
Santa Ana Mtns.

Anaheim Bay
ORANGE COUNTY

Palos Verdes
Peninsula
Point Fermin
Santa Ana
Santiago Peak

Bolsa Chica
O'Neill Park
Lake Elsinore

Huntington Beach
Irvine

Newport Bay

Santa Barbara Island
Laguna Beach

Dana Point
San Juan Capistrano
Temecula

San Onofre
Fallbrook

San Nicolas Island
Avalon
Santa Catalina Island

Santa Margarita River

San Luis Rey River
Pauma
Valley

Oceanside
Escondido
Buena Vista Lagoon
Carlsbad

Batiquitos Lagoon
Lake Hodges

San Elijo Lagoon
San Clemente Island
Solano Beach
SAN DIEG

La Jolla
Mission Go

Mission Bay

Pyramid Cove
- N -
Pt. Loma
SAN DIE
Coronado
San Diego Ba

Imperial Beach
Tijuana

Los Coronados Islands

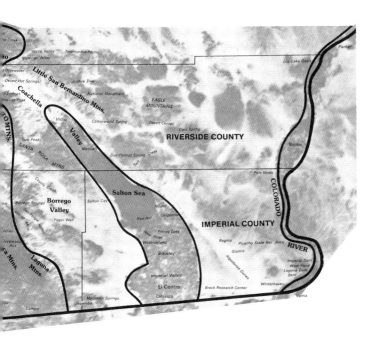

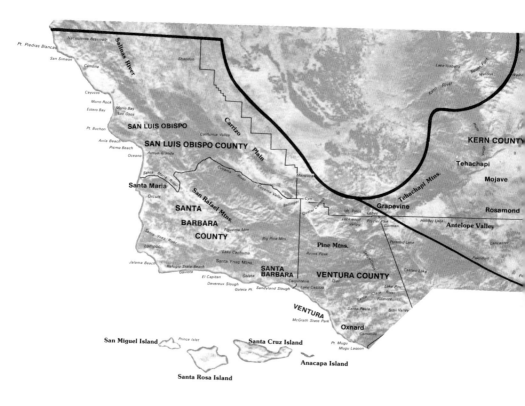

Pt. Piedras Blancas
Nacimiento Reservoir
San Simeon
Cambria
Cayucos
Morro Rock
Morro Bay
Estero Bay
Los Osos
Pt. Buchon
SAN LUIS OBISPO
Avila Beach
Pismo Beach
Oceano
Arroyo Grande

Salinas River

Shandon

SAN LUIS OBISPO COUNTY

Carrizo Plain

California Valley

Lake Isabella
South Fork
Weldon
Wofei
Kern River

KERN COUNTY

Tehachapi

Mojave

Santa Maria
Orcutt
San Rafael Mtns.
SANTA
BARBARA
COUNTY

Santa Maria River
Cuyama River
Cuyama Valley
Ballinger
Cyn
Maricopa
Cuyama River

Figueroa Mtn.
Big Pine Mtn.
Lake Cachuma
Santa Ynez Mtns.
Santa Ynez River
Refugio State Beach
El Capitan
Goleta
Devereux Slough
Goleta Pt.
Sandyland Slough

Quatal Canyon
Mt. Pinos
Lockwood
Valley
Foster Park
Gorman

Grapevine

Rosamond

Tehachapi Mtns.
Lebec
Holiday Lake
Antelope Valley

Lancaster

Pine Mtns.
Reyes Peak
Pyramid Lake

Palmdale

Lompoc
Jalama Beach

Gaviota

SANTA
BARBARA

Carpinteria
Lake Casitas

VENTURA COUNTY
Ojai

Castaic Lake

Lake Piru
Fillmore
Santa Clara River
Santa Paula
Simi Valley

VENTURA
McGrath State Park

Oxnard
Camarillo

Pt. Mugu
Mugu Lagoon

San Miguel Island
Prince Islet

Santa Cruz Island

Anacapa Island

Santa Rosa Island

34

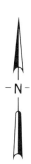

-N-

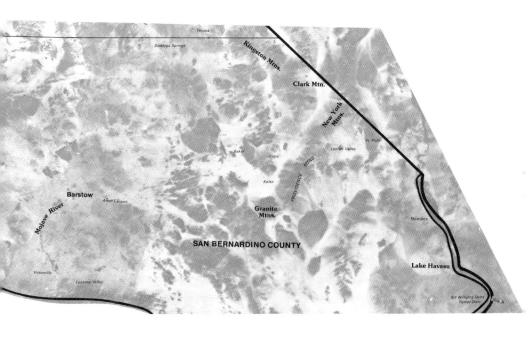

Tecopa

Saratoga Springs

Kingston Mtns.

Clark Mtn.

New York Mtns.

Ft. Piute

Baker

Cima

Lanfair Valley

Kelso

PROVIDENCE MTNS

Barstow

Afton Canyon

Mojave River

Granite Mtns.

Needles

SAN BERNARDINO COUNTY

Victorville

Lucerne Valley

Lake Havasu

Bill Williams Delta
Parker Dam

Ariz. B.

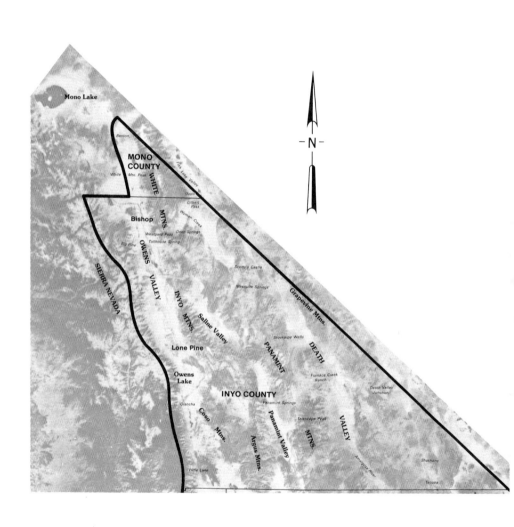

Mono Lake

Benton

MONO COUNTY

White Mtn. Peak

Fish Lake Valley

WHITE

Oasis

Gilbert Pass

Bishop

MTNS.

Wyman Creek

Westgard Pass

Deep Springs

Tollhouse Spring

Big Pine

OWENS

VALLEY

INYO MTNS.

Saline Valley

Scotty's Castle

Mesquite Springs

Grapevine Mtns.

Stovepipe Wells

Lone Pine

SIERRA NEVADA

PANAMINT

DEATH

Owens
Lake

INYO COUNTY

Furnace Creek
Ranch

Death Valley
Junction

Olancha

Panamint Springs

Coso

Mtns.

Panamint Valley

Telescope Peak

VALLEY

MTNS.

Argus Mtns.

Amargosa River

Shoshone

Little Lake

Tecopa

–N–

INTRODUCTION TO THE BAR GRAPHS

The following section will aid in the interpretation of the bar graphs which begin on page 42. It should be remembered that each bar graph is an oversimplified representation of a complex situation. While the graphs exhibit the major features of the geographical, seasonal, and ecological status of each species, they are not intended to stand entirely by themselves. The reader is urged to consult the text account for each species in order to learn the details of its geographical distribution within the region, its particular habitat preferences, specific citations of unusual occurrences, etc. In order to keep the graphs from being difficult to interpret, we have tried to establish a minimal number of habitat and district designations. However, the region is complex geographically, embracing correspondingly complex avian distributions. We therefore repeat that much information cannot be represented by the bar graphs, and that the reader will find it valuable to utilize the text accounts in all cases.

We have followed certain conventions in order to facilitate the interpretation of the bar graphs. For a given graph, district symbols are listed in decreasing order of importance to the species, with "importance" being a measure of how widespread and abundant the species is within the district. Habitat symbols are also given in decreasing order of preference shown by the species. If occurrence within a district is local or marginal, the district symbol is given in parentheses. If occurrence is extremely marginal, no graph may be presented for the district. When several graphs are presented for a species, they are given in order of decreasing abundance rather than in a fixed geographical sequence. For certain species, well-marked subspecies have separate graphs. In no case are separate graphs given for different habitats within a district, even though abundance and seasonal occurrence clearly may vary between habitats; such variations are discussed in the text. Marginal habitats are generally not shown for the graphs, but are discussed in the text. No habitat designations are given for most migrants and vagrants, or in other cases where the established designations might only prove confusing.

The bar graphs reflect the current status in the region of each species; historical trends are discussed in the text. We have taken into account both absolute abundance and detectability when formulating the graphs; if the graphs reflect a seasonal change in detectability (e.g. peaks in vocalizing during the breeding season) this is clearly stated in the text.

In some cases we have extrapolated from the record and made assumptions based on known weakness of coverage. Therefore the graphs sometimes reflect a "guessed" situation rather than a faithful regurgitation of records. This is usually explained in the text.

Records with indefinite dates (e.g. a bird present in "late summer 1965") are generally not graphed. In most cases, we have also not graphed records which pertain to birds found dead, unless there is evidence that they were freshly dead.

District Codes

C = Coastal district. Includes the open ocean, inshore waters, bays, harbors, salt water lagoons, ocean shore, estuaries, coastal lowlands, foothills, and interior valleys (west of the deserts).

M = Mountain district. Includes the higher ranges supporting coniferous forest, namely the Mt. Pinos region, the Transverse and Peninsular Ranges, the White-Inyo-Panamint Mountain region, and the higher mountains of the eastern Mohave Desert.

D = Desert district. The arid interior, including the Owens Valley, Death Valley region, Mohave Desert, Antelope Valley, Anza-Borrego region, and the Colorado Desert (exclusive of the Imperial, Coachella, and Colorado River Valleys).

S = Salton Sea district. Includes the Salton Sea and surrounding agricultural lands of the Coachella and Imperial Valleys.

R = Colorado River district. The lower Colorado River Valley, from the Nevada border south to the Mexican border.

Further details on this system of districts are found on pages 20 - 31. A few "problem" areas are difficult to represent with the district scheme employed. Among these areas is the Carrizo Plain in eastern San Luis Obispo Co., with desert and coastal elements but the absence of numerous species characteristic of either region. The Cuyama Valley near the juncture of San Luis Obispo, Santa Barbara, and Ventura Counties is included with District C, but has some desert affinites, while the Antelope Valley in Los Angeles and Kern Counties is considered part of District D but has many bird species atypical of that district. The forested mountains of San Luis Obispo and Santa Barbara Counties lack many species typical of District M, and most are considered part of District C. Although the status of many species on the Channel Islands is similar to that in the remainder of District C, this is certainly not always the case; the text should always be consulted for Channel Islands status. In cases such as these, the graphs cannot adequately express distributional complexities. Similarly, the graphs cannot take into account the cline from the relatively wet northwestern portion of District C (San Luis Obispo and Santa Barbara Counties) to that district's distinctly arid southeastern end (San Diego Co.). The predominantly rocky coastline of San Luis Obispo Co. cannot be distinguished on the bar graphs from the sandier beaches of the southern counties; nor can the northern deserts with their very cold winters and late springs be distinguished from the southern deserts with their relatively mild winters. The graphs may therefore represent an "average" for the entire district or, in some cases, represent a species' status in one portion of the district only. Such treatments are explained in the species accounts.

Habitat Codes

o = open ocean; generally more than 1 km offshore

i = inshore ocean waters, bays, harbors; generally less than 1 km offshore

b = beaches; including sandy and rocky shores, jetties; in District S, refers to shoreline of Salton Sea

e = estuaries; mudflats, tidal lagoons, and brackish waters affected by tidal action

r = riparian woodlands and thickets, including irrigated oases on the deserts

g = grasslands, fields, and agricultural areas

m = marshes, both freshwater and saltwater

c = chaparral, coastal sage scrub, and brushlands

w = woodland; including oaks, oak-conifer woods, pinyon-juniper associations, Joshua Tree woodland, parks, and suburban "woodland"

f = forest, dominated by conifers

d = desert scrub; sparse vegetation of desert flats, slopes, and washes

s = sagebrush and other brushy vegetation of cool, arid areas

l = lakes, reservoirs, large streams and rivers, and the margins of these areas

x = specialized or miscellaneous habitat; see text

A review of these habitat types will be found on pages 20 - 31, under the discussions of the individual districts. The habitat designations should not be taken too literally; habitats merge into one another almost imperceptably, and bird species vary in the extent to which they are tolerant of divergent habitat types.

Abundance Designations

Abundance designations are, of necessity, somewhat arbitrary. While we have developed general criteria for the employment of the various designations, we have also strived to keep them flexible enough to more accurately portray relative abundances between districts, between species, or between seasons. We have refrained from using rigid abundance criteria (e.g. numbers of individuals per day, percentage of trips found, etc.) in order to keep this flexibility.

Common to abundant; almost always encountered in proper habitat within the given district(s), usually in moderate to large numbers. When "abundant" is used, it implies that the species is always encountered under the indicated conditions, and in large numbers.

Fairly Common; usually encountered in proper habitat at the given season(s) in the given district(s), generally not in large numbers.

Uncommon; occurs in small numbers or only locally under the indicated conditions.

Rare; occurs annually (or virtually annually) during the season indicated, but generally in very small numbers. Also applies to species which breed extremely locally and in very small numbers.

Casual; records within a given district at the season indicated are few, but not cited individually. There may be no records in some (or many) years, but a general pattern of occurrence is suggested.

Individual record; details of the record are cited in the text. Generally used for species which have been recorded about ten times or fewer in the region, or which have been recorded only a very few times (the exact number varies) in that district or at that season.

Individual record; indicates a prolonged stay by the individual(s); note that a record spanning five days or less is represented by a single dot.

In many cases, year to year occurrence is markedly irregular; we represent this situation by showing broken abundance graphs:

Irregularly common, but may be uncommon, rare, or even absent in some years.

Irregularly common, but at least fairly common all years.

Species which are uncommon some years but very rare or absent other years are graphed by a solid "uncommon" line.

BAR GRAPHS

SPECIES	District	Habitat	January	February	March	April	May	June	July	August	September	October	November	December
Least Grebe	R	l										•		
Pied-billed Grebe	CSRMD	liem												
Horned Grebe	C	i												
	SR	l												
	DM	l												
Red-necked Grebe	C	i												
	D	l												
Eared Grebe	S	lm												
	CR	ilem												
	D	lm												
	(M)	lm												
Western Grebe	C	i												
	(R)S	lm												
	DM	l												
Short-tailed Albatross	C	o							•					
Black-footed Albatross	C	o												
Laysan Albatross	C	o												
	D													
Northern Fulmar	C	o												
Mottled Petrel	C			•	•									
Cook's Petrel	C	o											•	
Stejneger's Petrel	C	o											•	
Pink-footed Shearwater	C	o												
Flesh-footed Shearwater	C	o	•											
Buller's Shearwater	C	o												
	S	l												
Sooty Shearwater	C	oi												
	S	l												
Short-tailed Shearwater	C	o				•								
Black-vented Shearwater	C	oi												
Wilson's Storm-Petrel	C	o												
Fork-tailed Storm-Petrel	C	o												
Leach's Storm-Petrel	C	o	•		•								•	•
	S	l												
Black Storm-Petrel	C	o												
Ashy Storm-Petrel	C	o												
Band-rumped Storm-Petrel	C	o										•		
Galapagos Storm-Petrel	C	o								•				
Least Storm-Petrel	C	o												
	S	l												
White-tailed Tropicbird	C													
Red-billed Tropicbird	C	o			•									

42

SPECIES	District	Habitat	January	February	March	April	May	June	July	August	September	October	November	December
Red-tailed Tropicbird	C	o										●		
Blue-footed Booby	SRCMD	li	●		●			●						
Masked Booby	C	o	●											
Brown Booby	SR	l												
American White Pelican	S	lm												
	R	lm												
	C	lme												
	DM	l												
Brown Pelican	C	oieb												
	S	l	●											
	RDM	l												
Double-crested Cormorant	CR	ieblm												
	S	lm												
	DM	l												
Neotropic Cormorant	R	l												
Brandt's Cormorant	C	oib												
Pelagic Cormorant	C	oib												
Magnificent Frigatebird	CSR	li	●	●●	●●	●						●●		
American Bittern	SR	m												
	C	m												
	D	m												
Least Bittern	SR	m												
	C	m												
	D	mr												
Great Blue Heron	CSRM	mleb												
	D	ml												
Great Egret	SR	m												
	C	em												
	D	m			●							●		
Snowy Egret	SR	ml												
	C	mel												
	D	ml												
Little Blue Heron	S	m	●				●						●	
	C	me					●	●●						
	D	l					●●							
Tricolored Heron	C	me					●	●●						
	SR	m		●●	●								●●	
Reddish Egret	C	em												
	SR	m		●●●			●							
Cattle Egret	S	gml												
	RC	gm												
	D	mg												

SPECIES	District	Habitat	January	February	March	April	May	June	July	August	September	October	November	December
Green Heron	CSR	mle												
	D	l												
Black-crowned Night-Heron	CSR	mle												
	D	lm												
Yellow-crowned Night-Heron	C	me												
White Ibis	SC	m												
White-faced Ibis	S	m												
	R	m												
	C	m												
	D	m												
Roseate Spoonbill	SR	m												
	C	em												
Wood Stork	S	ml												
	R	ml												
	C	em												
Fulvous Whistling-Duck	S	m												
	R	m												
	D													
Black-bellied Whistling-Duck	S	m												
Whistling Swan	DCSR	lm												
Trumpeter Swan	C	l												
Greater White-fronted Goose	SCDRM	le												
Snow Goose	SR	mgl												
	DM	l												
	C	le												
Ross' Goose	S	mgl												
	CR	el												
	D	l												
Emperor Goose	C	e												
Brant "light-bellied"	C	ie												
"dark-bellied"	C	ie												
	S(M)	l												
	D	l												
Canada Goose	SRCMD	lmg												
Wood Duck	CD	lr												
	SR	l												
Eurasian Wigeon	CSM	lm												
	DR	l												
American Wigeon	CSRMD	lmg												
Gadwall	CMDSR	lm												
Baikal Teal	CS	l												

SPECIES	District	Habitat	January	February	March	April	May	June	July	August	September	October	November	December
Green-winged Teal (Eurasian)	CM	lm												
(American)	CSRMD	lme												
Mallard	CSRMD	lm												
Common Pintail	CSMRD	lme												
Garganey	C	lm												
Blue-winged Teal	SDR	lm												
	C	m												
Cinnamon Teal	CSRMD	ml												
Northern Shoveler	S	ml												
	CMRD	mle												
Canvasback	CMDR	l												
	S	l												
Redhead	S	lm												
	CMRD	lm												
Ring-necked Duck	CMDR	l												
	S	l												
Tufted Duck	C	l												
Greater Scaup	CSR	iel												
	D	l												
Lesser Scaup	CSDRM	le												
King Eider	C	i												
Harlequin Duck	C	i												
Oldsquaw	C	i												
	S	l												
	DRM													
Black Scoter	C	i												
	S	l												
White-winged Scoter	C	ie												
	S	l												
	DR	l												
Surf Scoter	C	ie												
	S	l												
	(M)	l												
	DR	l												
Bufflehead	CDSRM	le												
Barrow's Goldeneye	R	l												
	DCS	le												
Common Goldeneye	R	l												
	S	l												
	C	iel												
	DM	l												

SPECIES	District	Habitat	January	February	March	April	May	June	July	August	September	October	November	December
Hooded Merganser	CDRSM	le												
Red-breasted Merganser	C	ie												
	S	l												
	R	l												
	DM													
Common Merganser	R	l												
	CM	l												
	(D)	l												
	S	l												
Ruddy Duck	CSRMD	lme												
Turkey Vulture	R	g												
	C	gwc												
	MD	gdw												
	S	g												
California Condor	(MC)	cwg												
Osprey	C	el												
	SDM	l												
	R	l												
White-tailed Kite	C	gmr												
	DS	gr												
Mississippi Kite	CD													
Bald Eagle	MCR	le												
	SD	l												
Northern Harrier	CMSRD	mg												
Sharp-shinned Hawk	CD	wcr												
	M	wf												
	SR	r												
Cooper's Hawk	CDM	wr												
	SR	r												
Northern Goshawk	M	f												
	D	r												
	C	w												
Bay-winged Hawk	RS	r			*(extirpated)*									
Red-shouldered Hawk	C(M)	rw												
	D	r												
Broad-winged Hawk	C	w												
	D													
Swainson's Hawk	D	gw												
	SR													
	C													
Zone-tailed Hawk	CDM													

SPECIES	District	Habitat	January	February	March	April	May	June	July	August	September	October	November	December
Red-tailed Hawk	CDM	cwgdrs												
	SR	g												
"Harlan's"	C													
Ferruginous Hawk	(DM)	g												
	CSR	g												
Rough-legged Hawk	(D)	gs												
	RS(M)	g												
	C	g												
Golden Eagle	CMD	cwgds												
	S													
American Kestrel	CDM	gdwcs												
	SR	g												
Merlin	CDMSR	wr												
Peregrine Falcon	C	e												
	S	lr												
	DRM	lr												
Prairie Falcon	D(M)	dgws												
	CSR	g												
Blue Grouse	(M)	f												
Sage Grouse	(M)	s												
Gambel's Quail	SRD	rdw												
California Quail	C(MD)	cwr												
Mountain Quail	M(CD)	wfc												
Yellow Rail	C	m												
Black Rail	(R)	m												
	S	m												
	C	m												
Clapper Rail	(C)	me												
	RS	m												
	D													
Virginia Rail	RS(D)	m												
	C	m												
Sora	CSDR	m												
	(M)	m												
Purple Gallinule	C													
Common Gallinule	SR	ml												
	D	ml												
	C	ml												
American Coot	CSMDR	lme												
Sandhill Crane	(SR)	g												
	CMD	g												

SPECIES	District	Habitat	January	February	March	April	May	June	July	August	September	October	November	December
American Oystercatcher	C	b												
	S	b												
Black Oystercatcher	(c)	b												
Black-necked Stilt	S	bm												
	C	elm												
	DR	lm												
	M	l												
American Avocet	S	bm												
	DRM	lm												
	C	eml												
Black-bellied Plover	C	beg												
	S	gb												
	DRM	lg												
Lesser Golden Plover	C	eg												
	S	bg												
	DR	lg												
Snowy Plover	C	b												
	S	b												
	D	l												
	R	l												
Wilson's Plover	CS	be												
Semipalmated Plover	C	eb												
	S	b												
	DRM	l												
Piping Plover	C	b												
Killdeer	CDSRM	ge												
Mountain Plover	S(D)	g												
	CR	g												
Greater Yellowlegs	CS	eml												
	DMR	lm												
Lesser Yellowlegs	CS	eml												
	DMR	lm												
Solitary Sandpiper	CMDR	lem												
	S	lm												
Spotted Sandpiper	CSR	bl												
	D	l												
	(M)	l												
Wandering Tattler	C	b												
	S	b												
	D	l												
Willet	CS	bel												
	DMR													

48

SPECIES	District	Habitat	January	February	March	April	May	June	July	August	September	October	November	December
Upland Sandpiper	CDR	g												
Whimbrel	C	beg												
	S	gb												
	(D)	lg												
	R	lg												
Long-billed Curlew	S	bg												
	C	bge												
	(D)	gl												
	RM	gl												
Hudsonian Godwit	D	l												
Bar-tailed Godwit	C	e												
Marbled Godwit	C	beg												
	S	gb												
	DRM	l												
Ruddy Turnstone	C	be												
	S	l												
	DR	l												
Black Turnstone	C	b												
	SR	lb												
Surfbird	C	b												
	S	b												
Red Knot	C	eb												
	S	b												
	DR	l												
Sanderling	C	be												
	S	b												
	DRM	l												
Semipalmated Sandpiper	S	b												
	CD	el												
Western Sandpiper	CS	el												
	DRM	l												
Red-necked Stint	S	b												
Least Sandpiper	CS	elb												
	DRM	l												
White-rumped Sandpiper	S	l												
Baird's Sandpiper	DM	l												
	CSR	elb												
Pectoral Sandpiper	C	elm												
	DMR	l												
	S	b												
Sharp-tailed Sandpiper	C	e												
Rock Sandpiper	C	b												

SPECIES	District	Habitat	January	February	March	April	May	June	July	August	September	October	November	December
Dunlin	C	be												
	S	b												
	DRM	l												
Curlew Sandpiper	CS	eb												
Stilt Sandpiper	S	lb												
	C	e												
	D	l												
Buff-breasted Sandpiper	C	ge												
Ruff	C	bel												
	D													
Short-billed Dowitcher	C	e												
	S	b												
	DMR	l												
Long-billed Dowitcher	C	eml												
	S	b												
	DMR	l												
Common Snipe	CSR	lme												
	DM	lm												
Wilson's Phalarope	C	elm												
	S	l												
	DMR	l												
Northern Phalarope	C	iel												
	S	l												
	DMR	l												
Red Phalarope	C	oie												
	S	l												
	DR	l												
Pomarine Jaeger	C	oi												
	RS	l												
Parasitic Jaeger	C	i												
	S	l												
	R	l												
Long-tailed Jaeger	C	o												
	RS	l												
South Polar Skua	C	o												
Laughing Gull	S	lgb												
	C	ei												
	DR	l												
Franklin's Gull	C	oibel												
	S	lb												
	DMR	l												
Little Gull	CS	iel												

SPECIES	District	Habitat	January	February	March	April	May	June	July	August	September	October	November	December
Black-headed Gull	C	i												•
Bonaparte's Gull	C	ibel												
	S	lb												
	DMR	l												
Heermann's Gull	C	oieb												
	S	lb												
	DMR	l												
Mew Gull	C	ieb												
	S	lb												
Ring-billed Gull	CSR	ibel												
	DM	l												
California Gull	C	oibel												
	S	lb												
	DMR	l												
Herring Gull	S	oiebl												
	C	lb												
	R	l												
	MD	l												
Thayer's Gull	C	oie												
	S	lb												
Western Gull	C	oibe												
	R	lb												•
Yellow-footed Gull	S	lb												
	C					•			•					•
Glaucous-winged Gull	C	beoi												
	S	lb												
Glaucous Gull	C	eboi												
	S	l												
Great Black-backed Gull	C	e								•				
Black-legged Kittiwake	C	oibe												
	SR	lb												
Sabine's Gull	C	o												
	SR	l												
	D	l												
Gull-billed Tern	S	lm	•											
Caspian Tern	C	ibel												
	S	lb												
	DM	l												
	R	l												
Royal Tern	C	oibe												
Elegant Tern	C	ibe	•											

SPECIES	District	Habitat	January	February	March	April	May	June	July	August	September	October	November	December
Common Tern	C	ibe												
	S	l												
	R	l												
	DM	l												
Arctic Tern	C	o												
	DS	l												
Forster's Tern	C	ebil												
	S	lb												
	R	l												
	DM	l												
Least Tern	C	bei												
	S	l												
	R	l												
Black Tern	S	lm												
	R	lm												
	C	mei												
	DM	l												
Black Skimmer	S	lb												
	(C)	e												
Common Murre	C	oi												
Pigeon Guillemot	(C)	oi												
Marbled Murrelet	C	i												
Xantus' Murrelet *E.h. hypoleuca*	C	o												
E.h. scrippsi	C	o												
Craveri's Murrelet	C	o												
Ancient Murrelet	C	oi												
Cassin's Auklet	C	o												
Parakeet Auklet	C													
Rhinoceros Auklet	C	o												
Tufted Puffin	C	o												
Horned Puffin	C	o												
Red-throated Loon	C	i												
	RM	l												
Arctic Loon	C	i												
	RDS	l												
Common Loon	C	i												
	RSMD	l												
Yellow-billed Loon	C	i												
Band-tailed Pigeon	(C)M	wf												
	DS	rw												

SPECIES	District	Habitat	January	February	March	April	May	June	July	August	September	October	November	December
White-winged Dove	R	r			▬▬▬▬▬▬▬▬▬								
	SD	r												
	C				•••••••••• •	•							
Mourning Dove	CDSMR	cwgrd	▬▬▬▬▬▬▬▬▬▬▬▬▬▬▬▬▬▬▬▬▬▬▬▬											
Inca Dove	(R)	w												
Common Ground-Dove	RS	rw	▬▬▬▬▬▬▬▬▬▬▬▬▬▬▬▬▬▬▬▬▬▬▬▬											
	(C)	rw												
	D					•	•		•			••••••		
Yellow-billed Cuckoo	R(D)	r												
	CS	r					••••••••••••							
Greater Roadrunner	DSR	gdsr	▬▬▬▬▬▬▬▬▬▬▬▬▬▬▬▬▬▬▬▬▬▬▬▬											
	C	cg												
Groove-billed Ani	C											•	••••		
Barn Owl	CDSR(M)	gcrw	▬▬▬▬▬▬▬▬▬▬▬▬▬▬▬▬▬▬▬▬▬▬▬▬											
Flammulated Screech-Owl	M	fw	•								•			
	CDS						●●					●●		
Common Screech-Owl	CMDR	wr	▬▬▬▬▬▬▬▬▬▬▬▬▬▬▬▬▬▬▬▬▬▬▬▬											
Great Horned Owl	CMDR	wfcr	▬▬▬▬▬▬▬▬▬▬▬▬▬▬▬▬▬▬▬▬▬▬▬▬											
	S	w												
Northern Pygmy-Owl	(C)M	wfr												
Elf Owl	(R)	r												
Burrowing Owl	SR	g	▬▬▬▬▬▬▬▬▬▬▬▬▬▬▬▬▬▬▬▬▬▬▬▬											
	CD	gd												
Spotted Owl	M(C)	wf												
Long-eared Owl	D	rw												
	C	rw				•••••••••••••								
	SR	r	•••••••••••••••••••••••••											
Short-eared Owl	C	mge		••••					•••••					
	DSR	gm						● ●●						
Northern Saw-whet Owl	M(C)	fw	●●											
	DS		●●● ●		•		•		•			•	•	
Lesser Nighthawk	RS	gdr	••••••		▬▬▬▬▬▬▬▬▬▬▬▬						•••••••		
	D	drg		•										
	C	x	•••••••••									•••		
Common Nighthawk	(MD)	wgs					●		●		●	●●		
	CR													
Common Poorwill	DR	ds		▬▬▬▬▬▬▬▬▬▬▬▬▬▬▬▬▬▬										
	M	cw		▬▬▬▬▬▬▬▬▬▬▬▬▬▬▬▬▬▬										
	C	c			▬▬▬▬▬▬▬▬▬▬▬▬▬									
Whip-poor-will	(M)	w												
	CS		●●				●		●	●		●		

53

SPECIES	District	Habitat	January	February	March	April	May	June	July	August	September	October	November	December
Black Swift	M	x												
	C													
	DS													
Chimney Swift	C	x												
	DR													
Vaux's Swift	CDSR	x												
	M													
White-throated Swift	CSDMR	x												
Broad-billed Hummingbird	CDR	w												
Violet-crowned Hummingbird	C													
Black-chinned Hummingbird	C(D)	rwc												
	R	r												
	S	r												
Costa's Hummingbird	DR	rdw												
	C	c												
Anna's Hummingbird	C	cwr												
	SR(D)	wr												
	M	wf												
Calliope Hummingbird	M	fw												
	CDSR	crw												
Broad-tailed Hummingbird	(M)	w												
	DR	r												
	C													
Rufous Hummingbird	C	cw												
	M	wf												
	DSR													
Allen's Hummingbird *sasin*	C	crw												
	M	wf												
sedentarius	(C)	wcr												
Belted Kingfisher	CMR	lrbe												
	DS	lr												
Lewis' Woodpecker	CDM	w												
	SR													
Red-headed Woodpecker	S													
Acorn Woodpecker	CM	wf												
	D													
	SR													
Gila Woodpecker	R	rw												
	(S)	w												

54

SPECIES	District	Habitat	January	February	March	April	May	June	July	August	September	October	November	December
Yellow-bellied Sapsucker *varius*	DRC	rw												
nuchalis	R	r												
	D	wr												
	SC	w												
	(M)	f												
Red-breasted Sapsucker	M	f												
	C	wr												
	D	wr												
Williamson's Sapsucker	M	f												
	CD	w												
Ladder-backed Woodpecker	R	wr												
	D	wr												
	S	wr												
	C													
Nuttall's Woodpecker	CM	wr												
	(D)	r												
	S													
Downy Woodpecker	C	wr												
	DS	wr												
Hairy Woodpecker	M	fw												
	C	wr												
	D	wr												
White-headed Woodpecker	M	f												
	CD													
Common Flicker "Red-shafted"	CM	wfr												
	DSR	wr												
"Yellow-shafted"	CDRS	wr												
"Gilded"	(RD)	wr												
Olive-sided Flycatcher	M	fr												
	C	w												
	DSR													
Greater Pewee	CDSR	w												
Western Wood-Pewee	CM	wfr												
	DSR													
Willow Flycatcher	DSR	r												
	CM	r												
Least Flycatcher	DC													
Hammond's Flycatcher	CDSMR	wrcf												
Dusky Flycatcher	M	fwc												
	DSR													
	C													

55

SPECIES	District	Habitat	January	February	March	April	May	June	July	August	September	October	November	December
Gray Flycatcher	(M)	ws												
	DSR	rw												
	C	w												
Western Flycatcher	CM	wr												
	DSR	r												
Eastern Phoebe	CDSR	rwg												
Black Phoebe	CSR	rl												
	D	rl												
Say's Phoebe	DSR	dg												
	C	gcw												
Vermilion Flycatcher	DR	r												
	CS	r												
Dusky-capped Flycatcher	DR	rw												
Ash-throated Flycatcher	C	cwr												
	DR	dr												
	M	w												
	S	dr												
Great Crested Flycatcher	C													
Brown-crested Flycatcher	R(D)	r												
Sulphur-bellied Flycatcher	C													
Tropical Kingbird	C	gwr												
	DRS													
Cassin's Kingbird	C	w												
	(M)D	w												
	R													
	S													
Thick-billed Kingbird	C													
	R													
Western Kingbird	DSRC	grw												
	M	g												
Eastern Kingbird	D	gr												
	C													
	S													
Scissor-tailed Flycatcher	C													
	DRS													
Horned Lark	D	gd												
	CSR	g												
	M	g												
Purple Martin	CM	w												
	DSR													

56

SPECIES	District	Habitat	January	February	March	April	May	June	July	August	September	October	November	December
Tree Swallow	SR	lm												
	C	rml												
	DM	ml												
Violet-green Swallow	M	wf												
	C	w												
	DSR													
Rough-winged Swallow	SR													
	C													
	DM													
Bank Swallow	SDR	lm												
	CM	lmeb												
Cliff Swallow	CM													
	RS													
	D													
Barn Swallow	C													
	DSR													
Steller's Jay	M	fw												
	C	w												
	DR	wr												
Blue Jay	MD													
Scrub Jay	CM	wc												
	DSR	rw												
Pinyon Jay	(MD)	ws												
	C													
Clark's Nutcracker	M	fw												
	CD													
	SR													
Black-billed Magpie	(D)	rsw												
Yellow-billed Magpie	(C)	w												
Common Crow	C(M)	wgr												
	(D)	r												
	SR	gr												
Common Raven	D	dgw												
	CSMR	cwgd												
Mountain Chickadee	M	fw												
	C	w												
	D	rw												
	S													
Chestnut-backed Chickadee	(C)	rw												
Plain Titmouse	CM	wr												
Verdin	DSR	rd												

SPECIES	District	Habitat	January	February	March	April	May	June	July	August	September	October	November	December
Bushtit	CM	cwr												
	DR	wr												
Red-breasted Nuthatch	M	f												
	C	w												
	DR	wr												
	S													
Pygmy Nuthatch	M	fw												
	C													
	(D)													
White-breasted Nuthatch	MC	fw												
	DSR													
Brown Creeper	M	f												
	CDRS	wr												
American Dipper	(CM)	x												
Cactus Wren	DRS	wd												
	(C)	c												
Rock Wren	D	x												
	M	x												
	CSR	x												
Canyon Wren	CMD(R)	x												
Bewick's Wren	CM	cwr												
	DRS	rd												
House Wren	C	wrc												
	M	wrc												
	SR	dr												
	D	dr												
Winter Wren	C	rw												
	DR													
	S													
Marsh Wren	SR	m												
	C	m												
	D	m												
Gray Catbird	D													
	C													
Northern Mockingbird	CRS	cwdr												
	D	rdw												
Sage Thrasher	D	ds												
	(M)	s												
	CSR													
Brown Thrasher	CD													

SPECIES	District	Habitat	January	February	March	April	May	June	July	August	September	October	November	December
Bendire's Thrasher	(D)	w												
	SR													
	C													
Curve-billed Thrasher	DSR	r												
California Thrasher	C(D)	c												
Crissal Thrasher	R	r												
	DS	rw												
LeConte's Thrasher	D	d												
Western Bluebird	M(C)	wf												
	(D)	w												
	SR													
Mountain Bluebird	(M)	gsw												
	D	g												
	SRC													
Townsend's Solitaire	M	fw												
	D	wr												
	CSR	wr												
Varied Thrush	CM	wf												
	D	rw												
	SR													
Veery	CD													
Swainson's Thrush	C	rw												
	DSR													
Hermit Thrush	C	cw												
	DSR	r												
	M	f												
Wood Thrush	C													
Rufous-backed Robin	DR													
American Robin	C	w												
	M	fwr												
	DSR	wr												
Golden-crowned Kinglet	M	f												
	C	w												
	SDR													
Ruby-crowned Kinglet	CDSR	wrc												
	M	f												
Blue-gray Gnatcatcher	C	cwr												
	(M)D	wr												
	SR	dr												
Black-tailed *lucida*	DR	d												
Gnatcatcher *californica*	C	c												
Wrentit	C(M)	c												

59

SPECIES	District	Habitat	January	February	March	April	May	June	July	August	September	October	November	December
White Wagtail	C	e										••		
Red-throated Pipit	C	g										••••••		
Water Pipit	CDSR	geb												
	M	g												
Sprague's Pipit	CD	g										••••••••	•	
Bohemian Waxwing	CMD	wr											••••••	
Cedar Waxwing	C	w												
	DMSR	w												
Phainopepla	DR	rw												
	S	rw												
	C	rwc												
Loggerhead Shrike	CDSR	gwcs												
Northern Shrike	(D)	gr				•	•					••••••		
	CS	g												
White-eyed Vireo	D						•							
Bell's Vireo	C(DR)	r												
Gray Vireo	(M)	cw												
	C						•							
Solitary Vireo cassinii	C	w												
	M	w												
	DRS													
plumbeus	(M)	w												
	DRS													
	C													
solitarius	CS							•						
Yellow-throated Vireo	CD						•	••••	•			•	••••	
Hutton's Vireo	C(M)	wr												
	D		•									•	•	
Warbling Vireo	C	wr												
	M	wr												
	DSR													
Philadelphia Vireo	CD		•									••••••••	•	
Red-eyed Vireo flavoviridis	C											••••••••		
olivaceus	D													
	C											••••••••		
Blue-winged Warbler	CD							•				•		
Golden-Winged Warbler	CD						•••					•	•	•••
Tennessee Warbler	C													
	D		•			•		•				••••		
	S						•							

SPECIES	District	Habitat	January	February	March	April	May	June	July	August	September	October	November	December
Orange-crowned Warbler	C	cwr												
	M	cr												
	D	rw												
	SR	rw												
Nashville Warbler	CSDR													
	M	f												
Virginia's Warbler	(M)	w												
	C													
	DSR													
Lucy's Warbler	R	r												
	(D)	r												
	S													
	C													
Northern Parula	DSR													
	C													
Yellow Warbler	C	r												
	D	r												
	SR	rw												
Chestnut-sided Warbler	CDSR													
Magnolia Warbler	CD													
	R	c												
Cape May Warbler	CD													
	SR													
Black-throated Blue Warbler	CDS													
Yellow-rumped "Audubon's" Warbler	CRS	wrcg												
	D	rdwg												
	M	fw												
"Myrtle"	CDSR	r												
Black-throated Gray Warbler	CSR													
	D													
	M	w												
Townsend's Warbler	C	w												
	M													
	DSR													
Hermit Warbler	C													
	M	f												
	DSR													
Black-throated Green Warbler	CDS													
Blackburnian Warbler	CD													
Yellow-throated Warbler	C													
	D													

SPECIES	District	Habitat	January	February	March	April	May	June	July	August	September	October	November	December
Grace's Warbler	M	f												
	C													
Pine Warbler	CD													
Prairie Warbler	C													
	DS													
Palm Warbler *palmarum*	C													
	D													
	S													
hypochrysea	C													
Bay-breasted Warbler	CD													
Blackpoll Warbler	C													
	D													
Cerulean Warbler	CDS													
Black-and-white Warbler	D													
	CSR													
American Redstart	C													
	D													
	RS	r												
Prothonotary Warbler	CDR													
Worm-eating Warbler	CD													
Ovenbird	CD													
	R													
Northern Waterthrush	C													
	D													
	SR													
Louisiana Waterthrush	S													
Kentucky Warbler	CD													
Connecticut Warbler	CD													
Mourning Warbler	CD													
MacGillivray's Warbler	DSR													
	C													
	M													
Common Yellowthroat	SR	m												
	C	m												
	D													
Hooded Warbler	CD													
Wilson's Warbler	C													
	DSR													
	M	r												
Canada Warbler	C													
	DM													

SPECIES	District	Habitat	January	February	March	April	May	June	July	August	September	October	November	December
Red-faced Warbler	M	f												
	CD													
Painted Redstart	C													
	D													
	M	w												
Yellow-breasted Chat	CDSR	r												
Hepatic Tanager	(M)	w												
	C													
	D													
	R													
Summer Tanager	RD	r												
	C													
Scarlet Tanager	CDR													
Western Tanager	C													
	DSR													
	M	f												
Northern Cardinal	R	r												
Pyrrhuloxia	SRD	r												
Rose-breasted Grosbeak	C	wr												
	DR													
	S													
Black-headed Grosbeak	C	wr												
	DSR													
	M	wf												
Blue Grosbeak	CDSR	r												
Lazuli Bunting	C	cr												
	DSR													
	M	c												
Indigo Bunting	C(R)DM	rc												
	S													
Varied Bunting	DR													
Painted Bunting	C													
	DR													
Dickcissel	C													
	D													
	S													
McCown's Longspur	C	g												
	D													
	S	g													
Lapland Longspur	CD	g												
	S	g													

SPECIES	District	Habitat	January	February	March	April	May	June	July	August	September	October	November	December
Chestnut-collared Longspur	DM	g												
	C	g												
	S	g												
Snow Bunting	D													
Lark Bunting	CDR	g												
Fox Sparrow	M	wc												
	C	cw												
	DSR													
Song Sparrow	C	rw												
	SR	r												
Lincoln's Sparrow	CDSR	crg												
	M	r												
Swamp Sparrow	D	r												
	CSR	rm												
White-throated Sparrow	DCMSR	rwc												
Golden-crowned Sparrow	CM	cwr												
	DSR													
White-crowned Sparrow														
gambelii	CDSR	cdgw												
	M	c												
nuttallii	(C)	c												
oriantha	DSR													
	(M)	x												
	C													
Harris' Sparrow	DCSR													
Dark-eyed Junco														
"Slate-colored"	CDSMR	wcr												
"Oregon"	M(C)	wf												
	CD	cw												
	SR	wr												
"Pink-sided"	SR(D)	wr												
	C	w												
"Gray-headed"	(M)	w												
	RM	w												
	DSC													
American Tree Sparrow	D													
	C													
	SR													
Chipping Sparrow	C	wg												
	D	wr												
	SR	wr												
	M	wf												

SPECIES	District	Habitat	January	February	March	April	May	June	July	August	September	October	November	December
Clay-colored Sparrow	CD													
Brewer's Sparrow	DSR	dg												
	(M)	s												
	C													
Black-chinned sparrow	M	cw												
	C(D)	cw												
	SR													
Savannah Sparrow *nevadensis etc.*	CSRD	g												
	(M)													
beldingi	(C)	meb												
rostratus	S	m												
Sharp-tailed Sparrow	C	m												
	DR													
LeConte's Sparrow	D													
Grasshopper Sparrow	C	g												
	D													
	SR													
Vesper Sparrow	C	g												
	DSR	g												
	(M)	sg												
Lark Sparrow	CDR	wg												
	M	wg												
	S	wg												
Black-throated Sparrow	D	d												
	C													
Sage Sparrow *bellii*	C	c												
canescens	(D)	ds												
	(M)	s												
nevadensis	D	d												
canescens & nevadensis	SR	d												
Cassin's Sparrow	CDS	gd												
Rufous-crowned Sparrow	C	c												
scottii	(M)	w												
Green-tailed Towhee	M	csw												
	RS	dr												
	D													
	C													
Rufous-sided Towhee	CM	cwr												
	DSR	rw												
Brown Towhee	C(M)	c												

SPECIES	District	Habitat	January	February	March	April	May	June	July	August	September	October	November	December
Abert's Towhee	R	r												
	S	r												
Streak-backed Oriole	C													
	D													
Hooded Oriole	C	wr												
	DRS	r												
Northern Oriole "Baltimore"	C													
	D													
"Bullock's"	C	wr												
	D	wr												
	M	wr												
	SR	wr												
Orchard Oriole	C													
	DSR													
Scott's Oriole	D(M)	w												
	C													
Yellow-headed Blackbird	RS	mg												
	D	mg												
	C	mg												
Red-winged Blackbird	CDSMR	mgr												
Tricolored Blackbird	C(D)	mg												
	S													
Western Meadowlark	CDSRM	g												
Great-tailed Grackle	R	mgr												
	S	mr												
	D	gmr												
	C													
Common Grackle	DCR													
Rusty Blackbird	C	gl												
	D	lgr												
	R													
Brewer's Blackbird	CDM	gwsm												
	SR	gw												
Bronzed Cowbird	R	rgw												
	DS													
Brown-headed Cowbird	SR	gr												
	C	wrg												
	D	wrg												
	M	wf												
Bobolink	C	mg												
	D	mg												
	S													

SPECIES	District	Habitat	January	February	March	April	May	June	July	August	September	October	November	December
Pine Siskin	M	fw												
	CDSR													
American Goldfinch	C	rw												
	DSR													
Lesser Goldfinch	C	rwc												
	DM	rw												
	S	r												
Lawrence's Goldfinch	C	wrc												
	M	wr												
	(D)	wr												
	S													
	R													
Rosy Finch "Gray-crowned"	(M)	x												
"Black"	(M)	x												
Purple Finch	M	wr												
	C	wr												
	DRS													
Cassin's Finch	M	fw												
	D													
	C													
House Finch	CDMSR	cgrw												
Red Crossbill	M	f												
	C													
	DS													
Evening Grosbeak	D	rw												
	M	fw												
	C	wr												

HLJ 80

PODICIPEDIDAE: GREBES

LEAST GREBE
Tachybaptus dominicus

One certain record: 18-23 Oct 1946 West Pond near Imperial Dam IMP. On 18 Oct 1946 a pair of adults was observed; six adults and three young were observed on 23 Oct, with an adult male and a juvenile collected.

Additional reports, many published in *AFN*, have been discounted because of insufficient details. Since this species is a casual visitor to southern Arizona (where it has been recorded as far west as Organ Pipe Cactus National Monument) it appears likely to reach the southeastern portion of the region again.

PIED-BILLED GREBE
Podilymbus podiceps

Fairly common resident throughout most of the region; becomes common in winter in District C and in the southern areas of the interior.

In winter Pied-billed Grebes largely withdraw from the colder portions of the region. Occurrence in winter on lakes in District M is dictated by the availability of open water. Transients can occur almost anywhere in the region, including the Channel Is. For breeding, this species requires some emergent aquatic vegetation for concealment of nests. Freshwater marshes are inhabited throughout the year. At other seasons it may be found in a variety of open water habitats including harbors, bays, and, exceptionally, outer coastal waters and the open ocean.

HORNED GREBE
Podiceps auritus

Common winter visitant along the coast, with small numbers wintering on some lakes in District C and the interior. Very rare transient through the interior. Casual in summer.

The Horned Grebe is a common winter visitant to inshore waters, bays, and harbors. Most fall birds arrive by mid-November (exceptionally to 16 Sep 1976 Goleta SBA). Small numbers may remain through mid-April; a few individuals linger into early May. There are two summer records for the coast: 4 Jun 1967 San Diego Bay SD and 11-18 Jul 1967 Mission Bay SD. Although it is primarily a marine bird, this species is not often encountered on the open ocean. It is uncommon around the Channel Is.

Small numbers winter regularly on deep water lakes and reservoirs within District C; it is occasionally even fairly common (e.g. L. Cachuma SBA).

In Districts S and R it is a rare transient from late October to late January. It has proven to be regular in winter in small numbers on deep-water reservoirs along the Colorado R. (e.g. L. Havasu SBE); it is occasionally found through the winter at the Salton Sea. Six records of alternate-plumaged birds at the Salton Sea from late March to mid-May suggest an influx of spring transients. There are two summer records: 11-21 Aug 1976 NESS and 10 Jul 1977 NESS.

In Districts D and M it occurs regularly only as a rare fall transient from late October through mid-December. There are three earlier records: 9 Sep 1976 Tinnemaha Res. INY and 4-5 Sep 1976 and 22 Sep 1974 Furnace Creek Ranch INY. It is a casual spring transient through the deserts: 14-21 Apr 1973 Furnace Creek Ranch; 29 Mar-1 Apr 1976 Baker SBE; 25 Mar 1979 Furnace Creek Ranch; and 8 Apr 1979 nr. Lancaster LA. That there are only four records may reflect a lack of coverage in early spring. There are two winter records from Districts D and M: 4 Dec 1978-27 Jan 1979 L. Palmdale LA and 20-26 Feb 1979 L. Henshaw SD.

RED-NECKED GREBE
Podiceps grisegena

Very rare winter visitant along the north coast; one record from the interior of District C and one record from the true interior.

Along the coast it occurs very rarely; it prefers inshore waters, harbors, and, occasionally, lagoons. The earliest acceptable record is 17 Oct 1978 Santa Maria R. mouth SBE; the latest record is 20 Jan-2 May 1980 Ventura VEN. There are only two records of this northern species from south of Los Angeles Co.: 20 Dec 1969-2 Jan 1970 Sweetwater Res. SD (away from the immediate coast) and 14 Mar 1977 Imperial Beach SD.

There is one record from District D: 6 Nov 1977 Stovepipe Wells INY.

We have discounted some records which we feel represent questionable identifications.

EARED GREBE
Podiceps nigricollis

Common winter visitant through much of the region; primarily a transient through Districts D and M. Breeds locally in Districts C,D,M, and S.

A common to abundant winter visitant, it occurs along the coast and on lakes, ponds, and reservoirs throughout District C. This grebe is an abundant winter visitant at the Salton Sea, where tens of thousands are routinely seen in a day; it remains rather commonly through the summer at the Salton Sea, primarily around river mouths. This species also winters commonly on the Colorado R. Coastally, a few may summer on inshore ocean waters.

72

In District D the Eared Grebe is fairly common in migration and uncommon in winter in suitable habitat; it breeds locally. Although it breeds locally in District M (see below), it is primarily a transient there.

The species breeds, or formerly bred, locally and irregularly at many localities in all districts. Recent localities include most of the coastal estuaries of San Diego Co., Santa Clara R. estuary VEN, L. Sherwood VEN (1967), NESS, SESS (one nest in 1979), Baldwin L. SBE, near Lancaster LA, near Barstow SBE (1980), and near Olancha INY. The use of these and other breeding sites varies in accordance with yearly fluctuations in water level and other conditions. For example, few birds nest at Baldwin L. after a series of dry winters, but several hundred pairs may nest when water is plentiful. Former breeding localities include Elizabeth L. LA, Nigger Slough LA, San Jacinto L. RIV, San Pasqual Valley SD, L. Hodges SD, and L. Cuyamaca SD.

The Eared Grebe occupies a variety of aquatic habitats from open ocean, inshore waters, harbors, and lagoons to lakes, ponds, and reservoirs in the interior. Migrant flocks are often encountered well at sea. For nesting, marshes with adjacent open water are required. Because of changes in water level and the alteration of habitat, breeding at a locality may be ephemeral.

WESTERN GREBE
Aechmophorus occidentalis

Common along the coast, primarily in winter. Very local breeding resident in Districts C, S, and R. Transient and scarce winter visitant elsewhere in the interior.

A common winter visitant to the entire coast (less numerous around the Channel Is.), it frequents bays, harbors, and the inshore waters of the open coastline. In winter in the interior, Western Grebes are common in District C on some reservoirs (e.g. L. Cachuma SBA and L. Casitas VEN), fairly common to locally common along the Colorado R., uncommon at the Salton Sea, and rare in Districts D and M, where it is also an uncommon transient. Transients in the interior appear by late August.

In summer this grebe remains locally in small flocks along the coast. It is locally common in District R, stays uncommon in District S, and has been recorded a few times in Districts D and M. Breeding now occurs in District R at L. Havasu SBE (sizeable numbers), in District S at the Whitewater R. mouth NESS (since 1976), and, in the interior of District C, at Sweetwater Res. SD (nesting continuous through much of the year). It formerly nested at San Jacinto L. RIV (spring 1915) and small numbers may occasionally nest elsewhere in District C. The Western Grebe normally requires deeper water around its nesting marshes than does the Eared Grebe.

The relative status of the two distinct color morphs in the region awaits rigorous study. The dull-billed, dark morph does greatly predominate over the bright-billed, light morph in the region; both color morphs are known to breed in the region. Recent studies have suggested that these "morphs" in fact appear to represent reproductively isolated populations.

DIOMEDEIDAE: ALBATROSSES

SHORT-TAILED ALBATROSS
Diomedea albatrus

Formerly a rather common visitor offshore; the only record in this century is a sighting of an immature 145 km west of San Diego SD 28 Aug 1977.

Until late in the 19th century, this was a very common bird, with records in all coastal counties, often rather close to shore. However, heavy exploitation of the species on its nesting grounds off southern Japan brought it close to extinction. The last certain record prior to the recent record was 3 Apr 1898 off San Pedro LA (specimen).

Recent protective measures have allowed a gradual increase which will likely be reflected in future southern California records. There is a recent photographic record 20 Apr 1978 off Santa Cruz, some 130 km north of our region.

Large, massive-billed albatrosses seen off our coast in the future are likely to be of this species, although the Wandering Albatross (*D. exulans*) has been found once in northern California.

BLACK-FOOTED ALBATROSS
Diomedea nigripes

Year-round visitant well offshore; the largest numbers are present from early May through August.

The numbers and the regularity of occurrence of the Black-footed Albatross increase to the north; the species is fairly common (except in fall and early winter) off Morro Bay and other areas on the northern coast. The largest concentration known for the region is 112 birds 40 km w. of Pt. Loma SD on 6 Aug 1958. It is, however, likely that even larger numbers may be encountered in the poorly worked waters off the northern coast. It is only rarely observed inside of the Channel Is.

This species was abundant during the 19th century, but numbers declined sharply during the early 1900s because of destruction of colonies on the nesting islands in the mid-Pacific. It has once again increased in the last several decades, but numbers remain well below last century's levels.

LAYSAN ALBATROSS
Diomedea immutabilis

Casual offshore visitant in late winter and spring. One record for the interior.

There are six records offshore: 5 Apr 1909 San Nicolas I.; 15 Mar 1949 w. of San Miguel I. (2); 6 Feb 1958 eight km off San Pedro LA; 26 Mar 1968 80 km w. of Pt. Conception SBA; 12-13 May 1975 about 130 km off Pt. Arguello SBA; and 8 Mar 1980 vic. Davidson Seamount off n. SLO (3). The 1909 bird from San Nicolas I. represented the first record for California; the bird had been captured on the beach by the cook for a scientific expedition and served for a meal!

The interior record is: 5 May 1976 Morongo Pass near Desert Hot Springs RIV. The bird was flying west toward San Gorgonio Pass into strong headwinds and had undoubtedly been "trapped" in the Gulf of California.

Further investigation will likely reveal this species to be regular far offshore in late winter and spring, particularly in the northern portion of the region.

PROCELLARIIDAE:
SHEARWATERS, FULMARS, AND PETRELS
NORTHERN FULMAR
Fulmarus glacialis

Irregular winter visitant offshore, occasionally remaining into summer after flight years.

The fulmar is quite common off our coast some winters and nearly absent others; at least a few individuals are found each year. In flight winters it may be observed in inshore waters, around fishing piers, and even inside harbors; during such winters it may be abundant offshore. It is generally absent in summer, except after large flights when small numbers may remain. It may exceptionally be "numerous" into June, as in 1976.

Gray birds predominate in our region; white and intermediate plumaged birds are always in a distinct minority. However, the relative proportions of the different color morphs vary from year to year.

MOTTLED (SCALED) PETREL
Pterodroma inexpectata

Two records, both of birds found dead on the San Luis Obispo Co. coast: 28 Feb 1976 Cayucos and 31 Mar 1976 Cambria.

There are three additional records of this species from northern California. It is a more numerous visitant to the north and west of California.

COOK'S PETREL
Pterodroma cookii

One record: at least four present in the vicinity of Davidson Seamount, off northern San Luis Obispo Co., 17 Nov-1 Dec 1979. Possibly regular far offshore.

Four were present (along with two additional *Pterodroma* possibly of this species) 17 Nov 1979 vic. Davidson Seamount (one photographed). Two (plus five *Pterodroma* sp.) were seen there on 24 Nov 1979, and one was still present on 1 Dec 1979. These sightings have not yet been reviewed by the California Bird Records Committee. It is likely that this species is regular far offshore in the region; there are additional records more than 160 km off the southern California coast, and the species has also been recorded off Baja California. All specimens from the northern Pacific are of nominate *cookii* (breeding off New Zealand), and it is likely that our birds are of that race, although *P. c. defilippiana*, breeding on the Juan Fernandez I. off Chile and considered specifically distinct by some authors, cannot be absolutely excluded.

STEJNEGER'S PETREL
Pterodroma longirostris

One record: 17 Nov 1979 near the Davidson Seamount, off northern San Luis Obispo Co. Possibly regular far offshore.

The lone sight record has not yet been reviewed by the California Bird Records Committee. Additionally, five specimens were taken 1000 km off the central California coast on 14 and 19 Nov 1906, and it is likely that this species occurs regularly well offshore.

PINK-FOOTED SHEARWATER
Puffinus creatopus

Common summer visitant offshore, remaining rarely through the winter.

Pink-footed and Sooty Shearwaters are much the commonest members of their family in the region in summer. While aggregate numbers of Pink-footed are far less than those of Sooty, the former species often predominates far offshore. Numbers of both species decrease greatly far offshore (generally more than 150 km). The Pink-footed is only rarely observed from shore.

It is quite rare in winter, at which season it may be most regular in the northern portion of the region.

FLESH-FOOTED SHEARWATER
Puffinus carneipes

Very rare visitant offshore; most records are from spring, late summer, and fall.

The present breakdown of records consists of seven in spring, two in summer (July), eight in fall, and an isolated winter record (22 Jan 1978 off Morro Bay SLO). The latest fall records are 22 Nov 1968 off San Pedro LA (6+, the high count for a single day) and 24 Nov 1979 vic. Davidson Seamount off SLO.

This species is usually observed with Pink-footed Shearwaters well offshore. Some authorities have considered the Flesh-footed and Pink-footed Shearwaters to represent a single species; the two forms are allopatric breeders in the temperate southern Pacific.

BULLER'S (NEW ZEALAND) SHEARWATER
Puffinus bulleri

Rather rare fall visitant well offshore, but concentrations have been noted. One winter and two summer records from offshore; one interior record.

This shearwater is generally a rather rare fall visitant offshore, but numbers fluctuate and the species can be fairly common (and occasionally common) in the northern part of the region. The largest concentrations are: 2000 off San Miguel I. 26-28 Sep 1976 and 175 off Ventura VEN 27 Oct 1968.

There are only five records for the waters south of Ventura Co.: 2 Nov 1957 off San Clemente ORA (3); 22 Nov 1969 off San Diego SD; 22 Oct 1971 off San Diego (2); 15 Sep 1973 off San Diego (2); and 19 Feb 1976 La Jolla SD (dead on beach). Other winter records exist for northern California. Unseasonal were individuals at Pt. Mugu VEN 21 Jun 1980 (from shore) and s. of Anacapa I. 26 Jun 1976, but it has been recorded as early as mid-June in northern California.

Accidental in the interior: one at NESS 6 Aug 1966 (specimen). This bird undoubtedly came north out of the Gulf of California, even though the species is almost unknown in Mexican waters.

SOOTY SHEARWATER
Puffinus griseus

Abundant visitant offshore from April through September; quite uncommon in winter. Accidental in the interior.

An abundant spring and summer visitant offshore, the largest numbers are present from late April and early May to July and August (especially off the northern coast). Flocks of several thousand birds can often be seen in inshore waters. This is easily our commonest shearwater during much of the year, although it can be quite uncommon in winter. During winter it may be most numerous off the northern coast.

It is accidental in the interior: A bird was seen on the Salton Sea near Desert Shores IMP 14 Aug 1971. There is an additional interior record just outside our region near Yuma, Arizona.

SHORT-TAILED SHEARWATER
Puffinus tenuirostris

Rare late fall and winter visitant offshore.

The status of this species in the region is unclear because of frequent confusion with the very similar Sooty Shearwater. The Short-tailed Shearwater is probably a rare but regular visitant offshore in late fall and winter, especially in the northern portion of the region. Numbers appear to vary somewhat from year to year. In the winter of 1941-1942 numbers of up to 130 were seen within 0.5 km of La Jolla SD (many specimens). It was possibly more numerous historically than at present. The latest record is 20 Apr 1980 off San Diego SD.

Two recent sightings from shore came during northwesterly gales: 1 Mar 1976 La Jolla (3); and 2 Mar 1976 Goleta SBA (2).

This species should be identified with extreme caution in the region. We have dismissed a number of late spring and early summer records published in *AFN* because of insufficient details. Because of the difficulties of field identification of Short-tailed and Sooty Shearwaters, we feel that such unseasonal reports should be substantiated by specimens.

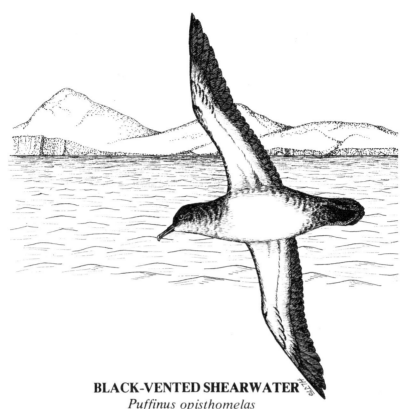

BLACK-VENTED SHEARWATER
Puffinus opisthomelas

Fairly common to common late fall and winter visitant, primarily off the southern coast. May linger through spring and remain casually through summer off San Diego.

Black-vented Shearwaters can be fairly common, common, or occasionally even abundant off the Orange and, especially, San Diego Co. coasts in late fall and winter (e.g. 12,000 off La Jolla SD 14 Nov 1979). Numbers there generally decline after early winter, although small numbers may linger well into spring and the species occurs casually through the summer.

It is irregularly fairly common in late fall and winter north along the remainder of the coast, although it is almost absent some winters. It may exceptionally be quite common, with maximal concentrations of 1500 off Pt. Mugu VEN 5 Jan 1980 and 200-300 off Pismo Beach SLO 6-14 Nov 1974. It is casual in spring north of San Diego Co.; there are no summer records.

This is a shearwater of inshore waters; the largest numbers are usually encountered within 5-10km of the coast, and it is frequently seen from shore. Most authorities now consider this species distinct from the Manx Shearwater, *P. puffinus*. A white-vented Manx-type shearwater, almost certainly not *opisthomelas*, was observed off Santa Rosa I. 10 Sep 1975.

HYDROBATIDAE: STORM-PETRELS

WILSON'S STORM-PETREL
Oceanites oceanicus

Three fall records: 31 Aug 1935 40km wnw of Pt. Loma SD; 5 Sep 1962 off San Clemente I.; and 7 Sep 1969 off Morro Bay SLO.
This species occurs regularly in fall with the rafts of Black and Ashy Storm-Petrels in Monterey Bay, north of our region.

FORK-TAILED STORM-PETREL
Oceanodroma furcata

In general, a casual winter and spring visitant offshore; occasional influxes have occurred.
Records of live, healthy birds extend from 15 Nov to 30 May. Additionally, a dead bird was found at Morro Bay SLO 3 Sep 1969 (not graphed), and an exhausted bird was at Cardiff Beach SD 9 Jun 1939.

In the spring of 1976 relatively large numbers occurred off the coast: 29 individuals were recorded in the Santa Barbara Channel 17-30 May (including one from shore at Goleta Pt. SBA 20 May), and others were recorded from Morro Bay 10 May, off San Diego SD 8 May, and from La Jolla SD (during a storm) 3 Mar. In 1916 another spring flight evidently occurred: 9 dead individuals were on Sunset Beach ORA 15 May-1 Jun and one was found the previous fall on 23 Oct 1915 at Playa del Rey LA (dead on beach).

Remaining records are: 23 Dec 1918 San Diego (dead); 15 Nov 1958 off Pt. Loma SD ("some"); 22 Nov 1958 Pt. Dume LA (3); 12 May 1975 150 km off Pt. Arguello SBA; and 1 Dec 1979 Davidson Seamount off SLO (2).

This species has declined off northern California in recent years. Little is known of its status far offshore, so we cannot speculate as to whether birds reaching our region are unusually far south or merely unusually close to shore.

Due in part to inaccurate representation in popular field guides, Fork-tailed Storm-Petrels have frequently been erroneously reported in the region. We have discounted numerous reports lacking convincing details.

LEACH'S STORM-PETREL
Oceanodroma leucorhoa

Fairly common visitant offshore, primarily from mid-June through September. Casual offshore in winter. Accidental in the interior. One or two small breeding colonies.
Leach's Storm-Petrels generally remain well offshore; storm-petrels inside the islands and in inshore waters are virtually never of this species.

However, they are seen regularly just off San Clemente and San Miguel Is. Small breeding colonies are located on San Miguel I., and possibly on Santa Barbara I.

There are four certain winter records: 25 Jan 1959 off Santa Barbara I.; 22 Mar 1904 between San Diego SD and San Clemente I.; and 17 Nov 1979 (2) and 1 Dec 1979 (20) Davidson Seamount off SLO. This species will likely prove to be regular in small numbers far offshore at this season.

It is accidental in the interior, where there is one record in the aftermath of Tropical Storm Kathleen: a dark-rumped individual was seen with Least Storm-Petrels at SESS on 15 Sep 1976.

White-rumped birds greatly predominate in our region. They are known to represent *beali* from northern California breeding locations and *socorroensis* from Guadalupe I.(this population also contains dark-rumped individuals). Birds breeding on the Channel Is. are small and show much white on the rump; they are tentatively assignable to *beali*. The population breeding on Los Coronados Is. just south of San Diego has been assigned to *beali* by some authors and called *willetti* by others; it certainly occurs in our southernmost waters. Dark-rumped individuals originate from Mexican waters; they have yet to be documented off our coast, but probably do occur. They would be composed of a segment of *socorroensis* and possibly the currently recognized *chapmani*, which breeds on the San Benitos Is. The taxonomy of Leach's Storm-Petrel is complex and has not been worked out adequately; future taxonomic change can be expected.

BLACK STORM-PETREL
Oceanodroma melania

Common summer visitant offshore; casual into early winter. One small breeding colony.

Almost always our commonest storm-petrel, this species is most numerous from late April through September; it diminishes in numbers through early October (present casually to mid-January and unrecorded in February and March). It prefers relatively inshore waters, and is the storm-petrel most likely to be seen from shore. The largest numbers are generally within about 20km of shore.

It breeds in very small numbers on Santa Barbara I. This is the only known colony in the United States.

ASHY STORM-PETREL
Oceanodroma homochroa

Fairly common to common summer visitant, primarily in the northern waters of the region. Breeds on some of the northern Channel Is. Very few winter records.

81

This is a fairly common to common summer visitor from late April through early October in the area from roughly Santa Catalina I. north. The largest numbers are usually encountered in May, although occasional concentrations have occurred in late August and September (e.g. "hundreds" between Goleta SBA and San Miguel I. 28 Aug 1977). South of Santa Catalina I., this species is a rare but regular spring and fall visitor. In winter it is probably a regular visitant to offshore waters throughout the region, although there are only about ten records between early December and early April. It is probably the storm-petrel most likely to be seen at this season.

This is the most numerous breeding storm-petrel in the region; large colonies are located on San Miguel, Santa Cruz, and Santa Barbara Is.

Ashy Storm-Petrels are recorded inside the Channel Is. as well as far at sea; they are occasionally seen close to the mainland and, exceptionally, from shore (especially during storms).

BAND-RUMPED (HARCOURT'S) STORM-PETREL
Oceanodroma castro

One record: 12 Sep 1970 off San Diego SD; carefully observed for an extended period.

The above record was reviewed and accepted by the California Bird Records Committee; it represents the only record for the west coast of North America.

GALAPAGOS (WEDGE-RUMPED) STORM-PETREL
Oceanodroma tethys

One record: 18 Aug 1976 s. of Anacapa I.

The above sight record is still being circulated through the California Bird Records Committee. A bird seen briefly vic. Davidson Seamount off SLO 1 Dec 1979 was also probably of this species; this record has not yet circulated through the CBRC. There are two additional records for the Monterey Bay area to the north of the region.

LEAST STORM-PETREL
Oceanodroma microsoma

Irregular late summer visitor offshore; occasionally abundant. One storm-related occurrence in the interior.

Generally present from mid-August through late September (and sometimes into October), Least Storm-Petrels are quite common some years and rare others. They are occasionally even abundant, especially off San Diego Co.; maxima include: 3200 off San Diego 8 Sep 1979; 3000 off San Diego 17 Sep 1970; 500 off San Diego 9 Sep 1978; and 500 off

Morro Bay SLO 7 Sep 1969. It is virtually absent some years and none was recorded in 1973. It is most regular in its occurrence off San Diego Co.; north of there it is recorded on the average of every other year.

Following Tropical Storm Kathleen, a wreck of some 500-1000 birds appeared on the Salton Sea; this constitutes the only record for the interior of the region. The birds were first noted on 12 Sep 1976, two days after Kathleen swept through the Imperial Valley from Baja California. The majority disappeared within two weeks, but small numbers remained well into October, with the last eight birds recorded on 21 Oct. No dead birds were found, which suggests that they may have departed successfully. Storm-blown birds were also recorded just outside our region on L. Mohave along the Colorado R.

PHAETHONTIDAE: TROPICBIRDS

WHITE-TAILED TROPICBIRD
Phaethon lepturus

One record: an adult was seen regularly at Upper Newport Bay ORA 24 May-23 Jun 1964.

The above bird was attracted to remote-controlled glider airplanes which hobbyists flew from the bluffs of the bay. The misguided bird actively courted and even attempted to copulate with these gliders! For a full account of this record, with photographs, see Hetrick and McCaskie, *Condor* 67: 186-187, 1965.

RED-BILLED TROPICBIRD
Phaethon aethereus

Rare summer and fall visitant offshore; probably casual in winter. One interior record.

Red-billed Tropicbirds are recorded most regularly in late summer and early fall; the extreme dates are from 6 Apr 1980 E. Anacapa I. and 10 May 1969 off San Diego SD to 17 Oct 1976 off Santa Barbara I. (with later records discussed below). The majority of records are from Santa Catalina I. south; scattered records exist for farther north. The northernmost records for the region are: 55 and 105 km off Pt. Arguello SBA 30 Sep 1979 and off Morro Bay SLO 7 Sep 1969. There are three records for northern California. Maxima are: 9 off San Diego 27 Jul 1968 and 8 off Santa Cruz I. 8 Sep 1974.

In late January 1977 at least three birds were recorded off the southern California coast (not graphed), indicating that this species is of at least casual status in winter.

A favored spot for tropicbirds is Pyramid Cove along the southern end of San Clemente I. (an area well covered by birders); it has often been seen in other areas just off the southern Channel Is., although it is very rare close to the mainland.

There is one record for the interior: an immature was caught by a dog at Morongo Valley SBE 11 Sep 1976, following Tropical Storm Kathleen. There are two additional records for southern Arizona.

It should be noted that Royal Terns offshore are frequently called tropicbirds by overzealous birders.

RED-TAILED TROPICBIRD
Phaethon rubricauda

One record within the region: 7 Oct 1979, 150 km off Pt. Buchon SLO.

There are three additional records from 160 to 320 km off the coast of southern California 30 Sep-8 Oct 1979, one 250 km w. of San Diego 16 Aug 1980, and one record from the Farallon Is. off San Francisco 3 Jul 1979. It has also been recorded off Baja California. The sighting for this region has not yet been reviewed by the California Bird Records Committee.

SULIDAE: BOOBIES

BLUE-FOOTED BOOBY
Sula nebouxii

Irregular late summer visitor to the Salton Sea; absent most years, although sizeable invasions have occurred. Also recorded in Districts R, D, M, and C, mainly during invasion years.

Principal invasion years on record for the Salton Sea are: 1953 (3 birds, from at least 18 Oct); 1966 (about 5 birds, from 4 Aug); 1969 (up to 30/day, from very late August); 1971 (up to 48/day, from 8 Aug); 1972 (up to 40/day, from 22 Jul); and 1977 (up to 11/day, from 24 Aug). Scattered records exist for other years. As shown above, the timing of these invasions is variable. Individuals may linger into late November, e.g. 23 Nov 1969 Salton City IMP. The boobies frequently congregate around the Whitewater R. dike at NESS; Salton City has also had concentrations.

There are only three records for District R: 4-10 Sep 1954 L. Havasu SBE; 14-24 Sep 1978 L. Havasu; and late Nov 1958-11 Apr 1959 L. Havasu. It has also been recorded around L. Mead, Nevada, outside of the region.

In some flight years, birds dispersing northward out of the Gulf of California may push northward beyond the Salton Sea, even reaching District C and the ocean. Many birds reaching the coast appear to have traveled westward through San Gorgonio Pass. Years of occurrence in District C (usually involving 1-2 birds) are 1947, 1954, 1964, 1965, 1969, 1971, 1972, 1974, and 1977. The only large coastal incursion was in 1971, when some 35 individuals were noted within the district. Some birds were even observed on the open ocean off Los Angeles Co., and later off San Diego Co. Thirty-seven were on Los Coronados Is. just south of the region, 21 Nov 1971. During the 1971 invasion, Blue-footed Boobies were also observed singly through much of the southern interior. The species is unrecorded on the northern deserts.

There are two records for District M: the first record of this species for California was obtained 1 Nov 1933 at Big Bear L. SBE and a bird was captured near L. Henshaw SD 18 Aug 1977.

Boobies arriving in southern California during invasions have remained on a few occasions for considerable lengths of time, e.g. the wintering bird on L. Havasu cited above; two at Puddingstone Res. LA from early Oct 1964 through May 1965; and one at L. San Marcos SD from late Aug 1972 until it was found dead 14 Dec 1972. A bird seen 8 Jan 1972 between Ventura VEN and Anacapa I. was probably a remnant of the invasion of the previous fall.

Birds seen 22 Jun 1976 at Gull I. off Santa Cruz I. and 16 Mar 1980 off Oceanside SD do not fit into the established pattern of occurrence.

Most Blue-footed Boobies in the region have been immature or sub-adult birds.

MASKED BOOBY
Sula dactylatra

One record: a near-adult bird was observed 16km s. of San Clemente I. 14 Jan 1977. This represents the only record of this species in California.

BROWN BOOBY
Sula leucogaster

Casual late summer visitant to the Salton Sea and Colorado River Valley. One record for the coast.

The Brown Booby disperses northward from the Gulf of California from late July into early fall; individuals sometimes remain in the region until early November. It is absent from the region in most years and has never occurred in such large numbers as the Blue-footed Booby. It is not a strikingly irruptive species as is the Blue-foot; it may appear in years in which the Blue-foot is nearly or completely absent (e.g. 1970, 1974). There is, however, probably some positive correlation between the appearance of these two species. It has been recorded in the following years at the Salton Sea and along the Colorado R.: 1946 (1), 1953 (1), 1957 (1), 1958 (2), 1966 (1), 1967 (1), 1969 (8), 1970 (1), 1971 (2), 1972 (3), 1974 (1), and 1977 (2). It was also recorded in 1943 on the Arizona side of the Colorado R. A bird seen 15 Jul 1972 standing in an irrigated field near Calexico IMP is the only record of this species in the region away from a body of deep water.

Prolonged stays by individuals include: 5 Sep 1958-7 Oct 1960 vic. Imperial Dam IMP and 19 Aug to mid-Dec 1977 L. Havasu SBE. An adult at NESS 25 Apr 1970 was either an unprecedented spring wanderer or, more likely, a bird remaining from the record invasion of the previous summer.

There is one record for the coast: one was present on Prince Islet off San Miguel I. during the summers from 1961-1968.

It should be noted that dark immature Blue-footed Boobies have often been called Brown Boobies. Caution should be exercised in the identification on this species. Most records in the region are of immatures.

PELECANIDAE: PELICANS

AMERICAN WHITE PELICAN
Pelecanus erythrorhynchos

Primarily a transient through the region, sometimes in large flocks. Commonest at the Salton Sea, least common along the coast. Winters locally; non-breeders may summer, especially at the Salton Sea.

At the Salton Sea it is a common transient in spring and fall; it is fairly common (in variable numbers) as a non-breeder through the summer. It nested there until 1957; up to several hundred pairs were sometimes present. The first spring transients may appear as early as late January; fall transients sometimes appear by late summer. White Pelicans are uncommon to rare in winter at the Salton Sea. Along the Colorado R. it is a fairly common spring and fall transient and is generally absent in summer and winter. Although it is infrequently observed through the remainder of the interior, migrant flocks can be quite large. The largest migrant flock recorded in the region was 3200 near Imperial Dam IMP 4 Oct 1956. It has wintered at L. Palmdale LA (1, winter 1978-1979) and at L. Elsinore RIV (25-30, winter 1967-1968). Near Lakeview RIV, 275 present 24-27 Dec 1979 may have wintered.

Along the coast this species regularly winters at Morro Bay SLO (50-100 birds), and a smaller flock is irregularly present on San Diego Bay SD. It is sporadic elsewhere; individuals or small flocks are noted primarily in fall migration and, less frequently, into early winter. It is unrecorded on the Channel Is. An unusual concentration in summer on the coast was 50 at Morro Bay 13 Jun 1962.

White Pelicans are usually found on large, open bodies of water, especially freshwater marshes and large, shallow lakes. At the Salton Sea they generally occur around freshwater inlets at the north and south ends. They frequently appear (and winter locally) on coastal estuaries, but they are virtually never seen on the open ocean.

86

BROWN PELICAN
Pelecanus occidentalis

Common throughout the year along the coast, with the largest numbers present in summer. Breeding colonies are located on Anacapa, Santa Barbara, and Santa Cruz Is. Regular post-breeding visitant to the Salton Sea, sometimes in numbers. Quite rare elsewhere in the interior.

Along the mainland coast it is least numerous in April and early May, when small numbers of non-breeding birds remain; however, breeding birds from Anacapa I. may be routinely noted foraging along the mainland coast from Pt. Dume LA to Santa Barbara SBA. Numbers of Brown Pelicans begin building in mid-May. The species is especially numerous from July through October, after the major post-breeding influx of birds from colonies in Baja California. Late in this period, the largest numbers of post-breeding birds may be found in the waters around the outer Channel Is. Along the mainland they remain common to mid-November; they are common throughout the year around the Channel Is.

At the Salton Sea the Brown Pelican is a regular post-breeding visitant from the Gulf of California. It has arrived as early as 15 May 1979, with numbers peaking in late July and August and falling off sharply thereafter. Numbers at the Salton Sea are variable; only a few are recorded some years. The maximum count was 105 on 12 Aug 1972. Late fall and winter records are: 30 Dec 1977 SESS (2) and 14 Jan 1978 NESS.

It has been recorded regularly from mid-June through fall on the Colorado R., especially in the vicinity of Imperial Dam IMP. Outside of this pattern was one present near Imperial Dam from 8 Aug 1978 until the spring of 1979 (not graphed), and another at Cibola L. IMP 31 Dec 1978. There are other scattered records for the interior, including District M and the interior of District C; all are from mid-July through mid-September except for 27 Dec 1979 near Lakeview RIV (imm. with White Pelicans). It is unrecorded on the northern deserts. Localities at which it has occurred in the interior include: L. Arrowhead SBE, Iron Mtn. Pump Plant SBE, L. Elsinore RIV, Seeley and Ocotillo IMP, and L. Cuyamaca SD. Birds at Hansen Dam LA 29 Aug 1971 and near Daggett SBE 20 Sep 1979 were the farthest from the Gulf of California. Only about 1% of the records from the interior pertain to full adults; the great majority are of first-year birds.

As a nesting species in the region the Brown Pelican has undergone a considerable decline which was first noticed in the late 1960s (only sketchy information is available for the 1950s and the early 1960s). The use of organochlorine pesticides has been convincingly implicated in this decline, which resulted primarily from decreased egg viability through eggshell thinning. The major current threat to Brown Pelicans in the region may be the commercial overharvesting of anchovies, a major food resource of this species. Historical nesting sites in the region were on the northern Channel Is.: Anacapa, Santa Barbara, San Miguel, and Santa Cruz. Although aggregate numbers of breeding birds were historically large, occupancy of particular rookeries was very irregular. By the mid-1970s the size and fledging success of colonies on W. Anacapa I. and around Santa Cruz I. had begun to increase somewhat. The most recent (1979) estimate of young hatched on W. Anacapa I. is 980 (out of over 1250 nests). About 50 active nests with 72 hatched young were on Santa Barbara I. (and adjacent Sutil Rock) in spring 1980. Eighty pairs nested on Scorpion Rock off Santa Cruz I. in 1975 (nesting also took place there in 1972 and 1974). This species nests commonly and successfully on Los Coronados Is. just south of the region.

The Brown Pelican is almost exclusively a bird of marine habitats, from the open ocean to inshore waters, bays, and harbors.

The California Brown Pelican (*P. o. californicus*) is the subspecies occurring in the region; it is considered endangered by the California and Federal governments.

PHALACROCORACIDAE: CORMORANTS
DOUBLE-CRESTED CORMORANT
Phalacrocorax auritus

Fairly common to common throughout the year along the entire coast, on some of the Channel Is., and along the Colorado R. Fairly common all year at the Salton Sea. A scarce transient elsewhere in the interior. Breeds locally on the Channel Is. and in Districts S and R.

While it is generally common along the coast and around the Channel Is., numbers on the mainland coast decrease in summer, when the species is fairly common (and may be quite uncommon in Los Angeles, Ventura, and Santa Barbara Cos.). It occurs locally on inland lakes on the coastal slope, sometimes commonly (e.g. L. Cachuma SBA and Sweetwater Res. SD). It breeds on San Miguel, Santa Cruz, Anacapa, and Santa Barbara Is. and on their adjacent islets.

It is a common species along the Colorado R. throughout the year; nesting is local (e.g. vic. Topock Marsh SBE). It is a fairly common resident at the Salton Sea; nesting is sporadic there, although the species has bred successfully in recent years at NESS and SESS. Away from Districts S and R it is a rare transient in the interior. It has summered very locally in District M — e.g. at L. Henshaw SD, where it formerly nested (to at least 1932).

This is the only cormorant to be seen inland, except for the very rare Neotropic Cormorant. In the interior it generally occurs around large lakes, reservoirs, and rivers. Along the coast it frequents estuaries, harbors, and bays. Over the open ocean it is the least common of our three coastal cormorants.

NEOTROPIC (OLIVACEOUS) CORMORANT
Phalacrocorax olivaceus

Three occurrences from along the lower Colorado R., most likely involving the same individual: a single bird was present with a flock of Double-crested Cormorants near Imperial Dam IMP 13 Apr 1971, 22-23 Apr 1972, and 7 Apr 1973.

This species is possibly increasing in New Mexico and southeastern Arizona; there it is mainly recorded in late summer and fall, but recent records exist for all seasons. It is likely to be found again in the southeastern part of the region.

BRANDT'S CORMORANT
Phalacrocorax penicillatus

Common resident along the northern coast and around the Channel Is., but primarily a winter visitant on the southern coast.

This is generally the commonest cormorant around the Channel Is. and on the coast of San Luis Obispo Co. South of San Luis Obispo Co. it is a common winter visitant which remains uncommonly to fairly commonly through the summer. These winter birds represent an influx from any of several sources: the north, Baja California, or the Channel Is. Large numbers observed moving up the coast past Goleta Pt. SBA in late February and March further suggest that a strong seasonal north-south movement does take place.

Breeding occurs primarily on the Channel Is. (except Santa Catalina I.); colonies occupy rocky headlands and islets. Breeding colonies are also located on the northern coast of San Luis Obispo Co. and possibly in northwest Santa Barbara Co. It formerly bred at La Jolla SD, and pairs nested on Pt. Loma SD in 1980.

This is by far the commonest cormorant over the open ocean. It wanders inshore to protected bays and harbors, but it generally stays in the outer portions of such areas. Although unrecorded inland, it has occurred once just north of us in Fresno Co.

PELAGIC CORMORANT
Phalacrocorax pelagicus

Fairly common resident on the northern coast and around the northern Channel Is. Primarily a winter visitant elsewhere along the coast.

The Pelagic Cormorant is fairly common throughout the year along the northern coast of San Luis Obispo Co. and around the Channel Is. south to Santa Barbara I. Breeding colonies are scattered through these areas (south to Pismo Beach SLO, with a pair also nesting at Pt. Sal SBA in 1980). Along the remainder of the coast it is a fairly common winter visitant, and it may remain rarely to uncommonly through the summer as a non-breeder. The bar graph reflects the status on the coast s. of San Luis Obispo Co.

This species requires steep cliffs for nesting, utilizing more vertical surfaces than the Brandt's Cormorant. It is rather local along the southern coast in winter, and it occurs mainly off rocky shorelines. It is rather "non-pelagic," being uncommon over the open ocean. Although unrecorded inland, it has occurred once just to the north of us in Mono Co.

FREGATIDAE: FRIGATEBIRDS
MAGNIFICENT FRIGATEBIRD
Fregata magnificens

Rare but regular summer visitant, primarily in July and August, to the Salton Sea and immediate coast; regular in the Colorado River Valley, but casual in Districts D and M, and in the interior of District C. Six winter and early spring records.

The Magnificent Frigatebird is a regular visitant from mid-June to early September to the Salton Sea and the coast; one to three are also recorded annually in District R. The great majority of records are for July and August, and the species is most frequently seen at the Salton Sea. Other interior records, most or all pertaining to birds originating in the Gulf of California, are: 24 Jun 1961 Palm Springs RIV; 15 Jul 1976 Grand Terrace SBE; 11 Sep 1976 w. of Blythe RIV (six birds, including five ad. males, after Tropical Storm Kathleen); 16 Jul 1978 Rancho Bernardo SD; 1 Sep 1978 Morongo Valley SBE (5); 16 Jul 1980 Big Bear L. SBE; 22 Jul 1980 vic. Cuyama VEN; and 5 Aug 1980 summit of Mt. Pinos (soaring with condors!). Additional records for the interior away from Districts S and R (one in winter, and five from the "invasion" of summer 1979) are noted below.

It is casual after September. Late fall, winter, and spring records are: 1 Oct 1977 near Imperial Beach SD; 9 Oct 1977 near Avalon, Santa Catalina I.; 29 Oct 1979 La Jolla SD; 4 Jan 1980 Redondo Beach LA (ad. female); 16 Feb 1977 Pismo Beach SLO; 20 Feb 1972 NESS (ad. male); 23 Mar 1977 Chino SBE (interior of District C); 25 Mar 1980 Redondo Beach LA; and 6 Apr 1976 San Miguel I. (ad. female).

The summer of 1979 was exceptional for this species in the region. At least 35-40 individuals were present along the coast, with records for all coastal counties; up to five were seen together. Numbers were also present at the Salton Sea; a maximum of 22 was seen together on 29 Jul 1979 NESS. Other inland records were: 13 Jul 1979 L. Hemet RIV (in District M); 30 Jul 1979 L. Castaic LA; 2 Aug 1979 L. Cuyamaca SD (5 in District M); 5 Sep 1979 L. Henshaw SD (in District M); and 7 Sep 1979 L. Hodges SD. Numbers declined after the first week of August; records after August were: 6 Sep 1979 Santa Clara R. estuary VEN; 23 Sep 1979

Salton Sea (3); 26 Sep 1979 Malibu LA; and the 29 Oct and 4 Jan records noted in the paragraph above.

This species is usually encountered soaring high overhead along the immediate coast or around the shore of the Salton Sea. It is occasionally recorded at sea or a short distance inland on the coastal slope. It has been noted several times around the Channel Is. (most frequently at Santa Catalina I.). The great majority of records pertain to immatures.

ARDEIDAE: HERONS

AMERICAN BITTERN
Botaurus lentiginosus

Primarily a winter visitant, uncommon in District C and fairly common in Districts S and R. Some remain through the summer, but very few recent nestings. Mainly a transient through District D.

An uncommon winter visitant in District C, it remains casually through summer. The only recent coastal nesting was in Goleta SBA in 1978. It was formerly a more widespread nester on the coastal slope; nesting was documented at localities such as Nigger Slough LA, Alamitos Bay ORA, Sunset Beach ORA, and, possibly, San Jacinto L. RIV (where considered fairly common in May 1911).

It is a fairly common winter visitant at the Salton Sea and Colorado R.; very small numbers remain there through the summer (nesting may occur at NESS). Most summer birds anywhere in the region are nonbreeders.

In the remainder of the interior this bittern is primarily an uncommon transient and very local winter visitant (e.g. Lancaster LA). It remains rarely through the summer and perhaps nests (e.g. Tecopa INY, Afton Canyon SBE).

There is one record for the Channel Is.: 31 Aug 1974 San Nicolas I.

American Bitterns are virtually restricted to dense beds of cattails and rushes, although transients may occur in atypical situations; they are partial to freshwater, and to the brackish portions of estuaries. Their secretive habits undoubtedly mean that many nesting pairs are overlooked.

LEAST BITTERN
Ixobrychus exilis

Common summer resident in Districts S and R; uncommon there in winter. Rather rare throughout the year in District C. Primarily a rare transient through District D.

Least Bitterns are common in summer and uncommon in winter at the Salton Sea and the Colorado R.; they are often seen in salt cedar scrub bordering dense marshes near sources of freshwater, as well as in the marshes themselves.

Elsewhere in the interior the species is mainly a rare transient that has been recorded from May through September. Transients have occurred quite out of expected habitat (e.g. at Mesquite Springs and Stovepipe Wells in Death Valley INY). It possibly nested recently in the Saline Valley INY (2 pairs on 25 Jul 1975) and it may nest very locally elsewhere in District D.

The Least Bittern is quite rare along the coast, but records exist from throughout the year. It has nested at Pt. Hueneme VEN (1 pair, 1978) and it possibly nests in the lagoons of southern San Diego Co. A very rare species in winter, it is more regular in summer, at least in the southern part of the region. It was formerly more numerous and widespread in District C; breeding was documented at Nigger Slough LA, San Jacinto L. RIV, Chino and Redlands SBE, and Guajome, San Luis Rey, and San Pascual SD.

This species has not been recorded in District M or on the Channel Is.

GREAT BLUE HERON
Ardea herodias

Fairly common resident throughout most of the region, becoming more numerous in the warmer areas in winter. Breeds very locally.

One of our commonest, most widespread, and hardiest herons, the Great Blue is found in a variety of aquatic habitats; it reaches peak abundance in coastal estuaries. They are often seen standing on kelp beds just offshore from the mainland and the Channel Is. In the deserts it is most likely to be seen during migration; it winters locally in suitable habitat. Warmer areas in Districts C, S, and R receive an influx of more northerly birds in winter; at this season it is locally common. It is much less numerous in District M.

Current breeding localities are Morro Bay SLO, Goleta SBA, L. Cachuma SBA, L. Casitas VEN, Pt. Loma SD, the Salton Sea, and the Colorado R. (e.g. Topock Marsh). Small rookeries may still exist elsewhere. Historical rookery sites, now abandoned, include several in Santa Barbara Co., Santa Monica LA (until 1901), Chatsworth LA, Santa Ana ORA, Laguna Beach ORA (until 1918), and San Onofre SD. Unchecked development in the coastal lowlands and the destruction of coastal lagoons has been largely responsible for the reduction of nesting localities in the region.

GREAT EGRET
Casmerodius albus

Primarily a fairly common winter visitor along the coast, common resident and breeder in Districts S and R, and uncommon transient through the rest of the interior. One recent nesting locality in the interior of District C.

In District C this egret is a common but local winter visitor that remains rarely to uncommonly through the summer, primarily as a non-breeder. There is one colony in the interior of District C: 20 pairs near Lakeview RIV in the summer of 1979. Important wintering localities include Morro Bay SLO, Santa Barbara and Goleta SBA, and coastal Orange and San Diego Cos. This is a scarce species in the interior of District C; the majority of birds are restricted to coastal *Salicornia* marshes and adjacent tidal channels and mudflats.

The Great Egret is a common breeding resident at the Salton Sea and along the Colorado R. It nests in mixed colonies of Great Blue Herons and other egrets. In District R this egret is found on mudflats, in open marshes, in agricultural fields, and along irrigation channels. At the Salton Sea it is restricted to the flats and marshes.

In District D it is uncommon in migration (primarily in spring). A few birds may remain through the summer. There is one winter record: Antelope Valley LA 20 Nov 1979-2 Mar 1980. It is probably a casual transient in District M.

There are only three records for the Channel Is.

SNOWY EGRET
Egretta thula

Common winter visitant along the coast, remaining uncommonly through summer. Common resident in Districts S and R. Generally an uncommon transient elsewhere.

Most birds summering on the coast occur in San Diego Co. Nesting recorded in District C has been recent: Sandyland Slough SBA (summer 1966), Buena Vista Lagoon SD (125 pairs in 1979), and Tijuana River Valley SD (three pairs in 1980). While common throughout the year in Districts S and R, Snowy Egrets nest only locally. Numbers of birds breeding at the Salton Sea have declined as a result of competition for nest sites with the recently increasing Cattle Egret.

This egret is generally an uncommon transient and summer visitant in District D, although it may be fairly common in spring at marshes and oases. It has nested once in District D: 6 May 1953 Klondike L. INY (1 egg set). This egret is a rare but regular transient through District M and a casual transient on the Channel Is.

The Snowy Egret is found in marsh and estuarine habitats and along river courses and irrigation channels. Small numbers occur in winter and migration on rocky shorelines. Dense marshes are required for nesting.

LITTLE BLUE HERON
Egretta caerulea

Casual visitant along the coast, primarily in fall and winter, and to the Salton Sea, in summer. About 55 records for the region. Two nesting records.

Most coastal records come from September through March (especially late October and November) and from late May and June. A movement that is apparently distinct from that of the wintering birds is the occurrence of adults along the coast in late May and June (as early as 29 Apr 1978 Goleta SBA). This movement is apparently correlated with the arrival of birds in the interior. A record for Goleta 15 Apr-10 June 1979 (imm.) does not fit the pattern of wintering birds; adults at Pt. Mugu VEN 8 Jul 1979 and Santa Ynez R. mouth SBA 23 Jul 1980 were late. A pair nested in the Tijuana River Valley SD summer 1980, successfully raising two young (not graphed).

In the interior it is a rare but regular summer visitant at the Salton Sea. All but three of the sightings are from the extreme southern end; the others are from NESS: 4 Jun-10 Sep 1973, 7 May 1977, and 30 Jul 1980. It is occasionally seen around egret rookeries at SESS in summer; a pair nested in a heronry at Seeley IMP in 1979 and raised three young. It has wintered once in District S: 7 Dec 1974-8 Feb 1975 SESS.

There are two spring records for the northern part of District D: 8 May 1976 Furnace Creek Ranch INY and 30 May 1977 Oasis MNO. Another was at Lakeview RIV (in the interior of District C) 9 May 1979. All three were adults.

This species is poorly represented in popular field guides; it should be identified with caution. A number of reports of immature Little Blue Herons have turned out to be Snowy Egrets; adults have been confused with Reddish Egrets.

TRICOLORED (LOUISIANA) HERON
Egretta tricolor

Rare but regular winter visitant and casual summer visitant along the coast. Casual visitant to the Salton Sea. One record for District R.

The great majority of coastal records are from Orange and San Diego Cos. and come from the period from late October through March. North of Orange Co. it has been recorded nine times: 9-10 Nov 1963 Santa Barbara SBA; 25-27 Aug 1972 Marina del Rey LA; 1 Jan-mid-Feb 1972 Pt. Mugu VEN (2); 30 Dec 1972-4 Feb 1973 Pt. Mugu (up to 3); 12 Oct 1975 Goleta SBA; 14 Jul 1976 Morro Bay SLO; 2 Jun 1977 Goleta; 31 Aug 1978 Santa Barbara; and 21 Mar-6 Apr 1979 Pt. Mugu. There are five summer records for District C: the Morro Bay and Goleta records above; 1 Jun 1977 Penasquitos Lagoon SD; 31 Jul-11 Sep 1977 s. end San Diego Bay SD; and 31 May 1978 Imperial Beach SD.

This heron is casual at the Salton Sea in spring and summer (nine records). There are three winter records: 22 Dec 1969-20 Mar 1970 SESS; 22 Nov-14 Dec 1972 SESS; and 19-27 Feb 1979 SESS. It has been recorded once in District R: 8-30 Sep 1955 Imperial Dam IMP.

All birds in District C have been found in the immediate vicinity of the coast. They usually occur along channels in *Salicornia* marshes.

REDDISH EGRET
Egretta rufescens

Casual visitant, primarily in fall, winter and spring; about 40 records for the region. Recorded along the coast (mainly Orange and San Diego Cos.) and in Districts S and R.

Along the coast it has been recorded only four times north of Orange Co.: 9 Jul 1962 Morro Bay SLO, 22 Apr 1968 Pt. Mugu VEN, 18 Aug mid-Nov 1969 Pt. Mugu, and 20-22 May 1977 Pt. Mugu. The great majority of records are for San Diego Co. There are five coastal records for July and August: the Morro Bay and Pt. Mugu records cited above; 26 Jul-29 Aug 1970 San Diego Bay SD; 31 Jul 1970 Newport Bay ORA; and 16 Jul-8 Sep 1978 Imperial Beach SD. A wintering bird remained in San Diego SD until 30 Jun 1978.

There are four records for District S and six for District R; most are from July to November. Outside of this pattern were birds at Imperial Dam IMP 1 Oct 1954-3 Mar 1955 and NESS 8 May 1978. Since 1963 it has been recorded only once on the California side of the Colorado R.: 11 Feb-3 Mar 1979 Imperial Dam (also unseasonal).

Reddish Egrets are primarily birds of open tidal mudflats and *Salicornia* marshes. The majority of the records are of immatures, but several spring records pertain to alternate plumaged adults. Inadequate representation in the popular field guides has occasionally led to confusion of immature birds with Little Blue Herons in the region. Note that white-phase birds do not occur in our western population, *E. r. dickeyi*.

CATTLE EGRET
Bubulcus ibis

Very common and increasing resident in District S; primarily a winter visitant along the coast and the Colorado R., summering locally (nests in three localities in District C). Rare transient through the rest of the interior.

In District S thousands of birds may now be found routinely in a day at the south end of the Salton Sea and in the surrounding agricultural areas. It is less numerous, but still generally common, at NESS. This species was first found nesting at the Salton Sea in 1970. It is now the commonest breeding heron in this area and it has largely displaced Snowy Egrets from prime nesting sites. The largest rookery is at Seeley IMP; it also nests at the mouth of the Whitewater R. RIV and, at least formerly, at the mouths of the New and Alamo Rivers IMP.

Along the Colorado R. the Cattle Egret occurs primarily in winter; it is decidedly less common here than it is at the Salton Sea. The largest numbers occur in the southern areas. It is not known to nest in the district.

Along the coast the Cattle Egret is mainly a fall and winter visitant and is occurring in ever increasing numbers. It is most common in the San Diego area, where up to 325 have been recorded in a day at Imperial Beach SD, but large winter concentrations have also been noted recently around Chino SBE (500 in winter 1978-1979). The largest numbers are present along the coast from late September through early November. It now summers fairly commonly but very locally within District C at L. Hodges SD, Imperial Beach (20 pairs nested in 1980), Buena Vista Lagoon SD (100 pairs nested in summer 1979), vic. Lakeview RIV (20 pairs nested in summer 1979), and Chino. This species also nests locally to the north of our region (Central Valley, Humboldt Bay).

A rare transient through District D, Cattle Egrets are most likely to be seen at oases, ponds, and agricultural and pasture areas; they can occur almost anywhere on the deserts.

Agricultural fields (especially when flooded) and livestock pastures are used for foraging. Transients are occasionally found at coastal estuaries. Transient flocks and individuals have also been noted on several of the Channel Is. and over the open ocean. At the Salton Sea, birds which forage during the day in the fields may be seen late in the afternoon flying in large flocks to roosting areas along the shore of the sea and at Seeley. Favorite sites for roosting are partially drowned trees.

The Cattle Egret was first recorded in California 7 Mar 1964 at Imperial Beach. Its phenomenal increase in the region has been paralleled by few bird species and is part of a global pattern of increase of this highly adaptable heron.

GREEN HERON
Butorides striatus

Uncommon to fairly common resident in the region, but seasonal status varies with locality.

In District C the Green Heron is generally uncommon in summer (locally fairly common). It becomes somewhat more widespread and numerous in winter. At the Salton Sea the species is fairly common throughout the year; aggregate numbers are probably higher in summer. In District R it is fairly common in summer, but only uncommon in winter.

An uncommon and local species in summer in District D, it is generally fairly common as a transient. It remains rarely through winter. In District M it is a rare transient. This heron has been recorded only twice on the Channel Is.

A fairly widespread nester, the Green Heron requires good riparian growth (primarily willows) and access to foraging areas along streams or the borders of marshes. Winter birds are less tied to riparian and marsh habitats, and are frequent in coastal estuaries. Transients are frequently recorded away from the vicinity of water.

BLACK-CROWNED NIGHT-HERON
Nycticorax nycticorax

Fairly common but local resident in Districts C, S, and R; nests locally. Uncommon transient and rare winter visitant in District D.

In District C Black-crowned Night-Herons are most numerous around Morro Bay SLO and in San Diego Co.; current nesting localities include Morro Bay, Santa Barbara SBA, and San Diego SD. Some former nesting localities include Inglewood LA and San Jacinto L. RIV. It is a rare visitant to the Channel Is., with records scattered throughout the year.

This heron is currently only a scarce transient through District M, but it formerly bred in the Big Bear Valley in the San Bernardino Mtns.

This species occupies a variety of water-edge habitats where trees or dense marshes are located nearby for roosting or nesting. Foraging takes place in coastal estuaries, lakeshores, and freshwater marshes and channels. It also frequents the shores of bays and harbors; pilings and piers are especially favored.

YELLOW-CROWNED NIGHT-HERON
Nycticorax violaceus

Casual straggler to District C from the south; eleven records as follows: "late June" 1951 Venice LA (not graphed); 3 Nov 1962 Imperial Beach SD; 27 Mar-3 Apr 1963 Claremont LA; 30 May-2 Jun 1963 Harbor L. LA; 22-25 Oct 1963 Imperial Beach; 1-11 Nov 1963 San Elijo Lagoon SD (the only immature in the region); 11 May 1977 San Joaquin Marsh, Irvine ORA; 3 Apr 1979 Mission Bay SD; 15 Apr-2 May 1979 Imperial Beach; 20-26 Apr 1980 Ventura VEN; and 18-26 Jul 1980 Imperial Beach.

It has been recorded once on the Arizona side of the Colorado R.: a subadult near Imperial Dam 17 Apr 1973.

THRESKIORNITHIDAE:
IBISES AND SPOONBILLS
WHITE IBIS
Eudocimus albus

Four acceptable records, probably only involving three individuals: 20 Nov 1935 Pt. Loma SD (imm.); 10-24 Jul 1976 NESS (ad.); 5 Aug 1976 SESS (ad.; probably the same bird that was present at NESS the previous month); and 25 Jun-14 Jul 1977 SESS (ad.).

An additional record for March 1914 at Palo Verde IMP lacks supporting details. Several sightings of subadult and adult White Ibis from Pt. Mugu

VEN south to northern Orange Co. after spring 1978 likely pertain to escapees; unbanded White Ibis are known to have escaped from a source in the San Fernando Valley LA prior to these sightings. One of these recent sightings from the greater Los Angeles area involves a White X Scarlet Ibis hybrid.

WHITE-FACED IBIS
Plegadis chihi

Fairly common transient and summer visitant at the Salton Sea, breeding locally and irregularly; remains uncommonly there in winter. Primarily an uncommon transient through the rest of the interior. Uncommon transient and very local winter visitant along the coast, with one recent nesting. Formerly more numerous, particularly on the coastal slope.

At the Salton Sea it is a fairly common transient and summer visitant. Three to four pairs that nested in 1977 at SESS were the first breeding in the region in 20 years; about 15 pairs nested in 1978 at NESS. It remains uncommonly through the winter at the Salton Sea. Formerly this species was more common at the Salton Sea; the wintering populations in the early 1950s numbered in the thousands, and breeding was more regular.

Along the Colorado R. it is primarily a spring and fall transient. In District D it is an uncommon spring transient and a rare late summer and fall transient (as late as 11 Nov 1979 nr. Lancaster LA).

Along the coast this ibis is an uncommon fall transient and scarce and local winter visitant. The principal wintering localities are the Pt. Mugu VEN area and the vicinity of Oceanside SD. Scattered individuals may occur elsewhere along the coast in winter. Although it is now casual along the coast in summer, eight pairs did nest at Buena Vista Lagoon SD in spring 1979.

This ibis was formerly much more common in all areas at all seasons. Breeding occurred locally on the coastal slope, e.g. at San Jacinto L. RIV (where 200-300 nests were found from May 1911 until 1917 when the lake was drained), and at Guajome SD (about 12 nesting birds in 1901). Steps should be taken to preserve the nesting habitat of this species, which is declining throughout its range. Extensive marshes are required for nesting. Foraging and transient birds may be found in flooded fields, marshes, ditches, and occasionally in estuaries.

ROSEATE SPOONBILL
Ajaia ajaja

Rare and irregular post-breeding summer visitant to the Salton Sea and, to a lesser extent, the Colorado R. Casual along the coast, being recorded only during large flight years.

It was first definitely recorded in California 22 May 1927 SESS (previous sight records lacked details). Since then it has been recorded as follows in Districts S and R:

1951: SESS (up to 6, 23 Jun-8 Oct)
1956: SESS (4 on 28 Oct)
1959: "California Swamp" IMP (up to 19, 30 Jul-13 Aug)
1966: SESS (2 birds 23-25 Sep; one on 18 Nov)
1969: SESS (one bird 20-22 Jul; 2 on 1 Sep)
1970: SESS (2, 30 Aug-19 Sep)
1972: SESS (up to 7, 8 Jul-8 Oct); NESS (one, 20 Aug-8 Sep)
1973: SESS (up to 35, 14 Jun-26 Oct); NESS (up to 14, 14 Jun-late Oct); Parker Dam SBE (6 birds 15 km south of dam, 24 Jun; numerous other records for the Arizona side of the river, particularly around the Gila R. mouth); Palo Verde IMP (one, 1 Dec 1973-21 Mar 1974, for one of two interior winter records for the region)
1976: NESS (one, 5 May; possibly the same individual at SESS 13 Jun to mid-Sep)
1977: SESS (up to 17, beginning 3 Jun; 14 still present 19 Oct); Imperial Dam IMP (6, 15 Jun); vic. Parker, in San Bernardino Co. (7, Jun-Sep); Draper L., above Imperial Dam IMP (2, 24 Jun); NESS (one, 25 Aug-23 Sep); vic. Needles SBE (one, 7 Sep); one at SESS 29 Jan-12 Mar 1978 was undoubtedly a remnant from this invasion, and what was possibly the same individual was at NESS from 19 May-19 Aug 1978
1980: SESS (one, 27 Jul-7 Sep; the only record of an adult for California)

Along the coast, spoonbills have been recorded only during the two largest flight years, 1973 and 1977. In 1973 a bird was at Marina del Rey LA in mid-July. Following that, there was a series of records that possibly involved the same group of birds: three at Zuma Beach LA 20-29 Jun; two at Pt. Mugu VEN 4-20 Jul; two at Goleta SBA 30 Jul-14 Sep; two at Laguna L. SLO 13-14 Jul; and one at Morro Bay SLO 15 Sep. In 1977 a series of records again possibly involved the same group of birds: three at the mouth of the Santa Margarita R. SD 24 Jun; three at San Joaquin Marsh ORA 26 Jun (with two remaining to 4 Oct); one at Goleta SBA 12 Sep-5 Oct; and lingerers at Malibu LA 4 Dec and at Pt. Mugu VEN 17 Oct and again 13 Jan 1978.

Just outside of the region there is a record for Buttonwillow KRN 2 Oct 1966.

The Roseate Spoonbill is clearly an invasive species in the region. It frequents shallow, open water, often in the company of egrets and Wood Storks.

CICONIIDAE: STORKS

WOOD STORK
Mycteria americana

Common post-breeding visitant, primarily from June through early September, to the south end of the Salton Sea and adjacent portions of the Imperial Valley. Quite rare at the north end of the Salton Sea. Uncommon post-breeding visitant to the Colorado R. Now strictly casual along the coast; formerly more numerous. Two records for District D.

Wood Storks usually begin arriving at the Salton Sea in late May and peak in July and early August. Numbers fall off rapidly after early September; the last individuals usually depart by mid-October. Extreme dates are 3 May 1980 NESS to 29 Oct 1953 (exceptionally to 10 Apr 1980 NESS and 30 Nov 1919 Calexico IMP). There is one winter record for District S: 18 Feb-12 Mar 1978 SESS; what was probably the same individual was seen there 15 and 23 Apr 1978. Numbers, while always large, vary somewhat from year to year. A recent high count was 650 at SESS in late Jul 1977. A very late high count was 1000 at SESS 18 Sep 1964. Curiously, this species is quite rare at NESS — there are only seven records. The majority of birds at the Salton Sea are immatures. They forage in shallow bays and channels, primarily around the mouths of the Alamo and New Rivers where there is a good growth of salt cedars and partly submerged trees and shrubs.

Wood Storks are much less numerous and somewhat irregular along the Colorado R. and generally occur from Blythe RIV south (occasionally north to Parker Dam SBE). The timing of occurence in District R is similar to that at the Salton Sea. A count of 52 at Imperial Dam IMP 7 Oct 1960 was large and exceptionally late for District R.

There are two records for District D: Death Valley (recorded in both San Bernardino and Inyo Cos.) Jul-Aug 1935, and Furnace Creek Ranch INY 15 Jul 1979.

It was formerly a fairly common post-breeding visitant to the coast from Orange Co. south. It was regular in small numbers north through Los Angeles and (occasionally) Ventura Cos.; scattered records exist north through San Luis Obispo Co. The bird was recorded inland to Lakeview RIV, the lower montane lakes of San Diego Co., and Simi Valley and "Sespe R." VEN. Numbers of birds reaching the coast varied from year to year. Several old winter records exist for District C and adjacent montane areas: 17 Mar 1918 near San Diego (2); 14 Jan 1921 Mission Valley SD; 12 Mar 1961 L. Mathews RIV; 12 Dec 1964-14 Feb 1965 Goleta SBA; 15 Oct-"mid-Dec" 1965 Santa Barbara SBA and early Jan 1966 at the mouth of the Ventura R. VEN (probably the same individual); and 28 Dec 1968 Morro Bay SLO.

Along the coast it is currently strictly casual. Numbers declined sharply along the coast in the 1950s; the last concentration was 18 at San Elijo Lagoon SD 29 Aug 1961. Since 1965 there have been 12 records for the coast; the five since 1971 are: 30 Jul-3 Aug 1975 San Elijo Lagoon SD; 15 Aug 1975 Santa Barbara; 13 Sep to late Oct 1979 San Pedro LA (and what was believed to be the same individual at Whittier Narrows LA 4 Nov 1979-12 Mar 1980); 6 Nov 1979 Dunes Lakes SLO (2); and 24 Aug-2 Sep 1980 Whalen L. SD.

ANATIDAE: SWANS, GEESE, AND DUCKS

FULVOUS WHISTLING-DUCK
Dendrocygna bicolor

Fairly common (but declining) summer resident at SESS, remaining rarely through winter. Very rare along the Colorado R. Five records of transients elsewhere in the interior. Formerly a summer resident in District C, but recent records there likely pertain to escapees.

At the Salton Sea this species is recorded sporadically through the winter. Numbers begin increasing in mid-March; flocks in late February possibly represent very early spring arrivals. Numbers in summer vary somewhat from year to year, but appear to have declined over the years. Curiously, it has been recorded only twice at NESS: 15 Jul 1977 (19) and 2 May 1971.

It is now a very rare or casual summer visitant along the Colorado R.; it was formerly more numerous. Recent records come primarily from the vicinity of Palo Verde IMP.

Elsewhere in the interior there are four relatively recent records: 30 Oct 1965 Saratoga Springs SBE; 28 May 1966 Oasis MNO (5); 24 May 1970 California City KRN (9); and 25 Sep 1973 Furnace Creek Ranch INY. It was also recorded 8 May and 1 Jun 1891 at "Little Owens Lake" in the Owens Valley.

Along the coast Fulvous Whistling-Ducks were formerly regular summer visitants in small numbers; they bred north to Los Angeles Co., and were recorded north to San Luis Obispo Co. The species was recorded regularly and nested at Playa del Rey LA until the early 1950s. Other former nesting sites include Nigger Slough LA, San Jacinto L. RIV, the San Luis Rey Valley SD, and, just outside our region, Buena Vista L. KRN. Late fall and winter records for District C are: 21 Oct 1956 Warner Springs SD; 14 Dec 1954 w. of Santee SD; and 31 Jan 1900 Bolsa Chica ORA. There is also a record for San Diego SD from "December" in the late 1800s.

There are still occasional reports from the coastal slope, e.g. 1-8 Feb 1970 San Bernardino SBE (13); 10 Sep 1972 San Elijo Lagoon SD; 19 Nov 1977 El Dorado Nature Center, Long Beach LA (5); 2 Apr 1978 San Joaquin Marsh ORA (3); 13 Aug 1978 Imperial Beach Pier SD (10); 18 May 1980 Santa Maria R. mouth SBA/SLO; and summer 1980 Santa Clara R. estuary VEN. Free-flying Fulvous Whistling-Ducks are common at collections, e.g. Lion Country Safari in Orange Co. and Sea World and San Diego Wild Animal Park in San Diego Co. It is therefore likely that most, if not all, recent coastal sightings pertain to escapees.

Dense marshes of cattails and adjacent shallow water are favored around the south end of the Salton Sea. Finney L. and the freshwater impoundments above the mouth of the Alamo R. are the most reliable places for this duck in the Imperial Valley.

BLACK-BELLIED WHISTLING-DUCK
Dendrocygna autumnalis

Five records, all for District S: "fall of 1912" SESS (not shown on graph); 12 Jun 1951 SESS; 2 Jun-5 Aug 1972 SESS (up to 4); 15 Oct-4 Nov 1973 SESS (up to 3); and 4-14 Aug 1977 near Brawley IMP.

Just north of our region there is a record for near Bakersfield KRN 19 Nov 1973 (3).

As this species is frequent in waterfowl collections, records falling outside the pattern of summer and fall dispersal to the southern interior most likely pertain to escapees (e.g. 28 Jul-1 Aug 1970 San Joaquin Marsh ORA).

WHISTLING SWAN
Cygnus columbianus

Primarily a rare late fall visitant, with relatively few birds remaining through the winter. Recorded in all districts, but most regular in the northern interior.

The majority of Whistling Swan records are for December in the northern interior, from the Owens Valley (especially) south to the Antelope Valley. The species is extremely rare south of the Los Angeles/San Bernardino Co. axis. The largest concentration noted recently was 52 at Holiday L. e. of Gorman LA 11 Dec 1971; 25 at Morro Bay SLO 22 Feb 1953 is the most recent concentration along the coast. The latest record of a spring migrant is one at Death Valley National Monument INY 24 Apr 1964. One bird had summered in the region: an immature in Pasadena LA 27 Dec 1972 spent the next year associating with domestic geese (not graphed).

Although it is rare along the Colorado R., some concentrations have been reported (e.g. 35 at Imperial Refuge IMP in Jan 1956, with 15 still present on 9 Mar; and 53 there 25 Feb 1957). It is even rarer at the Salton Sea, where the largest concentrations have been six (SESS 8 Dec 1971) and seven (NESS 7 Dec 1976).

Historically, the Whistling Swan was much more numerous. Large flocks from the 1900s include: up to 44 at Hope Ranch, Santa Barbara SBA from mid-Nov to 24 Dec 1919; up to 75 on L. Henshaw SD in Dec 1917; and 151 on "Crane Lake" in the Antelope Valley "around 1919." In recent decades only singles or very small flocks have been reported away from the norther interior.

Whistling Swans are most likely to be seen on the larger open reservoirs and lakes in the Owens Valley (e.g. Tinnemaha Res. INY); south of there, open lakes, ponds, marshes, and coastal estuaries may be frequented. This species is unrecorded on the Channel Is.

It is also called the Tundra Swan. The Old World "Bewick's Swan" (*C. bewickii*; considered conspecific with *C. columbianus* by many authors) has been recorded with flocks of *columbianus* in northern California, and should be looked for in the region.

TRUMPETER SWAN
Cygnus buccinator

Two certain records as follows: 13-22 Jan 1973 Carrizo Plain SLO (ad.) and 1 Jan -17 Feb 1975 El Monte LA (ad.), with what was almost certainly

the same individual at nearby Covina LA 13-15 Mar 1975 (these are graphed as one record).

Probably also correct is a record of three (ad. and 2 imms.) at the Santa Clara R. estuary VEN 17 Nov 1974. Two purported specimens from Los Angeles Co. were subsequently destroyed by fire. We can find no substantiation for comments that the Trumpeter was "more common" than Whistling Swans in Ventura Co. in the early 1880s.

Sight records of Trumpeter Swans should be made with extreme care; adults are safely separable from Whistling Swans only with critical study and comparison; immatures of the two species are virtually inseparable.

GREATER WHITE-FRONTED GOOSE
Anser albifrons

Mainly an irregular transient; also a rare winter visitant. Most numerous at the Salton Sea, although large groups of transients can be encountered almost anywhere in the interior. Now rather rare along the coast.

Fall migration begins in late September and continues into November, with a peak in mid-October (early for a goose). Spring transients are recorded from late January through early March. It was formerly common in late fall and winter at the Salton Sea; numbers of wintering birds are now much reduced. This goose is generally only a transient through Districts D and M. In spring this species is sporadic in its occurrence, but it is more widespread than in fall and can occur in greater concentrations (e.g. 2000 near Lakeview RIV Feb 1978, and 600 there 10 Feb 1979). A pair (one bird crippled) summered at NESS in 1974 (not graphed).

This species is fairly rare on the coastal slope, particularly in the immediate vicinity of the coast. However, while generally a transient in District C, it is now more likely to be seen on the coastal slope than in the true interior in mid-winter. It was formerly more common along the coast (e.g. "abundant" on Santa Rosa I. in November 1907). There is one coastal summer record: a bird associating with domestic geese in Santa Barbara SBA from winter 1979-1980 through summer 1980 (not graphed).

SNOW GOOSE
Anser caerulescens

Winter visitant; abundant at SESS, locally common along the Colorado R., and very local (and greatly reduced) in District C. Uncommon transient through the remainder of the region.

Snow Geese are quite abundant at refuges and adjacent grainfields at SESS, primarily from mid-November through February. The earliest recorded fall arrival here is 4 Oct 1957 (7). Small numbers, usually cripples, remain casually through the summer. It is uncommon at NESS.

It is locally common in winter along the Colorado R., where flocks winter below Needles SBE and irregularly above Yuma IMP.

This species is an uncommon fall transient and rare spring migrant through most of District D and on montane lakes; it is casual in winter, although a small flock often winters in the Antelope Valley near Lancaster LA. Extreme dates of transients are 18 Sep 1974 Little L. INY and 26 Apr-5 June 1964 Jacumba SD.

Along the coast it is now a rare fall transient and winter visitor to marshes, shallow lakes, and adjacent fields. It is recorded casually through summer. The largest flock currently wintering on the coast is at Whalen L. SD (10-20 birds). Numbers wintering along the coast have dropped drastically in this century, which is probably indicative of a shift in winter range (to the Salton Sea?) rather than an overall decline in the population. Willett (1933) stated that the Snow Goose was "formerly one of our most abundant species in winter," referring to coastal southern California. It occupied grainfields and pasturelands and "when hunted persistently. . . feeding was done at night. . . the birds remaining out to sea during the day." Santa Cruz and Santa Rosa Is. were especially favored historical wintering grounds. Migrant flocks were still occasional along the coast as of 1933, and the species was abundant on Santa Rosa I. up to the 1950s. A flock of 30 did winter on Santa Rosa I. 1974-1975.

The dark morph, or "Blue Goose," winters rarely with the huge flocks of Snow Geese at the Salton Sea; 1-5 are recorded annually. There is also a record from Needles SBE 19 Feb 1978. Intermediate birds are almost as frequent as true "Blue Geese" in the region.

ROSS' GOOSE
Anser rossii

Fairly common winter visitant to SESS. Now quite rare but recorded annually in late fall and winter along the coast. Four records for District D.

At SESS it is usually found in the company of Snow Geese, although there is a tendency to form pure aggregations within mixed flocks. The maximum recorded here was 600-700 during the winter 1975-1976. Numbers wintering in this area have increased in recent years. It is generally quite rare at NESS. The latest record for District S is 25 Apr-7 May 1978 NESS. A few probably winter regularly with flocks of Snow Geese along the Colorado R.

There are four records, all in fall and early winter, elsewhere in the interior: 25 Nov 1973 Lone Pine INY; 11 Jan 1975 near Big Pine INY; 15 Nov 1975 Little L. INY (2); and 21 Nov 1979 Tecopa INY.

Along the coast it is now a very rare but annual visitant; there are records from all coastal counties. The coastal maximum of 7 was at Whalen L. SD 1 Jan 1979. It has been found inland on the coastal slope to the San Bernardino Valley SBE and L. Piru VEN. Willett (1933) states that it was "formerly comon (along the coast) in company with Snow Geese south to Orange Co."

EMPEROR GOOSE
Anser canagicus

Casual winter visitant to coastal bays and salt marshes; seven records.
Our records come from only three winters, winters which correspond to flight years in northern California. Recorded as follows: 12 Dec 1966-12 Feb 1967 Morro Bay SLO (two present 12 Dec, one thereafter); 12 Dec 1966 Oceano SLO; 18-30 Dec 1968 San Simeon SLO; 15 Dec 1968 Laguna ORA; 15 Dec 1968-8 Mar 1969 Seal Beach ORA (initially five, with three remaining to late Dec, and one thereafter); 15 Dec 1977 Pismo Beach SLO (captured by dog); and 1 Jan-20 Feb 1978 Pt. Mugu VEN.

BRANT
Branta bernicla

Very locally common winter visitant along the coast; common to abundant transient (mostly in spring) past coastal promontories. Erratic spring transient at the Salton Sea and very locally elsewhere in the southern interior; very rare in the northern interior. A few remain occasionally through summer on the coast.

In winter large flocks occur at Morro Bay SLO and at the San Diego R. mouth and on San Diego Bay SD. Elsewhere along the coast scattered individuals or very small groups may winter on virtually any estuary. The centers of abundance are characterized by shallow water and a dense growth of Eelgrass. It is a common to abundant transient in spring past coastal promontories; several thousand may sometimes be counted in a single day at the peak of migration (late March to mid-April, with flocks well into May). A notable late spring concentration was 800-1000 at Pt. Mugu VEN 24 May 1957. The southbound migration in fall generally takes place well offshore; flocks are only infrequently seen from coastal points. Brant are occasionally found around the Channel Is., mainly in migration. A few individuals routinely linger at coastal localities through the early summer, and birds occasionally spend the entire summer. It was formerly more abundant and widespread in winter along the coast (e.g. in kelp beds off San Pedro LA).

In the interior, birds coming north out of the Gulf of California in spring are regularly recorded in the southeastern portion of the region. They are most regular at the Salton Sea, where flocks of up to 500 have been recorded at NESS. There seems to be a bimodal pattern of spring abundance at the Salton Sea. Many birds are recorded in late March and then again from late April to early May; relatively few are found in early and mid-April. Small numbers often linger through late spring and into the early summer. Birds at SESS on 24 Feb 1974 (2) and 16 Feb 1978 were probably very early spring transients. The two fall records at the Salton Sea (11 Nov 1969 Salton City IMP and two on 21 Oct 1976 SESS) might represent birds that summered there.

Elsewhere in the interior, small flocks are sporadically encountered northwest to San Gorgonio Pass RIV, L. Elsinore RIV, and L. Cuyamaca SD. The largest interior concentrations away from the Salton Sea are: 211 on L. Henshaw SD 4 Mar 1980; 50 over the Banner Grade, Laguna Mtns. SD 13 Mar 1977; 38 at L. Cuyamaca 22 Apr 1967; and 30 at San Gorgonio Pass 24 Mar 1974. Additional interior records are: 14 Apr 1978 n. of Blythe RIV (the only record for District R, although several records exist for the Arizona side of the Colorado R.); 1 May 1965 Morongo Valley SBE; 6 Mar-8 May 1976 Tinnemaha Res. INY; 7 Jul-Aug 1979 Lancaster LA; 29 Dec 1977-17 Apr 1978 Lancaster (the only record of a bird wintering in the interior); and, just north of our region, Jun-Jul 1969 Buena Vista L. KRN and 21 Apr-2 May 1978 Mono L. MNO.

There are three records for District C away from the ocean: 11 Mar 1973 Whittier LA; 5 Jun 197 Arcadia LA; and 22 Mar 1979 L. Hodges SD. Note that the two March records fit the spring pattern for the southern interior.

The above account pertains to the "dark-bellied" or "Black" form *B. b. nigricans*. The "white-bellied" or "American" form *B. b. hrota*, is a casual (but perhaps somewhat regular) winter visitant among large brant flocks; the majority of records are from the vicinity of San Diego Bay. Other records are: 9 Mar-4 Apr 1970 Goleta SBA; 27 Nov 1973-8 Jan 1974 Malibu LA; and 29 Mar 1977 Goleta Pt. SBA (flying up the coast with other brant).

CANADA GOOSE
Branta canadensis

Common winter visitant virtually throughout, although local in distribution and primarily only a transient through District D. Peak numbers occur from mid-November through early February; a few (often cripples from preceding hunting seasons) may remain through the summer in Districts C, D, and, especially, S.

It is most abundant around the Salton Sea (where thousands may winter) and locally along the Colorado R. (e.g. Cibola IMP, Imperial NWP IMP, and vic. Needles SBE). Favored localities nearer the coast include Whalen L. SD, L. Henshaw SD, Lakeview RIV, San Fernando Valley LA, and L. Cachuma SBA. It is a rare transient and winter visitant on the Channel Is. It is a transient and local winter visitant on montane lakes. In District D it winters only very locally (e.g. Owens Valley INY and Antelope Valley LA).

The Canada Goose is most numerous in managed habitats where grain fields are interspersed with lakes and ponds (e.g. wildlife refuges at SESS). It may be seen, however, in a variety of wetland habitats where fields are available for foraging. There has been some decline in wintering numbers on the coastal slope since the early 1900s.

107

Of the several subspecies which occur in the region, *moffitti* ("Giant" Canada Goose) and *parvipes* ("Lesser" Canada Goose) are the most numerous and most closely fit the distributional information outlined above. The "Cackling" Canada Goose, *B. c. minima*, is a rare late fall and early winter visitant throughout (most winter to the north). This easily recognized small form is somewhat regular in the northern coastal counties and in the Antelope Valley. Farther south it is quite rare; it has been recorded only three times in San Diego Co. since 1969 (Nov-Dec). Reports from the far interior are: 28 Feb 1970 SESS; 26 Oct-3 Nov 1973 Desert Center RIV; and 5 Nov 1978 Furnace Creek Ranch INY. Reports by Willett (1933) indicate that there was a decline, possibly sharp, of this race in southern California in the early 1900s. The "Aleutian" Canada Goose, *B. c. leucopareia*, is an endangered subspecies; it has been recorded twice recently at SESS: six were discovered there on 3 Dec 1975 and two or more were present through the winter of 1977-78.

Subspecies names above follow Palmer (1976); our knowledge of the distribution of the various subspecies of Canada Goose is still fragmentary.

WOOD DUCK
Aix sponsa

Rare to uncommon transient and rare winter visitant, occurring primarily in District C and, as a transient, in the northern portions of District D. Summers casually in District C. A few recent nestings.

In District C it becomes increasingly rare to the south. It appears to be most numerous as a transient in fall, when it is uncommon from mid-October through early November. Wood Ducks are regularly found wintering, especially from Los Angeles Co. north. This species is casual during the summer in District C. The only recent nesting in District C has been at L. Sherwood VEN (1979) and along the upper Santa Ynez R. SBA (several broods in 1979 and 1980). It also nested in 1950 (and possibly 1951) along the Santa Ana R. in Riverside RIV. There are several additional records of pairs in summer along the Santa Ynez R. and its tributaries. Pairs seen elsewhere in summer (e.g. Pasadena LA and Santa Barbara SBA) may or may not represent wild birds.

In District D this duck is primarily a fall transient from early September through early December; the majority occur in October and November. It is generally restricted to the northern deserts. A few occasionally winter within District D (e.g. at Furnace Creek Ranch INY and Holiday L. in the Antelope Valley LA). In spring transients have occurred as late as 1 Jun. It has nested at Bishop INY in the Owens Valley (female with young 10 Jun 1978).

The Wood Duck is a very rare winter visitant in Districts S and R, where it is perhaps most regular between Parker Dam SBE and Blythe RIV. The one summer record for District S is 18 Jun 1973 NESS.

There is one record for the Channel Is.: a flock of 15-20 on Santa Cruz I. 27 Oct 1978, with 4 still there on 9 Nov 1978. This is one of the largest concentrations recorded in the region.

Wood Ducks generally occur on ponds, streams, ditches, and other small bodies of water which are heavily bordered with tall vegetation; migrants are sometimes found on more open bodies of water. This is a common species on park lakes and in ornamental waterfowl collections. A number of out of season and southerly reports may not pertain to truly wild birds.

EURASIAN WIGEON
Anas penelope

Rare winter visitor with flocks of American Wigeon. The majority are found along the coast, but it is frequently recorded in the interior.

In District C typical localities include Upper Newport Bay ORA, Whalen L. SD, and vic. Lakeview RIV, where the maximum of five males occurred on 24 Dec 1979. The latest regional record is 31 Mar -6 May 1979 Pt. Mugu VEN. It is unrecorded from the Channel Is.

There are nine winter records for District S, where it is probably of annual occurrence. This wigeon is probably more or less regular on L. Hemet in the San Jacinto Mtns. and on the lakes in the San Bernardino Mtns.

A casual bird in District D, it has been recorded as follows: 7 Nov 1969 Little L. INY, 25 Oct 1975 - 1 Mar 1976 Furnace Creek Ranch INY, and 24 Nov 1976 Furnace Creek Ranch. There is one record from the California side of the Colorado R.: 16-17 Dec 1947 near Topock SBE.

Eurasian Wigeon are to be looked for among the large flocks of American Wigeon which occur where freshwater lakes or brackish estuaries are surrounded by fields and lawns (for grazing). Almost all records are of males; many females are undoubtedly overlooked.

AMERICAN WIGEON
Anas americana

Common to abundant winter visitor except in District D, where local and somewhat scarce. In summer quite rare but regularly observed, especially at the Salton Sea. Not known to nest. Rare transient on the Channel Is. except on Santa Rosa I., where it remains a common winter visitor.

This is a bird of freshwater lakes and ponds, including the backwaters of coastal estuaries. It is largely a grazing species which prefers open, grassy areas (e.g. golf courses) and fields for foraging. American Wigeon are quite abundant on montane lakes, although, as is true of most waterfowl wintering in the mountains, flocks will depart if winter freezes are severe.

GADWALL
Anas strepera

Fairly common, but somewhat local winter visitor to freshwater lakes, marshes, ponds, and coastal estuaries throughout. Uncommon to locally fairly common summer resident, with nesting recorded in all districts except S. Only two records (fall) for the Channel Is.

Examples of nesting localities include West Pond IMP (2 females with chicks, 1 Jul 1957); Owens Valley INY and vic. Lancaster LA in District D; Baldwin and Big Bear Lakes SBE in District M; and, in District C, the San Luis Rey and Santa Margarita R. mouths, Peñasquitos Lagoon, and Tijuana River Valley SD; Goleta SBA; Santa Clara R. estuary and Pt. Mugu VEN; and (formerly) San Pedro LA and San Jacinto L. RIV. The breeding status of this and many other duck species·in the region is poorly known; in the future such determination should receive considerable attention.

BAIKAL TEAL
Anas formosa

Two records: 29 Dec 1946 Calipatria IMP (ad. male; specimen); and 12 Jan 1974 near Riverside RIV (imm. male; specimens).

There are three additional specimens for northern California and two from the Pacific northwest. There are also several fall records for the west coast of Alaska. While the pattern of vagrancy along the Pacific Coast of North America is not as clear as it is for certain other primarily Palearctic waterfowl species (e.g. Tufted Duck, Garganey), this species has been accepted by the CBRC.

GREEN-WINGED TEAL
Anas crecca

Common to abundant winter visitant in all districts. A few remain through summer; two nesting records. The Eurasian form is a casual transient and winter visitant west of the deserts.

This is one of our most numerous dabbling ducks. Fall migrants begin arriving in very late July and early August; most birds have departed by late April. A few may remain through summer, particularly at the Salton Sea; it is casual in summer on the coastal slope.

The only known nestings are: San Luis Rey Valley SD 18 May 1931, and Carrizo Plain (Soda L.) SLO (egg set taken on 30 Apr 1978, with nesting also suspected there the following year).

Green-winged Teal occur with other dabbling ducks in a variety of shallow freshwater habitats and in brackish coastal estuaries. They are uncommon winter visitants to the Channel Is.

The Eurasian "Common Teal" has been recorded 15 times in the region, all since 1962. All records but two are from District C and involve all coastal counties; the exceptions are of birds at L. Cuyamaca SD in

District M 11 Mar 1979 and 16 Mar 1980. A bird at L. Sherwood VEN, found on 3 Jan 1971, was also recorded during the three subsequent winters and was last seen on 2 Feb 1974. The earliest arrival date is 28 Nov 1975 Westlake LA; the latest spring date is 2 Apr 1975 Legg L. LA. Only males of the Eurasian form have been recorded (although females would obviously be overlooked). Males showing mixed characters of the Eurasian and American forms have been noted in the region. Although there are no specimens from the region, it is likely that *A. c. crecca* is the subspecies involved, as there are specimens of this race from northern California and British Columbia.

MALLARD
Anas platyrhynchos

Fairly common winter visitant throughout; perhaps most numerous in the northern interior. Uncommon to locally fairly common in summer. Nests in coastal counties and on montane lakes. Rare winter visitant on the Channel Is.

The natural status of Mallards in the region is difficult to determine because of the widespread establishment of feral birds, many of which appear fully wild. Feral birds are established on lakes and ponds throughout much of the region.

Freshwater lakes, ponds, and marshes are occupied as are, to a lesser extent, coastal estuaries. The aggregate number of wild birds has probably been reduced during the present century.

COMMON PINTAIL
Anas acuta

Common to abundant and widespread winter visitant throughout; in general the commonest *Anas* duck. An early fall arrival, the first transients are noted by mid-July and the species is common by late July. Uncommon and local nester.

Pintails are found virtually wherever open water permits; migrant flocks are even frequently noted on the Channel Is. and over the open ocean.

It is generally uncommon and local as a nesting species in the region, although it may be fairly common locally, e.g. on lakes in the Big Bear Valley, San Bernardino Mtns. Some known breeding localities include: SESS; Deep Springs Valley and Owens Valley INY; L. Cuyamaca and formerly, L. Henshaw SD; Big Bear and Baldwin Lakes SBE; vic. Lakeview and L. Elsinore RIV; and many of the major coastal estuaries in the region. Even in localities which pintails currently use, nesting involves few pairs and tends to be sporadic.

GARGANEY
Anas querquedula

Two records of males: El Dorado Nature Center, Long Beach LA 15 Mar 1972, 4 Apr 1974, and 19 Mar 1975 (these records almost certainly pertain to the same individual); and 21 Mar-4 Apr 1979 L. Elsinore RIV.

There are numerous recent records of migrants (mainly in spring, but easily overlooked in fall) in western Alaska; transients have also been recorded in Hawaii, the Pacific Northwest, and western Mexico. This highly migratory species seems quite capable of reaching southern California as a vagrant.

BLUE-WINGED TEAL
Anas discors

Uncommon spring and fall transient in all districts, remaining rarely but regularly through the summer. Rare in winter, when most birds are along the coast.

The exact status of this species in fall is unclear because of the difficulty of identifying eclipse-plumaged and immature males, as well as the always hard-to-identify females. There is a tendency for spring transients to arrive earlier along the coast than in the interior. It is a rare spring transient in District M. There are six records for the Channel Is. (five in spring).

This teal is rare but regular in summer on coastal lagoons (e.g. at Goleta SBA and San Elijo Lagoon SD). It is also recorded very rarely but annually in summer in the interior from the Owens Valley south to the Salton Sea and Colorado R. There is only one definite nesting record for the region: one, possibly two, pairs with broods at the Santa Clara R. estuary VEN during the summer of 1980.

Along the coast this teal is rare in winter, although 10+ have often been found around Goleta at this season. It is casual in winter in the interior (Colorado River Valley, Salton Sea). It is unrecorded in winter in District D.

This species is most often found in the company of Cinnamon Teal, generally on marshy ponds, lakes, and coastal estuaries. Male Blue-winged X Cinnamon Teal hybrids are noted annually in the region, especially in spring.

CINNAMON TEAL
Anas cyanoptera

Common to abundant spring transient, common fall transient, and fairly common breeder and summer resident in all districts. Uncommon in winter, with the majority concentrated along the coast; very uncommon to rare in winter in the interior, especially away from the Salton Sea.

Spring migration begins quite early. Since flocks of migrants arrive by 10 Jan, it should not be assumed that Cinnamon Teal present in January have wintered locally. It is an uncommon to fairly common transient on the Channel Is. and has nested once (San Nicolas I.).

Cinnamon Teal may be found in virtually any freshwater habitat and on estuaries. Freshwater marshes are required for nesting.

NORTHERN SHOVELER
Anas clypeata

Common winter visitant to all districts; especially abundant at the Salton Sea, where tens of thousands may winter. Rare in summer, except at the Salton Sea, where it may remain uncommonly. Several known nestings, only two recent.

Historically, the shoveler undoubtedly nested sporadically in or near District C (Gorman LA, San Jacinto L. RIV, etc.), although only one set of eggs has been taken in the region: 23 May 1897 Nigger Slough LA. The recent nestings are: in District C, near Oceanside SD Jun 1973; and in District D, at Tecopa, summer 1979.

Northern Shovelers inhabit a variety of freshwater and estuarine habitats where extensive shallows are available for foraging. They are somewhat local in winter along the coast. Surprisingly, there are only five records (all in winter or migration) for the Channel Is.

CANVASBACK
Aythya valisineria

Fairly common winter visitant in all districts; common locally, e.g. at the Salton Sea. Rather locally distributed throughout. In summer, rare at the Salton Sea, casual elsewhere.

The Canvasback occupies open lakes, reservoirs, and larger ponds. It is uncommon and local in District R; Imperial Dam IMP is the only regular locality. It is rather scarce and local in District D, where little habitat with open water exists. There is only one record for the Channel Is.: 22 Mar 1977 Thompson Res., Santa Catalina I. The graph for Districts C, M, D and R largely reflects status in the former two districts.

There are about 20 summer records for the region, some 18 of which are for the Salton Sea. It is not known to nest in the region.

REDHEAD
Aythya americana

Status complex. Generally an uncommon to locally fairly common winter visitant through most of the region, remaining uncommonly and locally through the summer. At the Salton Sea it is a fairly common breeding bird and numbers are actually greater in summer than in winter.

This species summers rarely on coastal lagoons and ponds, with nesting recorded locally on the lagoons in the vicinity of Oceanside SD. It also summers rarely along the Colorado R. and, at least formerly, bred there. Redheads are local breeders in the Antelope Valley (vic. Lancaster LA) and perhaps also in the Owens Valley INY and at Baldwin L. SBE. Additional localities at which it formerly nested include Nigger Slough LA and San Jacinto L. RIV. It is to be looked for as a facultative brood parasite of other duck species.

There is only one record for the Channel Is.: 27 Feb 1976 Thompson Res., Santa Catalina I. (6).

Open marshes and ponds with some cover are required for nesting. In winter and migration deeper, more open lakes are inhabited.

RING-NECKED DUCK
Aythya collaris

Fairly common (to locally common) winter visitant in all districts except District S, where decidedly uncommon. Remains rarely into early June, but strictly casual through summer (when recorded in Districts C, D, M, and R).

Preferred wintering localities include L. Cachuma SBA; Los Angeles County Arboretum, Arcadia LA; Antelope Valley LA; Big Bear Valley SBE; Imperial Dam IMP; and, especially for transients in March, L. Cuyamaca SD. It is generally scarce on the immediate coast. On the Channel Is. it is a scarce winter visitant to Thompson Res., Santa Catalina I., and a casual transient elsewhere. In District S the latest spring record is 7 Jun 1969 (unrecorded in mid-summer).

This species was considered quite rare in the region before about 1930 (Willett 1933); it has apparently increased, perhaps in response to the proliferation of man-made lakes, a favored wintering habitat.

TUFTED DUCK
Aythya fuligula

Four or five records: an adult male at L. Sherwood Ven in late fall and early winter from 25 Jan 1973 to Jan 1977: 18 Apr 1978 Pt. Mugu VEN (ad. male); 9-11 Nov 1978 Santa Clara R. estuary VEN (imm. male); and 4 Dec 1978-26 Feb 1979 and again 10 Nov 1979-8 Jan 1980 Quail L., southeast of Gorman LA (ad. male). An adult male in the Cuddy Valley KRN 15 Jan 1980 may have been the same bird that was at nearby Quail L.

This Eurasian species has recently been found to be of nearly annual occurrence on the coastal slope of northern California. The L. Sherwood bird was with Ring-necked Ducks and departed the lake (with the Ring-Necks) when fishing season commenced around late January each year. It was recorded as early as 30 Oct 1974 and as late as 2 Feb 1974.

GREATER SCAUP
Aythya marila

Generally an uncommon winter visitor along the coast. Numbers decrease from north to south and vary from year to year. Rather rare in many winters, at least south of San Luis Obispo Co. Generally a rare transient and winter visitant in the interior, but concentrations have been noted in Districts S and R.

Along the coast the Greater Scaup varies from rare to locally fairly common. This duck primarily inhabits coastal estuaries and harbors, and it may occur rarely with sea ducks on inshore ocean waters. A few records exist for inland localities in District C. It may linger on the coast even as late as early May (to 19 May 1978 San Diego SD—4). It is occasionally seen migrating north with scoter flocks in spring.

In the interior it is generally rare; transients have been recorded in the northern interior only on 3 Nov 1974 Furnace Creek Ranch INY; 11 Nov 1973 Stovepipe Wells INY; and 25 Nov-11 Dec 1977 Furnace Creek Ranch. Recently it has been recorded regularly at Quail L. southeast of Gorman LA, with a maximum of six on 27-28 Jan 1979.

There are a number of records for District S, where it irregularly may even be fairly common. What may be the high count for the region was 60 noted at SESS 27 Feb-3 Mar 1979; 26 were there 24-25 Oct 1977 (exceptional for such an early date). Most are gone from the Salton Sea by late March; it has summered once: two on 11 Jun 1977 at NESS, with one remaining to 16 Jul.

In District R it is regular but very local. Concentrations have been noted below Parker Dam SBE (up to 20) and below Imperial Dam IMP (up to 12). Along the Colorado R. it prefers fast flowing waters, and is often seen with goldeneyes.

The status of this duck in the region is somewhat unclear because of its similarity to the common Lesser Scaup.

LESSER SCAUP
Aythya affinis

Common winter visitant throughout. Remains rarely to uncommonly through summer, when most numerous at the Salton Sea.

The Lesser Scaup is one of our commonest diving ducks, occurring from freshwater lakes, ponds, and reservoirs to coastal lagoons and harbors. In general it is less partial to saltwater than the Greater Scaup. It is somewhat local in District R, with large numbers only at Imperial Dam IMP and Parker Dam SBE. Lesser Scaup are rare winter visitants to the Channel Is.

This species does not nest in the region.

KING EIDER
Somateria spectabilis

One record: an immature male was present at Malibu LA 22 Nov 1973-28 Jan 1974.

This species is casual in northern California, but during the winter of 1973-1974 at least half a dozen individuals were noted there, indicating an exceptional southward flight.

HARLEQUIN DUCK
Histrionicus histrionicus

Very rare winter visitant along the coast; a few probably winter annually along the rocky coast of northern San Luis Obispo Co. and one or two are recorded farther south in most winters. Several summer records.

Harlequin Ducks approach casual status south of San Luis Obispo Co.; they have been recorded twice in mainland Santa Barbara Co.; seven times in Los Angeles Co.; four times in San Diego Co.; and once on the Channel Is. (San Miguel I. 6 Apr 1976 — 2 males). Unseasonal records are: 2 Aug 1914 Santa Barbara Co. coast; 29 Sep-6 Oct 1968 Goleta SBA; 20 Jun 1969 Cambria SLO; 26 Aug-30 Nov 1973 Montana de Oro SLO; 22 May 1978 Pt. Fermin LA; a male more or less continuously present at Playa del Rey LA from 3 Mar 1972 into 1976; and a male at Carlsbad SD from 31 Dec 1977 until at least May 1980.

This species frequents inshore waters along rocky coastlines and in the vicinity of breakwaters and jetties; it is occasionally noted in coastal lagoons.

OLDSQUAW
Clangula hyemalis

Rare but regular winter visitant along the coast, primarily from November to March. Remains casually into summer. Casual at the Salton Sea; six records elsewhere in the interior.

Along the coast Oldsquaws are often found with flocks of scoters on inshore waters, coastal bays, and harbors. It has been recorded in all coastal counties.

The Oldsquaw is casual at the Salton Sea, where it has been recorded on 13 occasions. Eight of the records are from winter and early spring (31 Oct 1972 SESS to 16 Mar 1967 SESS). There are four later spring records (April-May), which possibly represent birds moving north out of the Gulf of California, and one summer record: 9 Jul 1967 SESS.

The six records elsewhere in the interior are: 21 Dec 1959 China Lake SBE; 25 Feb 1961 Imperial NWR IMP (2); 12-13 Feb 1972 L. Castaic LA; 15 Apr 1973 L. Cachuma SBA; 29 Dec-2 Jan 1978 Lancaster LA; and 14 Jul 1979 nr. Lancaster.

BLACK SCOTER
Melanitta nigra

Regular winter visitant along the coast; generally rare, but considerably more numerous some years. Casual at the Salton Sea.

While in some winters only one or two Black Scoters may be reported in the region, it may border on uncommon some years and may exceptionally be almost common, e.g. 287 counted between Pt. Mugu VEN and Santa Monica LA 15 Nov 1959. It is always decidedly less numerous south of Los Angeles Co. It has been recorded only twice around the Channel Is.: 28 May-7 Jun 1968 San Miguel I. (8+) and 25 May 1976 Santa Rosa I. (2). Transients are noted every spring flying past coastal promontories; up to 50 birds total have been noted flying past Goleta Pt. SBA during the period from early March to late April. This species is casual during the summer along the coast (7+ records); some summer records have been dismissed as probably pertaining to worn female Surf Scoters.

There are four records, all recent, from the Salton Sea: 14 Aug 1976 SESS (male); 29 Jan-11 Feb 1977 SESS (imm. male); 9-27 Feb 1977 SESS (ad. male); and 1 May-19 Sep 1977 NESS (up to 5).

WHITE-WINGED SCOTER
Melanitta fusca

Irregular winter visitant along the coast, fairly common (exceptionally even common) some years and quite scarce others. Rare but somewhat regular in summer. Casual at the Salton Sea; seven records elsewhere inland.

This scoter occurs most regularly and in the largest numbers north of Pt. Conception SBA. It is quite irregular south of there; a series of poor flight years occurred through the mid and late 1970s, although there were moderate flights during the falls of 1978 and 1979. In spring, even in "off" years, transients are regularly seen migrating past promontories such as Goleta Pt. SBA, primarily in late March and April (peaks in mid-April). In summer it is rare but somewhat regular (and may be more numerous after flight years, e.g. 181 at Vandenberg AFB SBA 20-30 Jul 1980 and 54 at Pt. Mugu VEN 15 Jun 1980). This species is quite scarce around the southern Channel Is., although it can be common in winter off San Miguel I. and Santa Rosa I.

The White-winged Scoter is of almost regular occurrence at the Salton Sea. Since it was first recorded in 1957, the majority of the 17+ records have been from spring and summer.

It is casual elsewhere inland; the seven records are as follows: 8 Nov 1937 Redlands SBE; 28 Oct 1951 nr. Temecula RIV; 28 Dec 1957 Whittier LA (2); 30 Oct 1971 Chino SBE; 14 Nov 1976-23 Apr 1977 Imperial Dam

IMP; 24-27 Nov 1976 Furnace Creek Ranch INY; and 22-27 May 1979 Furnace Creek Ranch.

White-winged Scoters are usually encountered in pure flocks or with Surf Scoters on inshore waters, bays, and, particularly, around piers and harbors.

SURF SCOTER
Melanitta perspicillata

Abundant winter visitant and spring transient along the coast; uncommon in summer. Uncommon spring transient and rare fall transient and winter visitant at the Salton Sea; rare in summer. Flocks of spring transients are also noted irregularly on lakes in and near the southern part of District M. Rare transient elsewhere in the interior.

Surf Scoters are among the most numerous waterbirds of inshore waters, bays, and harbors during the winter and early spring. They can be very abundant as a spring transient past coastal promontories, particularly from Los Angeles Co. north (e.g. Goleta Pt. SBA where up to 10,000 have been encountered in a day during peak periods). Spring migration generally takes place from late March through early May, with peak numbers in early to mid-April. As with many other seabird species, fall migration takes place farther from shore and relatively few birds can be counted migrating past coastal points, particularly those south of Pt. Conception. A common bird in winter around the northern Channel Is., it is much less numerous around the southern islands. Surf Scoters remain uncommonly along the coast in summer; small flocks (exceptionally up to 100) are noted along the length of the coast. This species is casual away from the ocean in District C; most records are from quite near the coast.

At the Salton Sea it is an uncommon spring transient and rare fall transient and winter visitant. A few may linger through the summer (exceptionally up to 12, May-Jul 1977). This species is also an uncommon and irregular spring transient locally on lakes in the southern portion of District M and on the nearby Anza-Borrego Desert. These birds, like those at the Salton Sea, undoubtedly represent migrants moving north out of the Gulf of California. Maxima include up to 83 on L. Henshaw SD 22-24 Mar 1979 and up to 45 there 4-23 Mar 1980; and 50-75 on L. Cuyamaca SD 26 Mar 1967 and up to 22 there 15 Apr-6 May 1978.

In District R there are four records: 23 Oct 1949 and 20 Nov 1953 L. Havasu SBE; and 24 Oct 1959 and 3 Nov 1961 Imperial NWR IMP.

In the remainder of the interior (reflected in the graph) it is a very rare but regular fall transient through the northern deserts and a casual spring migrant; all records have been obtained since 1971. The 15 or so fall records come mainly from late October and November; the four spring records are: 15 Apr 1973 Little Rock Dam LA; 13 May 1978 Baker SBE; 22 May 1979 Furnace Creek Ranch INY; and 3 Jun 1979 Little L. INY.

BUFFLEHEAD
Bucephala albeola

Fairly common winter visitant in all districts; locally common along the coast (e.g. around San Diego SD). Casual in summer, with most records from the Salton Sea.

This is one of our latest ducks to arrive in fall; in spring it may linger to early May. It generally inhabits small ponds, lakes, and reservoirs, but also occurs on coastal estuaries and bays. It is not found on the open ocean. There are three winter records for the Channel Is., all from Thompson Res. on Santa Catalina I.

BARROW'S GOLDENEYE
Bucephala islandica

Very local winter visitant along the Colorado R.; casual elsewhere in the interior and along the coast.

This species has recently proven to be regular in small numbers (about 10) with wintering flocks of Common Goldeneyes along the Colorado R. below Parker Dam SBE. There are also scattered records south to Imperial Dam IMP, e.g. three at Senator Wash Dam IMP 17 Feb 1979. A small group regularly winters upriver at Davis Dam on the Nevada/Arizona border.

There are three records from the Salton Sea: 10 Dec 1978 NESS; 21 Jan 1979 Salton City IMP; and 1 Dec 1979 Salt Creek RIV.

The four records of late fall transients through District D are: 26-28 Nov 1976 Furnace Creek Ranch INY; 21-26 Nov 1977 Furnace Creek Ranch; 22 Dec 1978 Baker SBE; and 22 Nov 1979 Furnace Creek Ranch.

The five coastal records are: 5 Jan 1901 Newport ORA; 7 Mar 1964 Otay SD; 15-20 Feb 1975 San Diego Bay SD; 7 Jan and 9 Mar 1979 Otay; and 12 Dec 1979-24 Jan 1980 Bolsa Chica ORA.

Female and immature male Barrow's Goldeneyes can be very difficult to distinguish from Common Goldeneyes, and should be identified only with great caution.

COMMON GOLDENEYE
Bucephala clangula

Local winter visitant, fairly common to common along the Colorado R., uncommon to fairly common at the Salton Sea, and rare to locally fairly common in District C. Generally a scarce transient through Districts D and M.

It is a locally common winter visitant along the Colorado R., especially on the faster-flowing waters below Parker Dam SBE and nearby at the lower end of L. Havasu (up to several hundred birds may winter in

119

this area). Flocks are also encountered regularly downriver to below Earp SBE. Although it is less common elsewhere along the Colorado R., this species is still uncommon to fairly common throughout District R.

At the Salton Sea it is an uncommon to fairly common winter visitant; numbers vary from year to year. Fifteen were still present at the end of May 1963; there are at least six summer records.

Along the coast Common Goldeneyes are generally rare to uncommon, although they winter fairly commonly around San Diego Bay. Away from the San Diego area and, perhaps, the coast of northern San Luis Obispo Co., it is as likely to be found inland in District C as it is along the immediate coast. For example, small flocks have been noted on L. Cachuma and Gibralter Res. SBA, although the species is casual on the nearby, well-worked coastline at Goleta SBA. There are three records for the Channel Is.: 11-19 Apr 1970 Santa Cruz I. (2-8); 18 Apr 1970 Santa Cruz I. (1); and 29 Feb 1976 Santa Catalina I. Three summer records exist for Dictrict C: "summer 1967" San Diego Bay SD (not graphed); 6 Jun 1963 San Diego Bay; and 22 Jul 1956 Cambria SLO.

In Districts D and M it is primarily an uncommon late fall transient in the northern portion of District D and on montane lakes. A few birds may linger through the winter. Late spring transients on the desert are: 8-9 Apr 1979 Lancaster LA; 23 May 1970 Furnace Creek Ranch INY; and 26-27 May 1978 Furnace Creek Ranch.

The habitat on the Colorado R. is noted above. Along the coast goldeneyes occupy coastal lagoons and bays and, locally, inshore ocean waters. Birds in the interior occur on the deeper lakes and ponds.

HOODED MERGANSER
Mergus cucullatus

Rare but regular winter visitant, particularly along the northern coastal slope south to Los Angeles Co. Scarcer farther south along the coast, but recorded most winters. In the interior a rare fall transient and winter visitant in Districts S and R (with the vicinity of Parker Dam SBE being especially good) and in the northern portion of District D. Extremely rare in the remainder of District D.

Most birds are recorded in the region during the period from early November to mid-March; a bird at Santee SD 28 May 1977 had probably wintered locally.

Hooded Mergansers prefer streams and small ponds and lakes which are heavily bordered with vegetation; they are also found regularly on coastal estuaries. The species is unrecorded on the Channel Is.

RED-BREASTED MERGANSER
Mergus serrator

Common winter visitant along the coast, remaining uncommonly through the summer. In the interior, status complex, but primarily an uncommon spring transient and rare fall transient.

In the interior the largest numbers of transients occur in Districts S and R. It is a fairly common spring transient along the Colorado R.; an exceptionally large concentration was 880 on 19 Apr 1948 at L. Havasu SBE. A flock of 170 on 22 Feb 1957 at Imperial NWR IMP was unusually large for winter, and possibly represented early spring transients. This species summers irregularly at NESS; maxima of 150 birds were recorded during the summers of 1977 and 1978. There are scattered summer records for elsewhere in the interior (e.g. Furnace Creek Ranch INY). The few birds wintering in the interior are usually at the Salton Sea or along the Colorado R., particularly in the vicinity of Parker Dam SBE. This merganser is a rare to uncommon transient in the interior of District C.

Along the coast Red-breasted Mergansers are partial to inshore ocean waters and coastal estuaries and harbors, habitats which are rarely occupied by the Common Merganser.

COMMON MERGANSER
Mergus merganser

Uncommon transient and uncommon to locally common winter visitant, primarily on deep-water lakes, rivers, and reservoirs. Few summer records except at Parker Dam SBE, where regular.

In winter the largest numbers occur along the Colorado R.; most occur in the vicinity of Parker Dam SBE (especially) and Imperial Dam IMP. Although local, it is a fairly common to common winter visitant in District M and on the coastal slope (generally away from the immediate coast).

It is rare to uncommon at the Salton Sea; the majority of records are for mid-winter. This duck is generally a rare transient through most of District D, but flocks do winter locally (Owens Valley, Antelope Valley).

Small numbers have summered at Parker Dam; elsewhere it is casual in summer, with records as follows: 5 Jun 1964 SESS; 16 Jun 1967 Laguna Dam IMP; 3 Aug 1968 SESS; and mid-Aug to late Sep 1977 NESS (not graphed).

Common Mergansers are partial to deep bodies of fresh water, especially the larger reservoirs in Districts C and M. They commonly inhabit the flowing waters below the spillways of the major dams along the Colorado R. They are not likely to be seen on the ocean, and are quite rare on coastal estuaries and harbors, where the Red-breasted Merganser is common.

RUDDY DUCK
Oxyura jamaicensis

Common winter visitant in all districts; may be very abundant locally, e.g. at the Salton Sea. Remains fairly commonly through summer, breeding locally in all districts.

The Ruddy Duck is widespread and occurs from open freshwater lakes and marshes to coastal estuaries and, less typically, inshore ocean waters. It is a common winter visitor on Santa Catalina I. (Thompson Res.) and it is casual on the other islands. It was formerly more widespread as a nesting species in the region. Ruddy Ducks nest on freshwater lakes bordered by marshes and, at the Salton Sea, around freshwater marshes at the river mouths.

CATHARTIDAE: NEW WORLD VULTURES

TURKEY VULTURE
Cathartes aura

Common transient and uncommon summer visitant throughout; common in summer in District R. Very local winter visitant, primarily along the coast and in Districts S and R.

In spring the largest numbers of migrants are seen from mid-February to mid-April, when flocks may sometimes total hundreds of individuals. Spring migrants may arrive as early as mid-January. It is generally less numerous as a fall transient, although large southbound groups are often encountered, especially in District D. Fall migrants may appear as early as late June; most occur from mid-July into October, peaking in September.

Turkey Vultures are generally uncommon summer visitants, although they are common at this season in District R. Birds seen in summer in District S are generally around the desert fringes of the Salton Sea.

In winter this vulture is generally rare to uncommon, although it is locally fairly common to common. At this season it is virtually absent from the cold northern interior (the only Owens Valley winter record, 18 Jan 1976, may actually represent a very early spring transient) and from District D in general. The species is locally fairly common in winter in Districts S (primarily in the vicinity of Brawley IMP) and R (primarily from Blythe RIV to Earp SBE), gathering at winter roost sites. Turkey Vultures are generally rare along the coast in winter, but they are locally fairly common to common in coastal Orange Co. and on other coastal plains (Oxnard Plain VEN, Santa Maria SBA, and Los Osos Valley SLO). Only birds found from mid-November to mid-January should be assumed to be wintering.

One or two have been irregularly noted on San Clemente I., and the species may be resident there (no evidence of nesting). It is unrecorded on the other Channel Is.

Turkey Vultures occur in a variety of open and semi-open habitats, generally at lower elevations. Curiously, they are unrecorded from Pt.

Loma SD (reknowned for its migrating raptors). For nesting they usually require rocky cliffs, but the distribution of nest sites in the region is imperfectly known and needs much study. There are indications of a substantial decline in nesting birds, at least in District C.

CALIFORNIA CONDOR
Gymnogyps californianus

Very rare resident in foothill and montane regions, primarily in Ventura, Santa Barbara, and Kern Cos. Nearing extinction; the 1980 estimates are of a population of no more than 30 individuals.

At present condors occur most regularly in the interior portions of Santa Barbara and Ventura Cos. and in montane Kern Co. They wander regularly to extreme nw Los Angeles Co., and a few birds are often present in e. San Luis Obispo Co. It is now a casual wanderer to the vicinity of the coast (e.g. Goleta SBA, Santa Monica Mtns. LA); these occurrences are increasingly infrequent. It is very exceptionally recorded northeast to the Owens Valley INY, e.g. two at Olancha in early Nov 1962 and one near Little L. 12 Oct 1952.

The California Condor was formerly more numerous and widespread, occurring over much of the montane and foothill regions west of the deserts. It formerly nested at localities such as Pasadena LA and Mt. Palomar SD (until 1900, and recorded there until at least 1910). Very few documented condor nestings have occurred in recent years. Two nests were located in 1980, one in Los Angeles Co. and one in Santa Barbara Co.; the former nesting was apparently successful. Condors are now most regularly observed from the lookout established on Mt. Pinos KRN/VEN (best from July through September). They are also frequently seen over the ridge to the south of the Edmonston Pumping Station e. of Grapevine KRN (mainly fall and winter). They are now only rarely observed at the established refuge in the Sespe region of Ventura Co.

The California Condor is on both the Federal and California lists of Endangered Species. A variety of factors have been implicated in its decline, including reduction or modification of foraging habitat, decrease in availability of food, disturbance around nest sites, shooting, poisoning, pesticide residues, and the general senescence of the species.

ACCIPITRIDAE:
OSPREY, HAWKS, EAGLES, HARRIERS

OSPREY
Pandion haliaetus

Rare to uncommon year-round visitant; most widely noted in fall and winter on the coast and in migration in the interior. Has nested sporadically in recent years. Formerly more numerous.

In District C it is most often encountered in fall and winter, although a few birds regularly remain through the summer. Ospreys are found along the immediate vicinity of the coast and around the larger inland bodies of water (including the larger lakes of District M, where primarily a rare transient). In the interior this species is primarily a rare transient, but records are scattered through the entire year (rarest in mid-winter). In District R it is uncommon as a transient and in mid-winter; a few often summer. Individuals will often take up prolonged residence at certain favored areas and remain for several years (e.g. around some of the open bodies of water along the Colorado R.). Migrants are occasionally seen away from aquatic habitats.

In recent years it has nested for certain only at Tinnemaha Res. INY (1974-1976) and at L. Casitas VEN (1974). It has also probably nested recently on San Antonio L. on the San Luis Obispo/Monterey Co. line (1975). Pairs may sometimes remain through summer on other lakes (e.g. L. Arrowhead SBE), suggestive of the possibility of additional nesting.

Ospreys formerly nested commonly on San Clemente and San Nicolas Is., and less plentifully on Santa Catalina I.; nesting has not been recorded since the 1930s. It is now reported as an occasional transient on the Channel Is. A few pairs formerly nested on the mainland coast (e.g. Laguna ORA and San Diego Bay SD). There are no recent nestings along the immediate coast.

Ospreys are now most frequently seen around large coastal estuaries (Newport Bay ORA, San Diego Bay, etc.) and certain large inland lakes (L. Cachuma SBA, etc.). This species is still quite numerous as a breeder south of our region in coastal Baja California and locally to the north through coastal and northeastern California.

WHITE-TAILED KITE
Elanus leucurus   Map p. 391

Uncommon to locally fairly common resident in District C. Rare visitant and very local nester on the western edge of District D; very rare visitant to the eastern part of the region. Has nested once in District S.

The centers of abundance in the region are the coastal valleys and plains of Orange Co. and San Diego Co., where this kite is fairly common and common, respectively. Winter roosts form in late August and early September and may contain over 100 birds. These roosts are often found in Goleta SBA, coastal Orange Co., and in the Tijuana River Valley SD. This species has undergone a tremendous increase in population in the region (and through much of the New World) since the earlier part of this century (when populations had been reduced to very low levels). There are indications that the increase in District C has leveled off, with strong local declines after a peak in the early and mid-1970s. Because of these major fluctuations, the current status is difficult to determine exactly.

In the interior it is generally a rare, non-breeding visitant. It is increasing on the western edge of the deserts and is now even an uncommon resident in the Antelope Valley LA (maximum of 15 on 15 Dec 1979). This raptor is very rare in the eastern part of the region; records are: 2 Jan 1976 China Lake KRN/SBE; 7 Sep-30 Nov 1975 Big Pine INY; and 18 Dec 1971 near Bishop INY. In District S there are five records at NESS from 11 Aug 1976 to 6 Mar 1965. At SESS it has been recorded at Brawley IMP where a pair was present from 28 Nov 1974 to the spring of 1975, when it nested. The one fledged young was found dead 23 May 1975 and an adult was last seen in the vicinity 7 Dec 1975. There are no convincing records for District R (there are four records from Arizona). Interesting records for District M are 10 Aug 1975 on the summit of Mt. Pinos VEN and 14 Sep 1979 summit of Mt. Palomar SD.

It has been recorded four times from the Channel Is., all in fall.

This species inhabits open country where grasslands, agricultural fields, marshes, and even roadside borders provide sufficient rodent prey. Marshy bottomlands with clumps of large trees are favored sites for winter roosts.

MISSISSIPPI KITE
Ictinia mississippiensis

Casual late spring visitant. Six records as follows: 18 Jun 1933 near Goleta SBA; 2-5 Jun 1968 Furnace Creek Ranch INY; 3 Jun 1970 Santa Barbara SBA; 21 May-3 Jun 1973 Furnace Creek Ranch (2 subadults present 21 May, with one remaining to latter date); 14 Jun 1973 Furnace Creek Ranch (subadult; definitely none present 4-13 Jun); and 25-26 May 1976 Furnace Creek Ranch.

In recent years this species has expanded its breeding range westward into Arizona, where its existence is now threatened by the destruction of riparian woodland.

BALD EAGLE
Haliaeetus leucocephalus

Local winter visitant, fairly common at a few favored wintering sites around inland bodies of water but generally rare otherwise. Casual in summer. Formerly resident on the Channel Is. and locally along the coast.

The largest concentrations occur in District M and in the interior portions of District C: Big Bear Valley in the San Bernardino Mtns. (up to 25-30 birds), L. Mathews RIV (up to 20 birds), and L. Henshaw SD (about 10 birds). Small numbers also winter along the length of the Colorado R., primarily in the Needles/Topock area SBE. It is only rarely observed elsewhere, although it is regular at L. Cachuma SBA and the Edmonston Pump Station KRN, and has been recorded almost annually at the Salton Sea. Other areas of repeated occurrence include the San

Luis Rey River Valley, Sweetwater Res., and Cuyamaca Res. SD; and L. Arrowhead and L. Silverwood SBE. There are scattered records in District C away from the areas cited above. In District D it is mainly a late fall and winter visitant in the Owens Valley INY, where it is probably regular in winter in small numbers on Tinnemaha Res. The Bald Eagle has also been recorded twice in the Antelope Valley LA, and, exceptionally, at Furnace Creek Ranch INY (26 Dec 1977).

Individuals may linger into late spring (e.g. 19 May 1978 Palo Verde IMP) and casually through summer on montane lakes. The population wintering in the Big Bear Valley generally begins arriving in the second week of November and the last individuals depart by mid-April.

Bald Eagles were formerly common residents on the Channel Is. and local residents along the mainland coast. Mainland nesting sites this century were at Dos Pueblos Ranch, w. of Goleta SBA (to the early 1950s); nr. Carpinteria SBA (to the late 1930s); La Jolla Canyon nr. Pt. Mugu VEN (1922); Zuma Canyon, w. of Malibu LA (early 1900s); Malibu Canyon LA (to 1931); Little Tecate Mtn. ("Lookout Mtn.") SD (egg taken 8 Mar 1936); and nr. Sweetwater Res. SD (early 1900s). They may also have nested locally on the larger inland lakes and reservoirs, e.g. L. Elsinore RIV. This species persisted as a nester on the Channel Is. until the late 1950s. It is now only an occasional winter visitant on the Channel Is.; recent records are only from Santa Rose I. Attempts were being made in the summer of 1980 to reestablish it on Santa Catalina I.

A bird at Seeley IMP 13 Aug-29 Oct 1977 (not graphed) was banded as a nestling in central Arizona. It had been recovered near Joshua Tree National Monument and returned to Arizona before it made its way to Seeley.

Wintering sites are generally deep inland lakes and reservoirs, where the eagles subsist largely on fish, coots, and waterfowl. Coastal birds are generally around the larger estuaries. Immatures predominate in the region.

The southern populations of the Bald Eagle are considered endangered by the U.S. Department of the Interior and are strictly protected.

NORTHERN HARRIER
Circus cyaneus   Map p. 391

Fairly common winter visitant to open marshes and fields in all districts. Now very scarce and local as a breeder.

Harriers can be found over freshwater marshes, coastal salt marshes and estuaries, open grasslands, agricultural fields, and, uncommonly, over open desert and brushlands. In winter they are sometimes locally common in District R, at SESS and locally in District D (e.g. Antelope Valley). In District D in winter, most are restricted to agricultural areas. Migrants are widespread, even over the open desert and locally in open areas in District M, where a few may winter. It is a rare transient and winter visitor on the Channel Is. (15 records from 16 Sep to 1 May).

This hawk currently nests at the mouth of the Tijuana R. SD, near Lakeview RIV (after wet winters), at Harper Dry L. SBE, in the Owens Valley INY, at Morro Bay SLO, vic. Camp Pendleton SD, and probably in the Antelope Valley LA and on Vandenberg AFB SBA. It probably also breeds locally elsewhere. It formerly bred along the length of the coast in areas such as Dune Lakes SLO (current status unknown), Saticoy VEN, Alamitos LA, Seal Beach ORA, and near Del Mar SD. Protected marshes or open grassy meadows are required for nesting.

SHARP-SHINNED HAWK
Accipiter striatus

Fairly common winter visitant in all districts; locally common fall transient. Scarce summer resident in District M; it has nested once in District C.

In winter and migration this is the most numerous *Accipiter* in the region. It can be common as a fall transient moving along coastal ridges and promontories in late September and October. This hawk becomes decidedly scarcer in the northern portions of District D in mid-winter. Sharp-shinned Hawks are uncommon winter visitants on the larger Channel Is. and rare transients on the remaining islands.

In District M it is uncommon in winter and is a rare summer resident; nesting records exist for Icehouse Canyon in the San Gabriel Mtns. (1975), L. Arrowhead SBE (egg set taken 16 May 1922), and Big Bear L. SBE (1904). There are many other summer records for the San Bernardino Mtns., the mountains of San Diego Co., and, particularly, the San Jacinto Mtns.; these records are possibly indicative of regular nesting. It has nested once in District C: Cambria SLO (1968).

COOPER'S HAWK
Accipiter cooperii

Uncommon permanent resident except in Districts S and R where it winters uncommonly but no longer breeds. Can be fairly common in District C in fall when transients are observed along coastal ridges and at coastal promontories.

The region's breeding population has been much reduced in recent decades, especially in lowland areas where much riparian woodland has been destroyed. Nesting is now mainly restricted to woodlands and open forests of District M (including the New York Mtns. and possibly the Mid Hills of the Mohave Desert). It breeds locally at oases in District D (Morongo Valley SBE, Owens Valley INY, etc.). It formerly bred in District R, but is apparently extirpated as a nester there. It is generally a transient and winter visitant in District D. In District C it is more numerous and widespread in winter than in summer. This species is a rare winter visitant on the larger Channel Is.

Cooper's and Sharp-shinned Hawks are frequently misidentified in the field; consequently, the relative abundances of the two species are often misrepresented on censuses such as the Christmas Bird Count. In reality, Cooper's generally predominates only during the summer months, and perhaps in winter in Districts D, S, and R. A variety of woodland and semi-open habitats are occupied. Breeding populations are generally restricted to riparian groves and mountain canyons.

NORTHERN GOSHAWK
Accipiter gentilis

Very rare resident in District M, principally in the San Jacinto Mtns. and possibly the San Bernardino Mtns. and Mt. Pinos. One nesting record. Otherwise a casual late fall and winter visitant, perhaps regular in the northernmost portions of District D. Somewhat invasive, with infrequent flight years bringing individuals farther south in the region.

In District M it has been recorded at least six times in recent years from 2000-2700m in the San Jacinto Mtns. RIV. Localities include Tahquitz Valley, Willow Creek, Skunk Cabbage, Humber Park, and L. Fulmor. All birds observed here have been adults present in mid-summer. In the San Bernardino Mtns. this species has been recorded at Big Bear L. 22 Jul 1947 and near Arrowbear 21 May 1978 (2). Records for Mt. Pinos KRN/VEN are from 1 Aug 1953 and 18 Jun 1976; an egg set was taken there 6 May 1904. Another adult was recorded on 23 May 1979 on Clark Mtn. SBE.

In the northern part of District D it has primarily been recorded in late fall and winter at Oasis MNO, Deep Springs INY, and, exceptionally, south to Furnace Creek Ranch INY, Tecopa INY, and China Lake KRN/SBE. An early fall bird was at Westgard Pass INY 2 Sep 1978; there are additional September records.

Along the coast goshawks have been recorded in recent years as follows: 6 Dec 1972 Santa Ynez Valley SBA (ad.); 19 Nov 1972 Hemet RIV (ad.); 23 Dec 1972 Santa Barbara SBA (imm.); 25 Jan-11 Feb 1974 San Pedro LA (ad.); 7 Dec 1974-3 Jan 1975 Big Sycamore Canyon VEN (ad.); and 18 Dec 1977-18 Feb 1978 Arcadia LA (ad.). A bird on Figueroa Mtn. SBA 6 Apr 1977, while technically in District M, probably fits the coastal pattern. Most older records for District C are for the fall and winter of 1916-1917 when a major flight occurred. During that season three were recorded from Ventura Co., four from Los Angeles Co., one from Riverside Co., and one from San Diego Co. Additionally, one was recorded from District R, 3 km south of Palo Verde IMP on 2 Nov 1916. Old occurrences within District C in other years were: Oct 1900 near Rialto SBE and 5 Jan 1928 Mesa Grande SD.

There is an anomalous summer record for District R: 6 Jun 1964 Earp SBE (ad.).

Transient and winter goshawks have been found in semi-wooded areas in the coastal lowlands and around isolated groves of trees on the extreme northern deserts. Records from District M come from pine and fir forests above 2000m.

Goshawks should be identified with extreme care in the region; large female Cooper's Hawks are frequently misidentified as goshawks.

BAY-WINGED (HARRIS') HAWK
Parabuteo unicinctus

Formerly a fairly common resident in mesquite bosques and adjacent cottonwood galleries along the length of the Colorado R. and also locally in cottonwood/mesquite clumps at the south end of the Salton Sea. Now extirpated from the region, primarily due to the destruction of riparian forests along the Colorado R. and to the drain of wild populations for falconry.

Populations persisted at SESS until the early 1950s, in the vicinity of Bard IMP until about 1960, and around Needles-Topock SBE until about 1965. One was seen north of Blythe RIV 28 Nov 1964. There have been no credible reports of wild birds since the mid-1960s.

In District C old records which may pertain to wild birds are: 17 Nov 1912 Mission Valley SD and 1-6 Nov 1942 Oceanside SD. Numerous recent records from District C undoubtedly pertain to escapees. This species is now very popular with falconers and some observed birds have had jesses, bells, etc. Escapees have also been noted around the Salton Sea, where the situation is currently confused by the release of birds confiscated by the California Department of Fish and Game. Released birds made an aborted attempt to nest in 1976 near Niland IMP. Releases are currently taking place along the Colorado R. (e.g. Martinez L., Arizona). Future reports of Bay-winged Hawks anywhere in the region will probably have to be treated as escapees or released birds.

Bay-winged Hawks have declined through much of the southwest. Although they still nest locally through southern Arizona, their existence there is threatened by planned water reclamation projects and by falconers. Attempts to re-establish this species in southern California seem futile unless riparian habitat can be restored and regulations banning the possession of the species are instituted and enforced.

RED-SHOULDERED HAWK
Buteo lineatus   Map p. 391

Fairly common resident in woodlands west of the deserts. Rare to uncommon visitor in District D, primarily in the western and northern portions. Casual in the extreme southeastern part of the region.

This hawk is largely confined to the coastal slope of the region, although it is resident locally in the lower portions of District M (to about

1500m, occasionally wandering as high as 2600m) and is locally resident on the desert slopes of the Transverse Ranges, e.g. at Valyermo LA.

Throughout the remainder of District D it is an uncommon (bordering on rare) fall transient and rare winter visitant. During fall and winter there is some expansion into the coastal plains. These slight but regular movements indicate that western populations of this species are less sedentary than previously thought. Many of the desert records are concentrated in the northern and western portions: Owens Valley INY, Deep Springs Valley INY, Furnace Creek Ranch INY, Oasis MNO, Morongo Valley SBE, and the Antelope Valley LA. It is somewhat regular (about 8 records) at NESS, but there is only one record from SESS: 24 Sep 1977 Finney L. SESS. There are only three records for District R: 16 Feb 1962 near Yuma, in Imperial Co.; 21 Jan 1978 near Needles SBE (2); and 26 Jul 1978 Needles. It has also been recorded on the Arizona side of the river at the Bill Williams delta. The only summer records from District D (excluding the western edge) are: 17 Jul 1968 Wildrose INY; 20 Jul 1977 Saline Valley INY; and 12 Jul 1978 Kelso SBE. These undoubtedly represent post-breeding wanderers.

It is unrecorded on the Channel Is.

This is a hawk of relatively mesic woodlands that are dominated by oaks and riparian growth. On the western edges of the deserts it may nest along cottonwood-lined watercourses. This species is infrequently seen migrating with other hawks along coastal ridges or coastal promontories.

BROAD-WINGED HAWK
Buteo platypterus

Rare fall transient and casual winter visitant. Several spring records, all from the interior. Fall records are concentrated along the coast. About 65 records for the region.

Most Broad-winged Hawks are observed in fall along the coast, especially at coastal points and ridges which normally concentrate migrating raptors (e.g. Pt. Loma SD). At Pt. Loma they have been recorded annually in recent years, with up to six birds in a fall (maximum of three in a day). There are also seven fall records for the interior: 14 Sep 1979 Joshua Tree National Monument to 19 Nov 1977 Mesquite Springs INY; all are from the Death Valley region north. Additionally there is a record of a very late fall migrant 7 Dec 1977 at Coyote Ck. SD. A bird at Heart Bar State Park in the San Bernardino Mtns. 18 Sep 1977 is one of only two records for District M (see also below).

There are about 20 winter records for District C, although some of these may pertain to very late fall transients. Winter records are scattered through District C; records are not concentrated along the immediate coast as they tend to be in fall. Some wintering birds have remained into April. There are only two winter records from the interior: 7-8 Jan 1978

Furnace Creek Ranch INY, and 28 Jan-18 Feb 1978 Brawley IMP (the only record for District S).

The seven spring records are all from the interior: 21 Apr 1973 Furnace Creek Ranch; 1 May 1975 Kelso SBE (2); 25-26 May 1976 Furnace Creek Ranch; 12 Jun 1973 Deep Springs INY; 3-5 May 1978 Morongo Valley SBE; 12 Mar 1978 Brock Ranch IMP; and 19 Apr 1979 Morongo Valley. An additional record for Mt. Palomar SD 2 Apr 1969 may represent a spring migrant or a bird that had wintered in the vicinity.

It is unrecorded in District R and on the Channel Is.

Wintering Broad-winged Hawks have occupied lowland areas with groves of trees. The surprising pattern of a regular fall coastal migration of this species is even more strongly reflected in northern California where up to 30 birds have been noted in a single fall at Pt. Diablo, Marin Co.

SWAINSON'S HAWK
Buteo swainsoni

Rare to uncommon transient and rare summer resident, with numbers greatly reduced in recent decades (although large flights are still occasionally noted). Most now occur in District D. Accidental in winter.

In recent years it has been quite uncommon as a transient through District D; large flocks have only occasionally been noted. It is generally less common in fall than in spring. Spring migrants in the interior generally occur from mid-March into May; migration peaks in the first half of April. The earliest record is 2 Mar 1980 w. Antelope Valley LA. Migration is later in the northern parts of the interior, with the first birds appearing in mid-April. Recent maxima in the interior include 120 in the Borrego Valley SD 10 Apr 1975 and 25 at the same locality 10 Apr 1976. In the interior it is encountered less often in fall, although small concentrations have been noted in the Imperial Valley and the Colorado River Valley. The majority of fall records are from mid-August (occasionally late July) to early October; stragglers occur through the end of October.

This hawk is currently very rare (bordering on casual) as a spring and fall transient in District C. Only about a dozen records exist since 1968 (five in spring, seven in fall), and nearly half of these were before 1970. Recent coastal maxima are: 21 at Camp Pendleton SD 22 Oct 1977; 12 at Rose Hills LA 29 Sep 1968; and, exceptionally, 500-600 at the Tejon Ranch KRN 26 Oct 1979, and 200 at Temecula RIV the following day (27 Oct 1979). There are no certain records for the Channel Is.

This species is currently a very rare summer resident on the higher deserts. It has nested recently in the Lanfair Valley SBE, the Owens Valley INY, the Fish Lake Valley MNO, and the Antelope Valley LA. It has also nested recently in e. San Luis Obispo Co. (technically within District C), and may nest near the Edmonston Pump Station KRN. There are scattered records of non-breeding birds in summer, from Brock Ranch IMP north; most of these records are from Districts R and S.

Fifty or more birds at Oasis MNO 21 May-4 Jun 1978 appeared to be non-breeders. For nesting, Swainson's Hawks require scattered trees (even Joshua Trees) or ranchyard groves surrounded by desert grassland or agricultural areas. Our nesting populations include a large proportion of dark morph individuals.

Migrants may be noted over any habitat, but spring concentrations are usually found over desert grassland and lush blooms of spring wildflowers which provide the hawks with a source of caterpillars.

There are three certain winter records: a light morph bird was studied carefully at Bard IMP 5 Jan 1974; an immature was near Santa Maria SBA 2 Dec 1979; and a specimen was taken at Upland SBE 17 Jan 1916 (subadult female). We discount numerous other winter reports, mostly from Christmas Bird Counts. All winter reports should have substantial documentation.

This species was formerly much more common in the region; large spring concentrations (often over 100 birds) were commonly noted. Migrants were found throughout the region, especially in early April. Smaller concentrations occurred in the fall. Maxima included: 520 over the se San Gabriel Mtns. 2 Apr 1951, and 470 in the same area the following day. The last major spring concentration in District C was 60 in the Tijuana River Valley SD 31 Mar 1962. As a nesting species it was also formerly much more widespread. Nesting localities within District C included Santa Monica LA, Corona and Temecula RIV, and a few sites in San Diego Co. (e.g. Santee). Its decline in District C was noted as early as 1933 by Willett. The decline in the number of birds migrating through the region was drastic by the late 1950s, and numbers have been at a sustained low level since the beginning of the 1970s. An overall decline has occurred throughout the far west and the southwest.

ZONE-TAILED HAWK
Buteo albonotatus

Casual visitant, primarily in fall; over 25 records. Has nested once in the region.

The 13 fall records are from 27-28 Aug 1972 Big Pine INY to 26 Nov 1906 National City SD and come mainly from the coast; the two fall records away from District C are: the Big Pine record cited above and 10 Oct 1977 Cuyamaca Ranch State Park SD. There are six spring records: five for the interior from 21-22 Apr 1978 Morongo Valley SBE to 22 May 1976 Ft. Piute SBE, and one for "late April or early May" 1945 Chula Vista SD.

There is an additional late spring or summer record: 17 Jun 1978 Ft. Piute, where a late spring bird was also noted 22 May 1976. There is one nesting record: in the Santa Rosa Mtns. RIV a bird was present in the summer of 1978, a pair constructed a nest in late Jul 1979 (nesting believed to have failed), and a pair constructed a nest in 1980 and two young were produced (later found dead). This species has nested in the Bill Williams R. delta on the Arizona side of the Colorado R.

There are six winter records, perhaps involving four individuals: 23 Feb 1862, 50km north of San Diego SD; 20 Dec 1916 San Diego; 22 Dec 1974 ne Orange Co.; and a series of sightings possibly involving the same bird — 13-15 Jan 1978 and again 13 Jan 1979 near Oceanside SD, and 1-29 Feb 1980 at nearby Vista SD (not on graph).

Most coastal records are for San Diego Co. (three for Pt. Loma); it has been recorded twice in Orange Co. (18 Oct 1975 in the northeastern part of the county and the above winter record) and once in Los Angeles Co. (14 Nov 1975 Pt. Fermin). Interior records are for Ft. Piute SBE (cited above); Morongo Valley SBE (9 May 1970 and the April record above); Cottonwood Springs RIV 14 May 1960; Finney L. SESS 24 Apr 1960; and (cited above) Big Pine and the Cuyamaca Mtns.

RED-TAILED HAWK
Buteo jamaicensis

Common resident through most of the region. Less numerous in agricultural lands of the Coachella, Imperial, and Colorado River valleys, where it is a fairly common winter visitant (common in District R) and a rather rare summer resident (although a common resident in surrounding desert foothill habitats). Uncommon to fairly common on the Channel Is.; breeds on most of the larger islands, but only casual on the smaller islands.

Aggregate numbers in the region are much higher in winter due to an influx of northern birds; migrants are commonly seen in fall along coastal ridges and promontories. The most widespread and generalized of our *Buteo* hawks, it shuns only the deepest woodlands and most heavily urbanized areas, although it is a common suburban bird.

Red-tailed Hawks in the region represent a variety of color morphs; lighter birds predominate but very black individuals are often seen. *B.j. harlani* ("Harlan's Hawk") of the northern interior of the continent has been recorded for certain only once in the region: 19 Jan 1975 near Santa Maria, in San Luis Obispo Co. This race can be difficult to tell from melanistic Red-tails of other races. Other records of *harlani* published in *AFN* and *AB* are not fully believable.

FERRUGINOUS HAWK
Buteo regalis

Fairly common winter visitant (mid-September to early April) to grasslands and agricultural regions of District D and some valleys in the interior of District C. Generally rare to uncommon along the coast and in Districts S and R.

Important wintering localities include: Fish Lake Valley MNO, Owens Valley INY, the Carrizo Plain SLO, Cuyama Valley SLO/SBA, Antelope

Valley LA/KRN, Lucerne Valley SBE, Lakeview-Perris area RIV, and L. Henshaw SD. Along the coast it is fairly common only on the Santa Maria R. plain SBA/SLO. It is unrecorded on the Channel Is.

The Ferruginous Hawk arrives in the northern part of the region in mid-September (very rarely to the beginning of the month). The earliest record is 27 Aug 1978 Kelso SBE. It has generally departed by the beginning of April; a few linger into mid-April. The latest record is 20 Apr 1980 Baker SBE. May records published in *AFN* are all from localities where the species is unusual in winter, are not documented, and are dismissed here as unlikely.

Ferruginous Hawks occupy much the same open habitats as the Rough-legged Hawk, but they tend to be more widespread in the region, especially on the coastal slope. Dark-phase birds are rare in the region, although they have been noted almost annually.

ROUGH-LEGGED HAWK
Buteo lagopus

Irregular and local winter visitant, primarily in the interior; most birds occur in the northern portions of District D. Generally present from mid-October through March.

This uncommon and somewhat irregular hawk occurs from the northern interior south and west locally to the Antelope Valley LA/KRN, the Carrizo Plain SLO, the Perris-Lakeview area RIV, and L. Henshaw SD (all are graphed with District D). It is also recorded annually in agricultural habitats at SESS, but it is generally absent over the expanses of the Mohave Desert. In most years it is absent from District C. During flight years (1973-1974 and 1977-1978 are recent examples) this hawk is almost fairly common in areas of regular occurrence in the interior and is more widespread in all districts, with small numbers occurring on coastal plains and locally in District M (Baldwin L. SBE and L. Hemet RIV). There is one record for the Channel Is.: 9 Nov 1974 Santa Cruz I.

The Rough-legged Hawk occurs from mid-October through March; birds occasionally linger into April after flight winters. Late dates are: 17 Apr 1978 Antelope Valley; 22 Apr 1978 Oasis MNO; 24 Apr 1976 Cedar Canyon SBE; and 5 May 1974 Big Pine INY. An exceptionally early bird was near Big Bear L. SBE 11 Sep 1977.

Open fields, grasslands, and agricultural areas are occupied; arid desert scrub is generally avoided. On the coastal slope Rough-leggeds are found on open coastal plains, in river valleys, and in interior valleys with grasslands. Light-phase birds greatly predominate in the region.

GOLDEN EAGLE
Aquila chrysaetos

Uncommon resident through most of the region, except on the Colorado Desert and along the Colorado R., where a casual winter visitant.

Rare visitant on the larger Channel Is. Only two records for District S. Golden Eagles avoid heavily forested mountains and are generally absent from the immediate coast and urbanized areas. They are more widespread in winter and are mainly a winter visitant in interior valleys (e.g . the Antelope Valley, Cuyama Valley, and Carrizo Plain) and to certain coastal plains such as the Tijuana River Valley SD. There are very few records for District R; most are in winter. The only two records for District S are: 29 Apr-6 May 1962 SESS and 23 Jan 1963 SESS. We suspect that most reports of Golden Eagles at SESS actually pertain to immature Bald Eagles.

Golden Eagles favor grasslands, brushlands, deserts, oak savannas, open coniferous forests, and montane valleys. Nesting is primarily restricted to rugged, mountainous country.

FALCONIDAE: FALCONS

AMERICAN KESTREL
Falco sparverius

Common permanent resident throughout, although some withdraw from the northern interior in winter and from the southern interior in summer; numbers in District C are greatly augmented in winter. Fairly common resident on the Channel Is.; recent colonist on Santa Barbara and San Nicolas Is.

This is one of our commonest birds of prey, occurring in virtually all open and semi-open habitats. Some trees are required for nesting. During the breeding season it is scarce only in the higher and more forested parts of District M and in the southern interior (Districts S, R, and southern D).

MERLIN
Falco columbarius

Uncommon fall transient and rare winter visitant through most of the region. Seldom seen before late September and after early March.

Merlins are most regularly found along the coast and in the higher valleys of the northern and western fringes of District D (e.g. Oasis MNO, Owens Valley INY, Antelope Valley LA/KRN, Carrizo Plain SLO, and Cuyama Valley SLO/SBA/VEN). Extreme dates are 11 Sep 1959 near San Diego SD (exceptionally as early as 23 Aug 1980 Tijuana River Valley SD) to 23 Apr 1979 Goleta SBA. The species is rare in fall over the majority of the desert areas, including Districts S and R. It is a casual transient and winter visitant on the Channel Is.; transients have been noted over the open ocean, e.g. 10 km west of Morro Bay SLO 19 Nov 1978. Fall migrants often pass along the immediate vicinity of the coast (e.g. over coastal estuaries); they also appear in inland and mon-

135

tane valleys with scattered groves of trees, and on the desert where open (especially agricultural) land is broken by clumps of trees. They are rarely found in heavily wooded areas or over open deserts.

Merlins seen in the region (especially along the coast) are likely to be nominate *F. c. columbarius* (including *bendirei* of some authors). The pale *richardsonii*, breeding in prairie regions of central-western Canada, winters regularly in the interior and is almost as frequent as *columbarius* in the eastern part of the region. Individuals of *richardsonii* are very rarely found southwest to coastal San Diego Co. The "Black Merlin" (*F. c. suckleyi*, a very dark race breeding in coastal British Columbia) is casual in the region. The eleven records (eight specimens) extend from 14 Sep 1947 near Santa Barbara SBA (unusually early for any Merlin) to 6 Apr 1932 Santa Barbara. Six of the records are from coastal Santa Barbara Co.; the others are for Claremont LA 6 Dec 1895; SESS 31 Oct 1954 (the only record for the eastern part of the region); Bloomington SBE 7 Jan 1953; Mill Creek Canyon SBE 29 Dec 1977; and Big Bear L. SBE 4 Jan-20 Mar 1980. This race is undoubtedly more regular in the region than the few records indicate. Since the subspecies of the Merlin are distinguishable in the field under good conditions, all sightings should be recorded by subspecies whenever possible.

PEREGRINE FALCON
Falco peregrinus

Primarily a rare fall transient and winter visitant along the immediate coast, with a few pairs remaining to nest in the northwestern portion of the region. Even rarer in the interior, where its status is complex. Has undergone a sharp decline in the last several decades.

In District C it is primarily a fall transient along the coast, particularly in the vicinity of estuaries and at traditional raptor migration sites (such as Pt. Loma SD, where migrant Peregrines are noted annually). This species is probably most regular as a transient on Santa Barbara I. and the northern Channel Is., where it approaches uncommon status in spring and fall; a few birds often winter on the larger islands. A few birds regularly winter along the coast. Along the coast it is encountered less often in spring than in fall.

Nesting birds are currently known only from Morro Rock SLO (where a well-publicized and well-guarded pair is usually in residence), and a few other sites on the northern coast. Other recent summer records exist for District C, particularly in the vicinity of San Diego SD (some of these birds may originate in Baja California).

In District S this falcon is primarily a rare transient and non-breeding summer visitant; birds noted in summer possibly originate in Baja California, where the species still nests in fair numbers. There are a few winter records for District S.

Elsewhere in the interior the Peregrine is a rare transient and casual visitant at other seasons. It was formerly considered regular in winter along the Colorado R. (Phillips *et al*, Birds of Arizona 1964), but has decreased there, with recent records coming primarily in fall.

It was formerly much more common in the region, particularly as a nesting bird. Willett (1933) considered it a fairly common resident on the Channel Is.; it also nested in smaller numbers along the mainland coast from San Luis Obispo Co. south to Pt. Loma SD and locally inland to such localities as Escondido SD.

Peregrines frequent coastal estuaries and other areas which concentrate migrant waterfowl and shorebirds. Transients through the interior have been noted mostly at well-watered oases which concentrate migrants. For nesting, Peregrines require cliff faces within range of foraging areas such as coastal estuaries.

F. p. anatum is the subspecies normally occurring in the region. The larger, darker *pealei* (breeding in coastal Alaska and British Columbia) is known as a specimen from San Diego Bay 31 Mar 1908, and several sight records of large, dark Peregrines may pertain to this form. The species is considered endangered by the Federal and California governments. Loss of habitat, harmful effects of certain pesticides, and a drain of wild populations for the practice of falconry have all contributed to the decline of this species in the region.

PRAIRIE FALCON
Falco mexicanus

Uncommon resident in the arid interior and rare visitant (primarily in winter) to the coastal slope. Recorded once on the Channel Is.

Prairie Falcons breed locally through most of District D and in the arid interior portions of the coastal counties; they also breed in the mountains in the northeastern part of the region. For nesting sites they require cliffs or rocky outcroppings adjacent to the open, arid valleys needed for foraging. In winter they expand into agricultural portions of District D, into Districts S and R, and locally into open coastal plains (Tijuana River Valley SD, coastal Orange Co., and, less commonly, to the north — e.g. vic. Santa Maria SBA). The one Channel Is. record is 7 Mar 1979 Santa Barbara I.

Although populations have generally held up in the region, there has been a decline on the coastal slope. Willett (1933) cited several instances of nesting on the coastal slope (e.g. Santa Ynez Mtns. SBA, Piru Canyon VEN, vic. Hemet RIV, Cajon Pass SBE, Santa Ana Canyon ORA, and coastal San Diego Co.). The species no longer nests in most or all of these areas; nesting was recorded in 1980 in the western Santa Monica Mtns. VEN.

Prairie Falcons are birds of open regions and shun heavily wooded areas. Open desert scrub and grasslands are preferred, with some shifting into agricultural areas during the winter months. They have been recorded from below sea level in Death Valley INY and from nearly 4000m in the White Mtns. MNO.

PHASIANIDAE: GROUSE AND QUAIL

BLUE GROUSE
Dendragapus obscurus

Rare resident in the mountains of the northern part of the region. Now virtually limited to the White Mtns. in Mono Co.; very rarely noted in the Inyo Co. portion of that range.

In addition to the White Mtns. populations, Blue Grouse probably persist as a very rare resident above 2000m in the Mt. Pinos region VEN/KRN. The last certain records here were in 1964; unsubstantiated reports continue from this area, however, and intensive field work would likely reveal its continued presence. It is not known if the species still occurs on Tehachapi Peak and in the Piute Mtns. KRN, as reported by Grinnell and Miller (1944).

A pair reported at "9000 feet" in the San Jacinto Mtns. RIV 27 May 1971 hints at the existence of a relict population in this range, although the unprecedented nature of this record calls for further substantiation.

Blue Grouse inhabit coniferous forests and especially favor dense stands of firs on north-facing slopes. Exceptionally low was an individual at Tollhouse Spring INY 24-29 May 1970. Just outside our region this species is a fairly common resident along the eastern flank of the Sierra Nevada.

SAGE GROUSE
Centrocercus urophasianus

Status unclear; probably an uncommon summer visitant (May to mid-September) in the extreme northern part of the region where recorded on sagebrush-covered slopes and flats in the higher parts of the White Mtns. in Mono Co. Records are few, but this probably reflects poor coverage. Has been recorded to about 3800m.

In the early 1900s this species was reported in the Owens Valley south to the vicinity of Big Pine INY, an indication that its range was formerly slightly more extensive.

Sage Grouse are closely tied to sagebrush *(Artemisia tridentata)* associations. The upslope movement which brings birds out of the lower valleys into the White Mtns. is also exhibited by this species to the north of our region.

MOUNTAIN QUAIL
Oreortyx pictus   *Map p. 391*

Fairly common resident, primarily in District M, but also locally in the higher portions of District C and on the western fringes of District D.

It occurs in all of the mountain ranges west of the deserts and also in the mountains of the northern interior (White, Inyo, Panamint, Grapevine, Coso, and Argus). A population in the Granite Mtns. SBE may be a relict or an introduction. In District C it occurs to near sea level in Santa Barbara and San Luis Obispo Cos. A small population is resident locally in the w. Santa Monica Mtns. LA/VEN. This species occurs on the western fringes of District D in the Little San Bernardino Mtns., on Eagle Mtn. RIV, and in extreme sw Imperial Co.

Mountain Quail mainly inhabit dense montane chaparral and brushy areas within coniferous forests. More locally on the lower slopes they inhabit pinyon-juniper-yucca associations; in this habitat they are resident in the Little San Bernardino and Eagle Mtns. and on the desert ranges of Inyo Co. They also occur locally in dense, arborescent coastal chaparral dominated by ceanothus, manzanita, and Scrub Oak.

GAMBEL'S QUAIL
Callipepla gambelii   *Map p. 391*

Common resident on the southern deserts, north locally to San Bernardino Co. and se Inyo Co.

A common resident along the Colorado R., it occurs west across the southern deserts locally through District S to the Borrego Valley SD and north along the eastern base of the San Jacinto Mtns. to San Gorgonio Pass and Whitewater Canyon RIV. It is also resident locally on the Mohave Desert north to the Amargosa R. (vic. Shoshone INY) and west to the vicinity of Victorville SBE. Gambel's Quail are replaced by the California Quail over most of the w. and n. Mohave Desert (for areas of overlap with California Quail, see that species). This species occurs up to 1500m in Joshua Tree National Monument SBE/RIV, where it overlaps with the Mountain Quail.

Gambel's Quail are commonest in desert riparian associations, but also occur in a variety of desert brushlands as long as drinking water is available. In District S it is almost restricted to the remaining clumps of mesquite and acacia; it is not commonly found in pure stands of salt cedar (*Tamarix*) which now occupy much of that district.

This species has been introduced to San Clemente I., where it is now common, and to Cow Ck., near Furnace Creek Ranch, Death Valley National Monument INY.

HL Jones '79

CALIFORNIA QUAIL
Callipepla californica   Map p 391

Common resident throughout District C, ascending locally to about 1500m in District M and also occurring locally in the western and northern parts of District D and on the Channel Is.

Within District C it occurs in brushy areas, chaparral, river bottoms, oak woodlands, and even suburban gardens. In District M this species occurs locally in coastal slope chaparral and on the lower desert slopes of the major ranges.

In District D this quail is resident on the western fringes of the Mohave Desert in localities such as the Antelope Valley LA/KRN, the extreme northwestern part of San Bernardino Co., and the Mohave R. drainage from the San Bernardino Mtns. north (at least formerly) to the river's sink. It also occurs along the desert base of the Santa Rosa Mtns. RIV and locally along the west side of the Anza-Borrego Desert (e.g. Agua Caliente and Yaqui Well SD and extreme sw Imperial Co.). In the northern deserts *C. c. canfieldae* occupies the Owens Valley and mountain ranges to the east (White, Inyo, Panamint, and Argus). It occurs north to Benton MNO on the northern boundary of the region, inhabiting riparian groves and bordering sagebrush from 1100m to 2700m.

The California Quail is resident on Santa Catalina I., where it has been described as a distinct subspecies *C. c catalinensis*. This race has been introduced to Santa Cruz and Santa Rosa Is.

California Quail overlap with the Gambel's Quail very locally in the vicinity of San Gorgonio Pass RIV (San Andreas Canyon, Whitewater

Canyon, Morongo Pass, etc.). Hybrids are known from this area. It coexists over a broad altitudinal range with the Mountain Quail on the lower mountain slopes and in dense chaparral on the flanks of all ranges west of the deserts.

RALLIDAE: RAILS AND COOTS

YELLOW RAIL
Coturnicops noveboracensis

Casual transient and winter visitant; five or six records as follows: 12 Dec 1896 Newport Bay ORA (specimen); 31 Jan 1914 near Corona RIV (specimen, with another obtained here several days later); 26 Dec 1914 Goleta SBA; 9 Oct 1917 Shandon SLO; and 15-19 Apr 1978 near Lakeview RIV.

There are breeding records from just north of the region: Crowley L. MNO (1922) and Bridgeport MNO (to 1950). The recent dearth of records may in part reflect a change in birding habits away from the use of dogs and devices to flush secretive marsh birds. We reject some recent sight reports which lack convincing details. This species is poorly depicted in many field guides; misidentifications are thus frequent.

Yellow Rail records for the region have come from the grassy or marshy borders of inland ponds and from coastal marshes.

BLACK RAIL
Laterallus jamaicensis

Fairly common along the Colorado R. in the vicinity of Imperial Dam IMP, primarily in spring and summer. Rare to uncommon in District S, with the majority of records from summer. Now primarily a casual winter visitant in District C; formerly bred.

Black Rails are fairly easily heard in the vicinity of Imperial Dam IMP when vocalizing peaks in spring and summer. Calls have been heard here through the winter, indicating that at least some remain at this season. It is unrecorded farther north in District R, although it was recorded on the Arizona side at the Bill Williams R. delta 18 Apr 1979. Note that the graph for District R largely reflects the peak periods of calling.

This species is uncommon and very local within District S; it is somewhat irregular and unpredictable here and the majority of records are for summer. It has been noted at several localities around SESS, including Finney L. (up to seven heard in 1977) and the vicinity of Seeley. This rail has also been recorded at Niland IMP, Salt Creek IMP, and, recently, at NESS (two in 1977). West of the Salton Sea it has bred at Carrizo Marsh in the Anza-Borrego Desert of extreme e. San Diego Co. Elsewhere in District D there is only a record from Little L. INY Feb-Mar 1964.

In District C it is now a casual winter visitant away from Morro Bay SLO, where it is probably still resident and breeding. The graph does not reflect summer status at Morro Bay. It was formerly more regular and widespread in the district, with breeding at San Diego Bay SD (to at least the early 1930s), Sorrento Valley n. of La Jolla SD (to 1960), Hueneme VEN (egg set 28 May 1936), and at Chino SBE (1931). Scattered records of winter birds and transients exist for all coastal counties. Interesting records of migrants include a bird which flew into the Pt. Loma SD lighthouse 4 Aug 1876, one that hit a window in downtown Santa Barbara SBA in 1939, and a bird found on the Los Angeles City College campus 11 Oct 1950. This species was detected in winter in coastal San Diego Co. up to about 1964. A few are undoubtedly present at Newport Bay ORA in winter, when they have been reported by careful observers. However, the authors doubt the validity of many of the recent sight records from this locality. This species is unrecorded from the Channel Is.

Around Imperial Dam Black Rails inhabit freshwater bulrush marshes, especially where the vegetation is less than about 1m tall; they seem to shun the taller cattails. In District C records are primarily from *Salicornia* marshes. The California Black Rail (*L. j. coturniculus*) is considered rare by the California Department of Fish and Game. Its decline on the coast is clearly tied to the destruction of salt marshes.

CLAPPER RAIL
Rallus longirostris

Fairly common but very local breeding resident in coastal salt marshes, and fairly common breeding summer resident (probably uncommon in winter) in freshwater marshes in Districts S and R. Recorded twice in District D.

Coastal birds, representing *R. l. levipes* ("Light-footed Clapper Rail") except as noted, are now primarily confined to the Seal Beach Marshes and Upper Newport Bay ORA, and the Tijuana R. estuary SD. Smaller populations exist at Mission Bay and the south end of San Diego Bay SD, and at Sandyland Slough, Carpinteria SBA. At Morro Bay SLO a small population (thought to represent the southern limit of *R. l. obsoletus*, the "California Clapper Rail") may still exist, but there are no recent records. A population may persist at Pt. Mugu VEN, but there is only one published report there since 1972 (12 Jan 1980). One at Goleta SBA 6 Sep 1969 suggests that some movement may occur in the coastal races, as the resident population at Goleta had been extirpated by that time. There are no records from the Channel Is.

The "Yuma Clapper Rail", *R. l. yumanensis*, is a fairly common to common summer resident along the length of the Colorado R. from Topock and vicinity SBE south to near Yuma in Imperial Co. Its exact status in winter is unclear due to its secretive nature; although it is regularly heard at this season, it appears to be rare. Some 700 birds were censused along the Colorado R. in Arizona and California in 1973. It is a fairly common summer resident at the Salton Sea, where it occurs in freshwater marshes along the New and Alamo Rivers SESS, the Whitewater R. mouth NESS, Salt Ck. IMP, and locally elsewhere (even at some distance from the sea at Dos Palmas Spring RIV). It is uncommon in winter in District S. That *yumanensis* is at least partially migratory is further suggested by two extralimital records of Clapper Rails heard in District D: 4-7 Jun 1977 Harper Dry L. near Barstow SBE, and 17 May 1978 Cronese Dry L. near Baker SBE.

Along the coast the Clapper Rail has declined drastically in recent decades because of the destruction of salt marsh habitat (especially favored by the rails are large estuaries dominated by *Salicornia* and *Spartina*). The coastal races are considered endangered. The species has been extirpated from Los Angeles Co. (recorded to at least 1949 at Playa del Rey) and perhaps from Ventura and San Luis Obispo Cos., and has been substantially reduced in all other areas. A recent census of coastal southern California marshes yielded only 203 pairs. The interior *yumanensis*, while restricted in distribution, has held up well in numbers and in fact appears to be quite adaptable, quickly occupying ephemeral marsh habitats. It occurs in a variety of marshy situations, from pure cattails and rushes to (marginally) stands of cane and flooded salt cedar.

VIRGINIA RAIL
Rallus limicola

Common resident in marshes of Districts S and R, and locally within District D. Fairly common winter visitant in District C, remaining locally and uncommonly through the summer.

In Districts S and R it is most conspicuous in spring and early summer when it is most vocal, although numbers may actually be higher in winter. In District D it occurs in scattered marshy habitats of almost any size (e.g. Antelope Valley LA, Mohave R. and Morongo Valley SBE, Owens Valley and Tecopa INY). It probably departs from the coldest northern sections of District D in winter.

The Virginia Rail is a fairly common and widespread winter visitant to District C, but at present it remains only locally through the summer (e.g. near Guadalupe SBA, Santa Clara R. estuary VEN, and Batiquitos Lagoon SD). The number of breeding birds on the coast has undoubtedly been reduced due to the destruction of marsh habitat.

The two records from District M are: 16-17 Jul 1921 and 16 Dec 1978 (2) Big Bear L. SBE; it undoubtedly is more regular as a transient in the mountains than the two records indicate. There are five records for the Channel Is. (September through January).

143

Freshwater cattail marshes and bulrush beds are preferred, but wintering birds also occur in salt marshes. In Districts D and C it may breed in cattail clumps within riparian woodlands.

SORA
Porzana carolina

Fairly common to common winter visitant in all lowland districts, at present remaining only rarely through the summer. Recent breeding records come only from District M and the extreme northern part of District D.

Soras summer uncommonly and probably breed regularly in District M. Breeding is known from Big Bear L. (1916, 1917, and possibly more recently) and from Fain Spring near Onyx Summit in the San Bernardino Mtns. SBE 25-26 Jul 1971. Two at Big Bear L. 16 Dec 1978 suggest occasional wintering in District M. It has bred in the Owens Valley INY (egg sets from Olancha 20 May 1939). Small numbers may summer in District S, but there is no evidence of breeding there. Much needs to be learned about the current breeding status of this species in the region. Willett (1933) listed numerous breeding localities for this species in the lowlands of District C south to Escondido SD. While it may still nest in the coastal lowlands (no recent efforts have been made to document this), it must do so quite rarely, and a decline is certainly indicated. Willett's comments that this species was "common in summer" in marshlands (and reduced in numbers in winter) are undoubtedly partly in error.

Soras inhabit freshwater marshes and the marshy borders of small ponds and lakes; in winter they also move into salt marshes. This rail is somewhat more widespread in winter than the Virginia Rail, especially in District C. As with the Virginia Rail, transients may be noted almost anywhere, even well away from the vicinity of water. It is an occasional transient and winter visitant on the Channel Is.

AMERICAN PURPLE GALLINULE
Porphyrio martinica

One record: an immature was picked up alive on Pt. Loma SD 1 Oct 1961; it died subsequently.

This species, noted for its vagrancy, breeds as near as Sinaloa, Mexico. It is casual in southeastern Arizona and has been recorded once just east of the region at Corn Ck., Nevada (2).

COMMON GALLINULE
Gallinula chloropus

Uncommon to fairly common; resident in Districts S and R, primarily a summer visitant in District D and a winter visitant in District C.

In District S it is a fairly common resident; it is also fairly common in District R, but it becomes less numerous in winter, when most birds occur in the southern part of the district. Elsewhere in the interior this species is an uncommon and local summer resident which remains only rarely through the winter. Regular wintering localities include the Antelope Valley LA, Mohave Narrows SBE, and possibly Furnace Creek Ranch INY. Though scarce, it can occur almost anywhere in District D during migration. It is probably also a casual transient through District M.

In District C the Common Gallinule is primarily an uncommon winter visitant throughout; it remains rarely through summer (breeding rarely, e.g. L. Elsinore RIV 1979). It was formerly more numerous as a breeding species in District C (in 1933 Willett termed it "formerly common"). The decline of breeding birds in District C can be attributed to the large scale destruction of freshwater marshes.

The species is unrecorded on the Channel Is.

Common Gallinules inhabit freshwater lakes, ponds, and channels where ample emergent vegetation exists. Unlike American Coots, they are only rarely seen on open bodies of water.

AMERICAN COOT
Fulica americana

Common breeding summer resident and abundant winter visitant on bodies of water throughout the region.

Huge concentrations may occur locally, e.g. at Big Bear and Baldwin Lakes SBE before severe winter freezes and at the Salton Sea. It is a regular transient and winter visitant on the Channel Is. and an intermittent breeder on Thompson Res., Santa Catalina I.; it has bred on Santa Cruz I.

Virtually any non-marine, aquatic habitat may be occupied. The species does occur in winter in coastal estuaries, harbors, and shallow bays; it is occasional in migration on the open ocean. Coots often graze on lawns surrounding ponds and lakes.

GRUIDAE: CRANES
SANDHILL CRANE
Grus canadensis

Very local winter visitant; several thousand winter on the Carrizo Plain SLO, and smaller numbers winter in the vicinity of Blythe RIV and south of Brawley IMP. Rare to casual transient elsewhere.

The flock on the Carrizo Plain numbers up to about 4000 birds and is present primarily from November through February. The first birds arrive in late September and the last depart by mid-March. The size of this flock varies from year to year. The flock roosts at Soda L. and feeds in the surrounding grasslands and grainfields. Note that this locality is not treated on the bar graphs.

It is a regular winter visitant in District S, where a flock of about 100 birds frequents the fields between Brawley and El Centro IMP. Along the Colorado R. birds occur in fields north of Blythe RIV and represent offshoots from a flock of up to several thousand which winters across the river in the fields south of Parker, Arizona. Several hundred also occur to the south in the Cibola area in n. Imperial Co. Much smaller numbers occur in the Needles/Topock SBE area.

An extremely rare (bordering on casual) species elsewhere, individuals or small flocks have been noted in District C (15 records in the last 30 years, only in Riverside, Santa Barbara, Ventura, and Los Angeles Cos.), District D (four recent records — three in the Owens Valley/Deep Springs Valley area INY, and one of a bird that wintered at Furnace Creek Ranch INY late Nov 1964-11 Mar 1965), and District M (seven at Lake Cuyamaca 24-30 Sep 1977 represent the only recent record for San Diego Co.). Most records for Districts C, D, and M are for late fall. The earliest record for the region is 12 Sep 1964 Deep Springs INY; the latest is of four spring transients at Santa Barbara SBA 29 Mar 1955.

Sandhill Cranes were formerly more widespread as transients, especially in District C. Their decline had already been noted by Willett (1933).

The great majority of sandhills wintering in the region are undoubtedly *G. c. canadensis* (the "Little Brown" or "Lesser Sandhill" Crane); the Carrizo Plain flock appears to be entirely of this race. The more southerly breeding *G. c. tabida* ("Greater Sandhill Crane") probably comprises part of the flock wintering near Brawley and apparently most of the birds in District R; the relative abundance of the two forms is imperfectly known. *G. c. tabida* was apparently more common formerly in southern California; it has declined over much of its range during the present century. The overall decline of the species in the region thus may be in part due to the decline of *tabida*.

HAEMATOPODIDAE: OYSTERCATCHERS

AMERICAN OYSTERCATCHER
Haematopus palliatus

Casual visitant to the Channel Is. and the rocky mainland coast, although some individuals have remained for long periods. One record for the Salton Sea.

On the Channel Is. one bird has been present on the south shore of W. Anacapa I. from 24 May 1964 to at least 19 Oct 1980, and from one to three have been resident at Fraser Pt. on the western tip of Santa Cruz I. since at least 11 Nov 1966. There is a specimen from 2 Jun 1863 at Santa Barbara I. A record for Santa Catalina I. 12 Feb 1910 was questioned by Grinnell (1915). On the mainland it has been recorded 16 May 1862 Pt. Loma SD; 25 Oct

1964-20 Feb 1965 Avila Beach SLO; 20-21 Apr 1978 Pt. Loma; and 22 Dec 1978-14 Jan 1979 Pt. Fermin LA. Old reports of occurrence and breeding on the Ventura Co. coast 1879-1881 are open to question. While this species may have been more regular on the southern California coast during the 1800s, there is no conclusive evidence of breeding.

At the Salton Sea three birds were present 14-19 Aug 1977 at Salton City IMP; they were subsequently seen 20-30 Aug 1977 along the opposite shore of the sea between North Shore and Salt Ck. RIV.

American Oystercatchers found in the the region usually associate with Black Oystercatchers on rugged, rocky coasts. The birds at the Salton Sea frequented the gravel and barnacle litter of the open shoreline of the sea.

The race occurring in California, *H. p. frazari*, breeds south of our area; one to three pairs are apparently resident on Los Coronados Is., only a few km south of the Mexican border. Northern populations of *frazari* often show considerable black flecking on the underparts. A hybrid American X Black Oystercatcher has been seen on Santa Cruz I., and a few such intermediates are known from the west coast of Baja California.

BLACK OYSTERCATCHER
Haematopus bachmani

Fairly common resident on the rocky coast of San Luis Obispo and western Santa Barbara Cos., and on some of the Channel Is. Rare visitant along the remainder of the coast.

This species is resident along the mainland coast south to the vicinity of Pt. Buchon and Port San Luis SLO and locally in w. Santa Barbara Co. to Pt. Arguello. It is also resident on the northern Channel Is. and on Santa Barbara I. It is a straggler to San Nicolas I., Santa Catalina I. (has bred), and San Clemente I. (has bred).

The Black Oystercatcher is a very rare visitant along the remainder of the coast (primarily fall and winter). Up to five birds have been irregularly present on the jetties at Playa del Rey LA for the past several years. Elsewhere it is most consistent at Pt. Mugu VEN, Palos Verdes/San Pedro LA, vic. Dana Pt. and Laguna Beach ORA, and Pt. Loma SD. However, it is quite rare at all of these localities, with long spans during which the species is unrecorded. There are scattered records elsewhere along the coast.

This species is very partial to rugged, rocky coastlines; it occurs exceptionally on mudflats (e.g. Pt. Mugu). It reappears rather commonly just south of the region in the vicinity of Punta Banda (on the mainland) and Los Coronados Is.

RECURVIROSTRIDAE: STILTS AND AVOCETS

BLACK-NECKED STILT
Himantopus mexicanus

Abundant summer resident at the Salton Sea, remaining rather commonly through the winter. Primarily a transient elsewhere in the interior. Common transient, fairly common but local summer resident, and uncommon to locally common winter visitant along the coast.

One of the most conspicuous birds summering at the Salton Sea, Black-necked Stilts nest along virtually the entire shoreline of the sea and at diked ponds throughout the Imperial Valley. Elsewhere in the interior they have nested along the Colorado R. (Headgate Dam SBE, Imperial NWR IMP), in the Antelope Valley, and undoubtedly elsewhere. Otherwise they are primarily a fairly common transient through the interior.

In District C it is a common transient and fairly common, but local, summer resident. Breeding localities include Vandenberg AFB and Goleta SBA; Santa Clara R. estuary and Pt. Mugu VEN; Bolsa Chica, Upper Newport Bay, and San Joaquin Marsh ORA; and most of the estuaries of San Diego Co. It also nests very locally inland in District C, e.g. at Whittier Narrows LA and L. Elsinore RIV (1979); otherwise it is primarily a transient. In winter, stilts are fairly common to common in coastal Orange and San Diego Cos., fairly common at Pt. Mugu and uncommon to rare elsewhere along the coast. In the interior of District C it winters in the vic. of Chino SBE, but it is otherwise very rare at this season.

There is one record for the Channel Is.: 25 May 1897 San Nicolas I.

Stilts forage in shallow water and prefer the extensive shallows of lakeshores, flooded alkalai flats, coastal estuaries, and flooded fields. For nesting they require open areas of dirt, mudflats, or dikes near foraging areas. They are well-adapted to nesting in extremely hot regions and adapt quickly to nesting in ephemeral or newly-formed habitats.

AMERICAN AVOCET
Recurvirostra americana

Very common to abundant year-round visitant to the Salton Sea. Fairly common to common transient elsewhere in the region, nesting very locally. Fairly common to common in winter along the coast (mainly in the southern counties); casual at this season in the interior away from District S.

At the Salton Sea large flocks of alternate-plumaged birds remain through the summer, but only a few pairs have been known to nest (e.g. five pairs at SESS in 1977 and 1978).

In the interior away from the Salton Sea (including the inland portions of District C), it is a fairly common transient; a few birds summer locally around marshes and shallow ponds. Recent nesting is known from the

Antelope Valley (fairly common near Lancaster LA), Furnace Creek Ranch INY (six nests in 1978), and Baker SBE (one pair in 1978). It has nested in the Owens Valley (e.g. Olancha INY in 1938-1939) and probably still does so. The avocet winters regularly in wetlands of District R and casually in District D.

In District C it is a fairly common to common transient along the coast; it remains commonly through the winter in coastal Orange and San Diego Cos., but is generally uncommon farther north (although common at Pt. Mugu VEN and fairly common at the Santa Maria R. mouth SBA/SLO). A few winter in the interior of the district (where it is primarily a transient). It nests sparingly in District C: for instance at several localities in coastal San Diego Co., at Bolsa Chica ORA, at the Santa Clara R. estuary VEN, and at Santa Maria SBA. It was formerly more widespread as a nester in the district, with known sites including Playa del Rey and Nigger Slough LA, vic. Santa Ana ORA, and L. Elsinore RIV.

This species is a rare transient on the Channel Is.

Avocets are found in areas of shallow water habitats such as coastal estuaries, alkalai ponds, and lakeshores.

CHARADRIIDAE: PLOVERS

BLACK-BELLIED PLOVER
Pluvialis squatarola

Common winter visitor along the coast, with smaller numbers of non-breeding birds remaining through the summer. Fairly common transient and slightly less numerous as a winter visitor at the Salton Sea. Generally a rare transient elsewhere in the interior.

The coastal range of the Black-bellied Plover includes the Channel Is. Numbers are lowest from late May to late June, when it is uncommon to locally fairly common (e.g. San Diego Bay).

Inland, including the interior of District C, it is generally a rare transient but it may be fairly common as a transient in the Antelope Valley LA/KRN (an area with strong affinities to the Central Valley); 53 were noted here 20 Mar 1979 and 15 were seen 31 Jul 1979. Fall birds are recorded into November. A very few may occasionally winter in the interior of District C (e.g. vic. of Chino SBE).

Black-bellied Plovers are one of the most numerous shorebirds wintering on sandy beaches and somewhat rocky shores; they reach peak abundance on estuarine mudflats. Flocks often feed in open fields, whether plowed or flooded; even lawns are sometimes used.

LESSER GOLDEN PLOVER
Pluvialis dominica

Status complex, with two subspecies involved. Generally an uncommon fall transient and rare winter visitant and spring transient along the coast. Casual or very rare transient at the Salton Sea; eight other inland records.

Along the coast fall transients may appear as early as mid-July, but the species is not regularly encountered until late August. Transients may linger into late fall and individuals and flocks regularly winter. Late fall and winter maxima include: 14 on San Clemente I. 8-9 Dec 1976; 11 at Newport ORA 27 Dec 1963; and 8 in Imperial Beach SD in early Jan 1966. Some 20-25 birds have remained into April during the winters of 1978-1979 and 1979-1980 near Santa Maria SBA. Numbers of transients vary somewhat from fall to fall; at this season it is perhaps most numerous on the Channel Is., where small numbers may also winter. Spring transients are only rarely noted along the coast, and many records pertain to lingering winter birds. A late spring transient was at Santa Clara R. estuary VEN 31 May-6 Jun 1980. Four records from late June and early July could pertain to very late spring birds or, more likely, very early fall transients: 17 Jun 1976 San Nicolas I.; 24-26 Jun 1977 El Toro ORA; 29 Jun 1978 San Miguel I.; and 2 Jul 1977 Santa Clara R. estuary (2).

At the Salton Sea it is a very rare transient and casual winter visitant. There are 11 spring records (19 Apr 1970 NESS to 25 May 1974 NESS) and 4 fall records (2 Sep 1962 NESS to 31 Oct 1976 SESS). Records falling outside of this pattern are: 13-19 Feb 1966 SESS; 13 Jun 1970 NESS; 11 Jul 1970 SESS; 16 Jul 1966 SESS; and 22 Jul-12 Aug 1967 SESS.

The only records for the interior away from District S are: 12 Oct 1977, 22 Sep 1978, and 18 Oct 1979 near Blythe RIV; 28 Jul 1979 near Lakeview RIV; 4 Nov 1979 L. Hodges SD; and 27 Apr 1980, 12 May 1980, and 24 May 1980 near Lancaster LA.

The majority of records, including most or all from the interior, appear to pertain to *P. d. dominica*. Most or all birds wintering in the region appear to be *P.d. fulva*, a smaller and brighter race with a primarily Siberian breeding distribution and a normal winter range in the islands of the Pacific. Individuals or small flocks of *fulva* often return year after year to favored wintering sites such as vic. Santa Maria SBA, Playa del Rey LA, and the San Diego R. mouth SD. There is no specimen evidence that nominate *dominica* winters in the region or anywhere else in North America (it normally winters in South America); however, we cannot state with certainty that all birds wintering in the region are *fulva*.

Lesser Golden Plovers may be found on estuarine mudflats and in agricultural areas and short grass fields a short distance inland. These same types of habitats are utilized at the Salton Sea. Wintering birds usually associate with Black-bellied Plovers.

SNOWY PLOVER
Charadrius alexandrinus

Fairly common, but somewhat local and declining resident on sandy coastal beaches (including some of the Channel Is.); numbers on the coast are augmented in winter. Primarily a summer resident in the interior, nesting at the Salton Sea and at various alkali lakes.

The Snowy Plover is much reduced along the coast as a nesting species; major remaining nesting areas are in San Diego Co. and at Vandenberg AFB SBA. Its breeding range includes some of the Channel Is. (especially San Miguel, Santa Rosa, and San Nicolas Is.). Numbers on the coast are augmented somewhat in winter, probably by the arrival of birds which nested in the interior.

It nests fairly commonly at the Salton Sea, where it is most numerous along gravelly beaches (generally avoiding mudflats). It remains rarely here through the winter, e.g. at Salton City IMP (where it may be uncommon).

A summer visitant to District D, Snowy Plovers opportunistically colonize sinks, playas, and receding lakeshores. Breeding localities in the interior include: Deep Springs L. INY; vic. Tecopa INY; Owens L. INY (499 counted summer 1978); Harper Dry L. SBE (up to 100 in Jun 1977); near Rosamond KRN; and near Lancaster LA. Aggregate numbers of breeding birds in the interior probably surpass those of the coast, but numbers at any one locality vary greatly from year to year. Transients and occasional non-breeding, summering birds may be scattered through the district and linger into November. In winter it is casual in District D where it has been recorded at Owens L. INY 3 Jan 1975 (2) and 11 Jan 1976. There is a record from 5 Nov 1978 at L. Henshaw SBE on the lower border of District M.

Along the Colorado R. it is a rare transient and non-breeding summer visitant; most records are for August.

This species is casual in the interior of District C, but it has nested at L. Elsinore RIV (3 juvs. on 23 Apr 1974). It has wintered in the interior of District C at L. Hodges SD (two or three during winter 1979-1980).

The preference of Snowy Plovers for sandy beaches has led to its decline as a nesting bird along the coast; such areas suffer from much human disturbance during the nesting season. The adaptability of populations nesting in the interior gives strong hope for the survival of this species as a breeder in the region.

WILSON'S PLOVER
Charadrius wilsonia

Five records: four come from the coast and one is a nesting record from the Salton Sea.

Along the coast it has been recorded as follows: 24-29 Jun 1894 Pacific Beach SD; 11 May 1918 Imperial Beach SD; 27-29 Jun 1977 Santa Clara R. estuary VEN; and 21 Apr-24 Jun 1979 Pt. Mugu VEN.

There is also an unpublished record of a pair of adults with three eggs near Mullet Is., SESS 20 May 1948 (eggs now in the San Bernardino Co. Museum).

These represent the only California records of this species (which breeds on both coasts of Baja California).

SEMIPALMATED PLOVER
Charadrius semipalmatus

Common transient and uncommon (to locally common) winter visitant along the coast. Transient through the interior, generally rare except at the Salton Sea where common in spring and fairly common in fall. A few remain locally through the summer.

Along the coast fall transients begin arriving in late June, not long after lingering spring transients have departed in late May. A few non-breeders remain through the summer. A few winter in the interior of District C (e.g. L. Hodges SD). This species is commonest on mudflats of coastal estuaries; it is much less partial to sandy beaches than the Snowy Plover.

It is an uncommon transient on the Channel Is.; it has been recorded once in winter: 25 Feb 1976 Santa Rosa I. (5).

In the interior this species is found primarily at the Salton Sea, where it is a common spring transient (exceptionally up to 2000 on 29 Apr 1962) and fairly common fall transient. A few regularly remain through the winter. Elsewhere in the interior, including the inland portions of District C, it is a rare (bordering on uncommon) transient; small flocks are sometimes noted, especially in spring. Concentrations in the interior include: 43 at Owens L. INY 29 Apr 1978; 16 at Big Pine INY 28 Apr 1973; 12 at Lancaster LA 10 May 1980; and 10 at Baldwin L. SBE 8 May 1976.

PIPING PLOVER
Charadrius melodus

Two records for the coast: one bird was found four consecutive years at Goleta SBA. First recorded 14-24 Apr 1971 (had probably wintered locally); it was subsequently recorded 16 Dec 1971-22 Apr 1972, 16 Dec 1972 to at least 21 Jan 1973, and 16 Dec 1973-3 Mar 1974. Another was at Malibu LA 18 Nov 1973-16 Apr 1974. What was likely the same individual was reported there 12 Oct 1974, but did not remain.

Both birds wintered with Snowy Plovers on sandy beaches. These represent the only certain records of this eastern species for California. There are several recent records from the Gulf of California, where this species may winter regularly in very small numbers.

KILLDEER
Charadrius vociferus

Common breeding resident near water, irrigated fields, and lawns

throughout; largely withdraws from the colder parts of the region in winter, but numbers are greatly augmented elsewhere at this season. Breeds locally on the Channel Is.

This is one of our most ubiquitous shorebirds; it is not often seen on beaches, but it is otherwise tolerant of a wide range of wetland and open field habitats. Large flocks form in winter in the agricultural areas of coastal valleys and the interior.

MOUNTAIN PLOVER
Charadrius montanus

Fairly common but very local winter visitant, with the largest numbers occurring in grasslands and agricultural areas of the interior. Usually present from mid-October to mid-February, with a few birds lingering later.

In winter flocks are regularly found on the Carrizo Plain SLO, the western San Joaquin Valley KRN (on the boundary of the region), SESS and the Imperial Valley IMP, and the Antelope Valley LA/KRN. Flocks may also occur, at least irregularly, in the Lucerne Valley SBE and along the Colorado R., where it is uncommon and occurs mostly in the vicinity of Blythe RIV. It lingers into late March along the Colorado R. (not graphed).

Elsewhere in the interior it is a rare fall transient. Individuals or small flocks are noted almost annually in Death Valley and the Owens Valley INY and it has also been noted recently in the Lanfair Valley SBE. Unusually early fall transients include one at Furnace Creek Ranch INY 1 Sep 1979, another there 3 Sep 1977, and two at Owens L INY 13 Sep 1968. In general, fall transients appear earlier in the northern portions of District D than elsewhere. A late fall migrant was at Oasis MNO 11 Dec 1977. A bird in late Feb 1972 six km north of Essex SBE was probably a spring transient, but this area receives little coverage in winter. Very early fall records for District S are: 5 Aug 1967 SESS; 28 Jul 1969 SESS; 25 Aug 1975 SESS; and 15 July 1979 SESS. That these represent early transients is supported by three records of fall transients at Mono L. just north of the region.

In District C this species is a rare transient and very local winter visitant; the earliest record is 21 Sep 1972 Tijuana River Valley SD (15). The largest numbers winter in the vicinity of Lakeview RIV (up to several hundred). Close to the coast it is most numerous in the Tijuana River Valley (e.g. 200 on 5-12 Nov 1972) and on Otay Mesa SD (e.g. 250 on 12 Dec 1971). It is probably regular on the Santa Maria R. plain SLO/SBA and the Oxnard Plain VEN; small numbers were recorded at both localities in fall/winter 1979-1980. It is now casual elsewhere in District C. It was formerly more numerous on the coastal plains of the region; the decline is largely attributable to the loss of suitable open habitat. For example, it formerly wintered in the San Fernando Valley LA and on the coastal plains of Orange Co. (present around Irvine ORA until at least the mid-1960s; now noted there only rarely); both of these areas today are virtually covered with housing tracts. The species formerly wintered on some of the Channel Is., but in recent years has only been recorded twice (both in fall on Santa Rosa I.).

SCOLOPACIDAE: SANDPIPERS

GREATER YELLOWLEGS
Tringa melanoleuca

Fairly common transient and uncommon to fairly common winter visitant along the coast and in District S. Primarily a transient elsewhere in the region.

The Greater Yellowlegs is most numerous and widespread as a transient, but it may be locally fairly common in winter in coastal Santa Barbara, Ventura, Orange, and San Diego Cos., and in the Imperial Valley IMP. It remains rarely through summer in Districts C and S as a non-breeder.

In the interior away from the Salton Sea this species is a fairly common transient. Fall records extend well into November and a few winter occasionally along the Colorado R. and possibly in the Antelope Valley in the vicinity of Lancaster LA (e.g. 15 on 15 Dec 1979). It is primarily an uncommon to fairly common transient and rare winter visitant in the inland portions of District C.

On the Channel Is. this shorebird is a rare spring and fall transient; there are two winter records.

Greater Yellowlegs occupy a variety of shallow water habitats such as coastal estuaries, flooded fields, marshes, and stream channels. They are only occasionally found on open beaches and jetties.

LESSER YELLOWLEGS
Tringa flavipes

Primarily a fall transient: fairly common in Districts C and S and uncommon elsewhere. Uncommon spring transient, but concentrations have been noted in Districts S and C. Winters locally along the coast and rarely in District S. Casual through summer.

Fall concentrations of up to 75 birds have been noted on coastal estuaries; this species may locally outnumber the Greater Yellowlegs at this time, although it is in general far less numerous. In fall, juveniles

154

predominate in the region. It is rather rare as a spring transient along the coast, but concentrations have been noted (e.g. up to 40 at Pt. Mugu VEN 25 Mar-2 Apr 1978). It is an uncommon spring transient in District S; 100 at SESS 22 Apr 1972 was a very large concentration. It is casual, though perhaps regular, on the coast and in District S in summer, when it is outnumbered by the Greater Yellowlegs. Birds wintering in District C are quite localized (e.g. vic. Santa Maria SBA, Pt. Mugu, and some of the coastal estuaries of San Diego Co.); numbers are generally small (exceptionally up to 23 at Pt. Mugu 20 Jan 1980). Concentrations of up to ten birds have been noted in winter in District S, but the species is less regular there.

Elsewhere in the region this yellowlegs is an uncommon transient; it is more numerous in fall (when it borders on fairly common) than in spring. Like most shorebirds it is primarily a fall transient in District M. This species is largely a rare fall transient in the interior portions of District C, with small concentrations occasionally noted. It has been noted in winter (exceptionally up to six near Chino SBE Jan-Feb 1980). There are two September records for the Channel Is.

The Lesser Yellowlegs is slightly more specialized in habitat preference than the Greater Yellowlegs, and is thus encountered less widely. This species is partial to coastal estuaries and, locally, flooded fields. Open mudflats around small ponds are especially preferred in District S.

SOLITARY SANDPIPER
Tringa solitaria

Uncommon fall transient and rare spring transient in all districts except District S (where rarer). Three acceptable winter records.

Spring records extend from 4 Apr 1978 Granite Mtns. SBE and 5 Apr 1973 Rancho Bernardo SD to 30 May 1968 Harbor L. LA; the majority occur from mid-April to early May. The only spring records for District S are 12 Apr 1949 SESS and 17 Apr 1976 SESS. Fall records extend from 18 Jul 1978 Baker SBE to 18 Oct 1975 Tijuana River Valley SD; the majority occur between 10 Aug and 25 Sep. It is a very rare fall transient in District S and on the Channel Is.

Records falling outside the above pattern, including mid-winter records published in *AFN*, lack details and should be disregarded, except for these three acceptable winter records: 26 Dec 1958 SESS; 12 Jan 1977 NESS; and 17 Dec 1978 near Colton SBE.

Solitary Sandpipers frequent water-edge situations with marshy or grassy vegetation, such as small ditches, stream channels, and the borders of small ponds and lakes. The great majority of fall birds are juveniles.

SPOTTED SANDPIPER
Actitis macularia

Fairly common winter visitant in Districts C, S, and R. Primarily a transient through District D and an uncommon transient and summer resident in District M. Also nests very locally in District C.

Small numbers breed very locally in District M, with recent nesting recorded at Big Bear L., Baldwin L., and L. Arrowhead in the San Bernardino Mtns. SBE. Because spring transients may pass through into early June and fall transients may arive in early to mid-July, care should be taken to determine whether birds around montane lakes (and elsewhere in the region) are truly summering. Scattered breeding records exist for District C; recent records are for the Santa Ynez R. SBA, Santa Clara R. estuary VEN (and locally up the Santa Clara R. to the Los Angeles Co. line), Ventura R. mouth VEN, and Azusa LA. Older localities include Santa Paula VEN (around 1900) and, in District D, "Amaja Marsh" in the Owens Valley INY (1931). Pairs staying through the summer in District R suggest possible breeding there.

Away from Districts C, S, and R, a few birds may winter in the Antelope Valley LA/KRN and perhaps elsewhere in District D. It is an uncommon visitant to the Channel Is. (mostly mid-Aug to Apr).

Transients and wintering birds occur along streambeds and the shores of ponds and lakes. Spotted Sandpipers are less often found in estuaries and on rocky shores. Most nests have been around grassy or marshy meadows or vegetated bars of gravel bordering lakes, ponds, streams, and estuaries.

WANDERING TATTLER
Heteroscelus incanus

Fairly common spring transient and uncommon fall transient and winter visitant to rocky coastal areas. Casual at the Salton Sea; also recorded twice in the interior of District C and once (spring) in District D.

The Wandering Tattler is quite local in winter; it favors the rocky coast of San Luis Obispo and w. Santa Barbara Cos., Playa del Rey and Palos Verdes Peninsula LA, and La Jolla and Pt. Loma SD. Scattered birds winter rarely elsewhere along the coast. It is much more widespread in migration. This species is decidedly more numerous on the rocky shores of the Channel Is., where it is a fairly common to common non-breeding visitant throughout the year (scarcest in June and early July). There are very few mid-summer records for the mainland coast, although the species may be regular at that season at favored localities.

It is casual at the Salton Sea; the eight records are as follows: 27 Apr 1974 SESS; 7 May 1972 Salton City IMP; 8 May 1971 Salton City (4 birds with one still present on 9 May); 11 May 1969 NESS; 11 Jun 1978 SESS; 12 Aug 1971 NESS; 22 Aug 1977 SESS; and 31 Aug 1961 SESS.

It has been recorded twice in the interior portion of District C: 1 Sep 1972 Sepulveda Basin LA and (an anomalous record) 3 Mar 1974 West-lake VEN/LA. There is one record for District D: 2 Jun 1978 Owens L. INY. Significant records just outside of the region are of one at Kern NWR KRN 14 Sep 1977 and birds at Mono L. MNO 14 Sep 1976 and 26 Aug 1978.

Tattlers are birds of rugged, rocky coastlines; jetties and breakwaters are also occupied. During migration they also occur on sandy beaches and coastal estuaries. Birds at the Salton Sea have generally been on rocky jetties.

WILLET
Catoptrophorus semipalmatus

Common to abundant transient and winter visitant along the coast and at the Salton Sea, remaining fairly commonly through the summer as a non-breeder. Uncommon transient through the rest of the region. May nest occasionally in the Owens Valley.

Willets are common to abundant through most of the year along the coast and on the Channel Is. They are less numerous, but still common, at the Salton Sea. Numbers are lowest from mid-May to mid-June, when the species is fairly common in these areas (locally common, e.g. San Diego Bay SD).

Elsewhere in the region, including the interior of District C, this species is a rare spring and uncommon fall transient. It is locally more numerous in fall in areas such as District R (where fairly common) and the Antelope Valley (e.g. 30 near Lancaster LA 8 Aug 1979). A very late record for District D was one w. of Lancaster 13 Nov 1977. It is primarily a fall transient in District M.

Willets were believed to have nested near Big Pine INY in 1975 and 1978 (not graphed), but no definite nesting evidence exists for the region. This species probably nests just north of us, in Mono Co.

Willets frequent the coastline (sandy or rocky), estuaries, and flooded fields near the shore. In District S they occur mainly along the shore of the Salton Sea.

UPLAND SANDPIPER
Bartramia longicauda

Eight records: 11 Sep 1952 Havasu Landing, w. shore of L. Havasu SBE; 13 May 1959 Furnace Creek Ranch INY; 10 Sep 1973 near Colton SBE (specimen); 23 May 1975 Santa Barbara I.; 15 May 1976 Furnace Creek Ranch; 28 May 1979 Deep Springs INY; 9 Sep 1979 Pt. Mugu VEN; and 23-24 May 1980 Furnace Creek Ranch.

There are four additional records for northern California.

157

WHIMBREL
Numenius phaeopus

Common transient and fairly common winter visitor along the coast, with non-breeding birds remaining uncommonly through the summer. Abundant spring transient and common fall transient at the Salton Sea, with a few remaining through the summer. Generally a rare to casual transient (mostly spring) in the rest of the interior, although large flocks may be noted in spring in the Antelope Valley. Common transient and winter visitant on the Channel Is. from late July to mid-May.

In District S spring flocks at SESS may number thousands of birds (e.g. 10,000 on 19 Apr 1970). Numbers are smaller in fall, with a maximum of 400 on 19 Aug 1973. Dates of departure in fall are unclear; concentrations have been noted as late as mid-September.

The status in District R is not entirely clear, but the species appears to be a rare spring transient (26 noted in mid-Apr 1979) and a rare fall transient. Eight birds at Imperial Dam IMP 1 Jul 1973 were probably early fall transients.

The Whimbrel is a common spring transient in the Antelope Valley LA/KRN, where concentrations of up to 1300 (16 Apr 1980) have been noted. It is an uncommon spring transient through the interior portions of District C. In District D away from the Antelope Valley it is a casual spring transient; there are eight records (8 Apr 1978 Owens L. INY to 31 May 1979 Furnace Creek Ranch INY), all since 1960. Two of these records involve up to four birds. There are only four fall records for District D: 22 Jul 1978 Big Pine INY; and 17 Jul 1979, 25 Jul 1980, and 7 Aug 1979 near Lancaster LA. There are no substantiated records of Whimbrels in the interior in winter.

Whimbrels occupy both sandy and rocky beaches and also forage in fields near the immediate coast (occasionally on lawns). Around the Salton Sea they prefer flooded fields. Flocks encountered recently in the Antelope Valley have been in alfalfa fields.

LONG-BILLED CURLEW
Numenius americanus

Uncommon to locally fairly common, or even common, transient and winter visitor along the coast. Common winter visitor in District S, and fairly common at this season in the Antelope Valley. Otherwise, generally a rare transient through the interior. Has nested once in the Owens Valley.

Important localities along the coast include Morro Bay SLO, Santa Maria R. plain SBA, Pt. Mugu VEN, Seal Beach and Newport Bay ORA, and San Diego Bay and the Tijuana River Valley SD. It is an uncommon transient (mostly fall) and rare to uncommon winter visitor elsewhere along the coast, even where habitat appears suitable. Small numbers of non-breeding birds summer along the coast, particularly in favored wintering localities. It is a rare year-round visitant on the Channel Is. This species is primarily a transient in the interior portions of District C; flocks do winter locally in areas such as pasturelands around Chino SBE.

A common winter visitant in District S, flocks of hundreds are often encountered at SESS (much less numerous at NESS). It remains uncommonly through June at SESS.

The Long-billed Curlew is generally a rare transient in Districts D, R, and M, except in the Antelope Valley LA/KRN, where it is a fairly common fall transient and winter visitant.

This species has nested recently in the Owens Valley (a pair with three juveniles near Big Pine INY in Jul 1978; may nest regularly here); it breeds in similar grassland habitat in northeastern California.

Transients and wintering birds frequent coastal estuaries (especially with *Salicornia*), agricultural fields, and, less commonly, sandy beaches. The largest concentrations of wintering birds occur on coastal plains and the largest coastal estuaries.

HUDSONIAN GODWIT
Limosa haemastica

Two records: near Daggett SBE 9 May 1975 and near Lancaster LA 9-19 May 1980.

There is an additional fall record for northern California.

BAR-TAILED GODWIT
Limosa lapponica

One record: one present along Ballona Creek, Playa del Rey LA 11 Feb-2 Mar 1976.

The above bird associated with Marbled Godwits and other shorebirds on the muddy bed of a tidal, concrete-lined channel. There are at least three additional records of this Eurasian species in northern California (all in fall). All California records appear to pertain to the east Asian race *L. l. baueri*, which is characterized by extensive barring on the lower back and rump.

MARBLED GODWIT
Limosa fedoa

Common winter visitant along the coast, remaining uncommonly through the summer as a non-breeder. Fairly common transient and winter visitant at the Salton Sea, with small numbers remaining through the summer. Generally a rare transient elsewhere in the interior.

It is less numerous on the Channel Is. than it is along the coast. Concentrations may occur locally on the coast in summer, e.g. on San Diego Bay SD.

159

In the interior away from the Salton Sea (including the interior of District C) it is primarly a very rare transient (bordering on casual). However, in the Antelope Valley (vic. Lancaster LA) it is recorded uncommonly in spring (maximum of 10 on 10 May 1980) and fairly commonly in fall (maxima of 15 on 9 Jul 1980 and 27-30 Aug 1980). A concentrations of 13 was near Lakeview RIV 15 Aug 1979. It is a rare spring transient and uncommon fall transient along the Colorado R.

This is a characteristic wintering bird of open shores, beaches, and estuarine mudflats. Foraging may also take place in *Salicornia* marshes and in flooded and irrigated fields in the immediate vicinity of the coast.

RUDDY TURNSTONE
Arenaria interpres

Fairly common to common transient and uncommon to locally common winter visitant along the coast, with a few remaining through the summer. Uncommon spring transient and rare fall transient at the Salton Sea; casual transient elsewhere in the interior.

Fall transients begin arriving on the coast in early July. A common transient and winter visitant in southern San Diego Co. (San Diego Bay and adjacent salt works), it is generally uncommon and somewhat local farther north in winter. It is fairly common on the larger Channel Is., where it occurs from August to April. A few birds regularly remain through summer along the coast, particularly in the San Diego region (e.g. up to 50, San Diego Bay in Jun 1966).

The Ruddy Turnstone is an uncommon spring transient and rare but regular fall transient at the Salton Sea. Spring maxima include 47 at NESS 12 May 1980, 30 at NESS 7 May 1977 and 9 May 1979, and 25 at NESS 2 May 1964. Maximal fall concentrations involve four birds. Extreme dates in District S are: 20 Apr 1978 Salton City IMP (exceptionally to 9 Apr 1978) to 3 Jun 1980 NESS, and again 19 Jul 1977 Salton City (3) to 15 Sep 1976 Salton City.

This species is a casual transient elsewhere in the interior. In District R it has been recorded 16 Sep 1952 (2) and 21 Aug 1953 at L. Havasu SBE; there are additional records for the Arizona side of the river. In District D it has been recorded 30 May 1974 Furnace Creek Ranch INY; 17 Sep 1977 Daggett SBE; and 31 Jul-4 Aug 1979, 11 Aug 1979, 2-9 Aug 1980, and 31 Aug 1980 (three, with one present to 4 Sep) near Lancaster LA. In the interior of District C there is a record for Lakeview RIV 27-29 Aug 1978. There are several records of transients at Mono L. MNO, just north of our region.

Ruddy Turnstones inhabit a variety of beaches; they particularly like marine vegetation, such as kelp, which has washed up on beaches. This species is less tied to rocky shores than the Black Turnstone; it often occurs in coastal estuaries.

160

BLACK TURNSTONE
Arenaria melanocephala

Common winter visitant along rocky coastlines, including those of the Channel Is. Casual spring transient in the interior, with seven records from the Salton Sea and one from the Colorado R.

Black Turnstones are normally present from late July through late April, with some birds lingering to mid-May. Unlike the Ruddy Turnstone, it is equally numerous along the length of the coast in winter, although it is somewhat localized to rocky shorelines (i.e. scarce in winter in coastal Ventura Co., which has little suitable habitat). It is common in San Diego Bay SD, where no rocky shoreline exists. A very few birds summer regularly along the coast.

The nine interior records are as follows: 12 Mar-22 Apr 1978 Salton City IMP (five sightings, probably involving two individuals); 30 Mar and 16 Apr 1979 Salton City; 26 Apr 1969 NESS; 2 May 1964 NESS (2); 7 May 1977 Salton City; 17 May 1930 Salton Sea IMP; 21 May 1948 Havasu Landing SBE; and 3 Jun 1980 NESS. Two other interior records (July, September) published in *AB* likely pertain to drab Ruddy Turnstones.

Black Turnstones are partial to rugged, rocky coastlines; they occur less often on sandy beaches, especially where kelp has washed ashore. Jetties and breakwaters form ideal artificial habitat.

SURFBIRD
Aphriza virgata

Fairly common but very local winter visitant, fairly common spring transient, and uncommon and local fall transient along rocky coasts and

161

jetties. Casual in the interior: three April records from the Salton Sea.

Primary wintering localities include the rocky coast of northern San Luis Obispo and western Santa Barbara Cos., Playa del Rey LA, and La Jolla and Pt. Loma SD. It is very rare in winter away from these localities. Fall transients are recorded most often at these known winter sites; birds occur very rarely elsewhere along the coast. Spring migration begins in late March; at this season flocks are found along the length of the coast on jetties and rocky shores and, to a lesser extent, on sandy beaches. It is casual along the coast in summer (five published records for June). The first fall transients may arrive in mid-July, although the species is not easily found until mid-August.

It is an uncommon transient on the Channel Is.; it has wintered on San Nicolas I.

The Surfbird is casual at the Salton Sea, where it has been recorded three times in April: 25 Apr 1967 NESS (5); 29 Apr 1967 North Shore Marina RIV (2); and 9-22 Apr 1978 Salton City IMP (up to five in a day, with perhaps as many as ten birds involved). Large flocks have been noted at the head of the Gulf of California; it is possible that some or all of these birds take an overland flight north and do not normally stop within the region.

RED KNOT
Calidris canutus

Common transient and winter visitant along the coast in the vicinity of San Diego SD; otherwise generally a rare to uncommon transient and very rare winter visitant along the coast. Fairly common spring transient and uncommon fall transient at the Salton Sea; only five records elsewhere in the interior, plus two for the inland portion of District C.

On San Diego Bay, at the mouth of the San Diego R., and at Mission Bay SD, it is very common; flocks of hundreds occur in spring, fall, and winter. In this area spring transients may occur into June, and alternate-plumaged fall adults may appear during the first week of July. A few birds regularly summer on San Diego Bay (maximum of 50 in summer 1966). Note that the bar graph does not reflect the status in the San Diego area. Elsewhere along the coast small numbers winter at Morro Bay SLO and Pt. Mugu VEN, with scattered birds away from these areas. Fall concentrations of transients rarely exceed a dozen individuals.

It has been recorded twice in the interior of District C: 25-28 Sep 1971 Hansen Dam LA and 7 Sep 1979 L. Hodges SD. There are five records of spring and fall transients on the Channel Is.

At the Salton Sea it is a fairly common spring transient and uncommon fall transient. The spring passage takes place from mid-March through mid-May; exceptional concentrations include 300 at NESS 6 May 1972, 225 there 12 May 1980, and 200 at Salton City IMP 22-23 Apr 1978 (spring maxima normally under 100 birds). Fall migration occurs from early July through early October and involves single birds or small groups (maxima of 45 at SESS 14 Jul 1979 and 15 at NESS 7-8 Sep 1971). Late fall records include 25 Oct 1971 NESS and 20 Nov 1976 SESS. There is one summer record of a bird in basic plumage at SESS 16 Jun 1976.

The Red Knot is casual elsewhere in the interior, where it has been recorded five times as follows: 1 Jun 1978 Stovepipe Wells INY; 25 Jul 1978, 11 Aug 1979, 9 May 1980 (3), and 31 Aug 1980 near Lancaster LA; and 9 Aug 1950 L. Havasu SBE. Very small numbers have been detected in fall at Mono L. MNO to the north of the region.

Red Knots inhabit estuarine mudflats and, occasionally, sandy shores. In winter large estuaries with salt marshes are preferred; the species has wintered on rocky jetties at Playa del Rey LA.

SANDERLING
Calidris alba

Common to abundant transient and winter visitant along the immediate coast and on the Channel Is., remaining uncommonly through the summer. Fairly common transient and rare to uncommon winter visitant at the Salton Sea. Very rare transient elsewhere in the region.

The Sanderling is the common *Calidris* of sandy beaches, where it feeds actively at the edge of the surf. Rocky shorelines and outer estuarine mudflats are also occupied, and river channels may be followed a short distance inland on coastal plains. Spring birds linger in fair numbers until late May; the first fall transients arrive in early July.

At the Salton Sea it is a fairly common transient and rare to uncommon winter visitant (e.g. up to 30 winter 1977-1978). Sanderlings are usually found on the gravelly shoreline. The largest numbers occur at Salton City IMP; it is very rarely recorded at SESS.

This shorebird is very rare elsewhere in the interior (bordering on casual); the majority of records are for spring. Although Phillips *et al* (1964) termed it a rare to uncommon migrant along the Colorado R., we know of only seven records (mostly spring) for the California side (maximum of 7 on 24 May 1959 West Pond IMP). Early spring dates for the Colorado R. are 14 Apr 1979 near Blythe RIV (2) and 15 Apr 1973 Imperial Dam IMP. Other records for the interior are: 11 May 1980 Harper Dry L. SBE (3); 19 May 1974 Desert Center RIV; 27 May 1972 Furnace Creek Ranch INY; 21 Jul 1971 Baldwin L. SBE; and 3 Oct 1979 Daggett SBE. This species may be a regular transient (at least in fall) near Lancaster LA where recorded 12 May 1980, 16 Aug 1978, 2 Aug 1979, 6-8 Aug 1979 (1-2), 11 Aug 1979 (2), 9 Aug 1980, and 30-31 Aug 1980. There is one record for the interior of District C: 17 Aug 1979 L. Hodges SD. Much information is needed on the passage of shorebirds through the interior, and we suspect that this species will prove to be regular in very small numbers away from the Salton Sea.

SEMIPALMATED SANDPIPER
Calidris pusilla

Rare spring transient, with most records for the Salton Sea, and rare fall transient, with a majority of records for the coast. Unrecorded away from the Salton Sea until 1977, with recent records indicating an increase in familiarity with the species.

In spring it is a rare but regular transient at the Salton Sea (some 18 records). Extreme dates are 21-24 Apr 1979 SESS to 6 Jun 1976 SESS. The majority of records are from 10 to 25 May. There are two spring records for the coast: 3 Jun 1979 Pt. Mugu VEN, and 6-8 May 1980 Santa Clara R. estuary VEN. It has also been recorded once in spring in District D: 24-27 May 1979 Tecopa INY. There is an additional spring record for Kern NWR KRN (just outside the region) 13 May 1979.

This species now appears to be regular along the coast in fall. Prior to 1980 it was recorded 10-11 Aug 1977 Goleta SBA; 9-15 Sep 1978 Santa Clara R. estuary (3); 10 Sep 1978 Imperial Beach SD; 31 Jul, 30 Aug-6 Sep (up to 3), and 20-23 Sep 1979 Santa Clara R. estuary; and 30 Aug-11 Sep 1979 nr. Oxnard VEN. In fall 1980, 11 were in Santa Barbara Co. (29 Jul-27 Aug), 26 were in Ventura Co. (2 Aug-3 Sep), and 15 were in San Diego Co. (9-31 Aug). Fall records for the interior include one from the interior of District C (15 Aug 1979 near Lakeview RIV) and one from District S (23 Aug 1975 SESS). Fall records for District D are: 28 Aug 1978 (specimen) and 8 Sep 1978 Baker SBE; 20 Aug 1980 Owens L. INY; and the following records from near Lancaster LA — 31 Jul-3 Aug 1979, 6-11 Aug 1979 (2 on 6 Aug), and 3-30 Aug 1980 (12 birds over this period).

As this species is easily confused with the Western Sandpiper, we suspect that intensive scrutiny of fall *Calidris* by increasingly aware observers will reveal a regular passage of Semipalmateds through areas where small sandpipers congregate in fall. The increase in records (65 birds in fall 1980) has been almost totally a function of increased observer awareness of the field marks of *Calidris*; however, the 1980 total may have been exceptional. All fall records have been of juveniles.

WESTERN SANDPIPER
Calidris mauri

Common to abundant transient throughout, except on the Channel Is. (where uncommon); uncommon to locally common winter visitant along the coast. Fairly common in winter at the Salton Sea, but casual elsewhere in the interior at this season.

The greatest numbers of wintering birds occur on the larger estuaries such as San Diego Bay SD, Newport Bay ORA, Pt. Mugu VEN, the Santa Maria R. mouth SLO/SBA, and Morro Bay SLO. It is very rare on many parts of the coast in winter, as well as in the interior of District C (flocks do winter around Chino SBE). A few regularly remain along the coast in summer, but it is quite scarce in late May and early June. The first fall transients arrive as early as mid-June.

Spring migration is skewed somewhat later at the Salton Sea than along the coast; fair numbers ocur well into May and a few birds linger into June.

This species is casual in winter in Districts D, R, and M. Care should be taken to document winter records in the interior away from the Salton Sea; the Least Sandpiper is the expected peep in these areas in winter.

RED-NECKED STINT
Calidris ruficollis

Two records: an adult male in basic plumage was collected at SESS 17 Aug 1974, and a juvenile was photographed in the Tijuana River Valley SD 10 Aug 1980.

While it appears to be correct, the Tijuana River Valley record must remain slightly tentative pending a better understanding of the identification criteria of this difficult species. A juvenile studied and photographed at the Santa Clara R. estuary VEN 1-6 Sep 1978 had been tentatively identified as this species, but appears to the authors to be a Semipalmated Sandpiper. Extensive documentation is clearly necessary (but perhaps not sufficient) for the acceptance of sight records of birds in juvenile or basic plumage. There are two additional records (May, June) of this Siberian species for Humboldt Co. in northern California.

LEAST SANDPIPER
Calidris minutilla

Very common and widespread transient and winter visitant; most numerous in Districts C and S. Non-breeding birds remain casually through the summer.

This is our hardiest *Calidris*, even wintering occasionally in District M and throughout all of District D except the coldest northern portions. It is variously uncommon to common as a winter visitant on the Channel Is. Spring birds have largely departed by the first of May, at which time large numbers of Western Sandpipers are still passing through. In District C non-breeding birds remain casually through the summer; Leasts are outnumbered in June by the Western Sandpiper.

A wide variety of habitats is occupied, particularly in migration. Least Sandpipers are much more widespread in winter than the Western. Small numbers may even winter on rocky coastlines and kelp-strewn beaches.

WHITE-RUMPED SANDPIPER
Calidris fuscicollis

Three records. There are two spring records for the Salton Sea: 7 Jun

1969 NESS and 16 Jun 1976 SESS; both birds were in alternate plumage. Also recorded 15-22 Aug 1980 near Lancaster LA (ad.).

The lateness of the spring dates matches the pattern of vagrancy to Arizona and northern California, and reflects the lateness of spring migration of this species in North America. Note that our spring records have come from the period of minimum abundance of our regular *Calidris*. The fall record is unique for western North America, except for one Alaska record.

BAIRD'S SANDPIPER
Calidris bairdii

Uncommon to fairly common fall transient, with the largest numbers passing along the coast, through District M, and especially through the northern part of District D. Casual in spring (eight records).

It is primarily an uncommon transient in Districts C and S, although concentrations have been noted along the coast (maximum of 24 at Santa Clara R. estuary VEN 22 Aug 1978). This species is a fairly common fall transient through much of District D (especially the northern part from the Antelope Valley north through the Owens Valley) and locally in District M (Baldwin L. SBE and L. Henshaw SD). Maximum concentrations in the interior are: 200 + at Tinnemaha Res. INY 20 Aug 1977, and 45 at Baldwin L. SBE 13 Aug 1977. It is a rare transient on the Channel Is., where it has been recorded from 6 Aug to 5 Oct. Fall transients usually begin appearing at the end of July (exceptionally to 18 Jun 1980 Santa Maria R. mouth SBA and 21 Jun 1954 Salton Sea — both ad.); the few mid-July records pertain to adults, whereas the great majority of birds passing through later in fall are juveniles. The latest record for the region is 29 Oct 1964 Tijuana River Valley SD; in general it is quite rare after the first of October.

The Baird's Sandpiper is casual in spring; the eight records are: 27 Apr 1917 "Fish Springs" SESS; 28 Apr 1968 NESS (2); 5 May 1973 Imperial Beach SD; 4 May 1977 Baker SBE (2); 15 May 1977 SESS (with 4 present on 20 May); 2 Apr 1979 near Blythe RIV; 5 Apr 1979 Baker; and 15 Apr 1980 Santa Clara R. estuary (3). Numerous spring records and all winter records published in *AFN* and elsewhere are unsupported and dismissed here as unconvincing. This species winters primarily in temperate South America and there are no valid winter records for North America. Sanderlings in alternate plumage are sometimes mistaken for this species in spring and early fall.

In the mountains and northern deserts Baird's Sandpipers occupy the shores of shallow lakes and ponds (including sewage ponds). Coastally, the brackish and freshwater upper portions of estuaries are favored.

PECTORAL SANDPIPER
Calidris melanotos

Uncommon fall transient, primarily along the coast; only casual in District S. Casual in spring (11 records).
While most fall transients pass along the coast and, to a lesser extent, through suitable habitat in the interior portions of District C, a few also pass through the northern interior, the Channel Is., and Districts M and R. Numbers of fall transients along the coast vary greatly from year to year; at least small numbers occur every year. In some falls it borders on fairly common; 480 were recorded in the region in fall of 1978, with an exceptional concentration of 109 near Oxnard VEN 30 Sep 1978. The first fall transients normally arrive in late August; peak numbers are from mid-September through mid-October (with juveniles greatly predominating). Well-documented records of very early fall transients are: 29 Jun 1977 San Elijo Lagoon SD; 29 Jun 1980 Santa Clara R. estuary VEN; 10 Jul 1977 Goleta SBA; 21 Jul 1980 nr. Santa Maria SBA; 4-13 Aug 1980 Santa Clara R. estuary; and, in District D, 18 Jul 1943 nr. Victorville SBE. All of these early birds have been adults, and the timing corresponds to the passage of large numbers of adults well to the east of the region. Late coastal records are: 12 Nov 1978 nr. Santa Maria; 14 Nov 1978 Santa Clara R. estuary; 15 Nov 1978 Goleta; and 24-25 Nov 1979 Goleta (latest record for the region).

In the interior transients are scarcer, but some are recorded annually (they are probably regular in the Antelope Valley). Exceptional interior concentrations are 30 near Lancaster LA 3 Oct 1979; 24 at L. Havasu SBE 14 Sep 1947; and 23 at Blythe RIV 27 Sep 1976. At the Salton Sea it has been recorded only four times in September and October and once in November (14 Nov 1969 SESS, the latest record for the interior; otherwise the latest interior record is 12 Nov 1979 Baker SBE).

This species is casual in spring; the 11 records are as follows: 17 Mar 1973 SESS (exceptionally early); 31 Mar 1979 SESS; 1 Apr 1979 nr. Lancaster LA; 14 Apr 1910 Santa Barbara SBA; 29 Apr 1972 Newport Bay ORA; 30 Apr 1978 Goleta; 15 Apr 1979 nr. Blythe RIV (2); 2 May 1975 Goleta; 9 May 1980 nr. Lancaster (3); 17 May 1964 Malibu LA; and 18 May 1968 SESS. A few other spring records published in *AFN* and lacking documentation are dismissed.

No acceptable winter record exists for the region. This species winters in South America; lingering fall migrants have been recorded into December in parts of the southern U.S. (e.g. 30 Dec 1957 Martinez L. on the Arizona side of the Colorado R.) and also 16 Dec 1979 San Jose, California.

Pectoral Sandpipers prefer the margins of freshwater ponds, the upper, freshwater portions of estuaries (sometimes onto estuarine mudflats), and flooded fields.

SHARP-TAILED SANDPIPER
Calidris acuminata

Casual fall transient in the immediate vicinity of the coast; 15 records. One additional winter record.

Fall records, by county, are as follows: 24-30 Sep 1973 Morro Bay SLO; 13-21 Sep 1969 Goleta SBA; 5 Oct 1977 Goleta; 24-30 Oct 1977 Goleta; 13 Dec 1977 Goleta; 1 Oct 1978 Santa Maria R. mouth SBA; 15-17 Oct 1978 Santa Maria R. mouth (2); 22-27 Oct 1978 nr. Santa Maria SBA; 19 Sep 1979 Goleta; 9 Nov 1977 Santa Clara R. estuary VEN; 21-29 Oct 1978 Santa Clara R. estuary; 13-14 Oct 1979 Pt. Mugu VEN (2); 27 Oct-2 Nov 1977 Tijuana River Valley SD; 16 Sep 1921 Mission Bay, San Diego SD; and 5 Oct 1976 Santa Catalina I.

It has been recorded once in mid-winter: 19 Jan-2 Mar 1980 Pt. Mugu (the only winter record for North America).

All regional records of this Asiatic species are of juveniles; the passage is rather late for a shorebird. While some have associated with Pectoral Sandpipers, many have been with Dunlin, Red Knots, or other shorebirds. All but three of the records are since 1976.

ROCK SANDPIPER
Calidris ptilocnemis

Casual winter visitant to rocky coastal areas; recorded as follows: 30 Dec 1966 San Simeon SLO; 13 Feb-10 Apr 1968 Cambria SLO (2, with one present to mid-May); 21 Nov 1968 San Pedro LA; "winter 1968-1969" Cambria; 14 Nov 1971 San Simeon; and at Playa del Rey LA five different winters from 1958-1959 to 1966-1967 (never more than two birds per winter).

Extreme dates for the region are 14 Nov-10 Apr, except for the lingering Cambria bird present to mid-May. It has not been recorded since 1971. This may in part reflect the poor coverage that the northern coast of San Luis Obispo Co. receives; with intensified coverage the species may even prove to be regular there.

This is a bird of rocky shores and jetties; it is usually found in the company of turnstones and Surfbirds. It winters annually in very small numbers on the rocky coasts of central and northern California.

DUNLIN
Calidris alpina

Common winter visitant along the coast. Fairly common spring and fall transient at the Salton Sea, remaining uncommonly through the winter. Elsewhere in the interior an uncommon transient, being largely absent in winter.

168

In District C, most winter birds occur on tidal mudflats and channels; a few appear a short distance inland in coastal valleys, where the Dunlin is more numerous as a transient. It is primarily a transient through the interior, slightly more numerous in fall than in spring; the maximum for District D in spring was 50 nr. Lancaster LA 9 May 1980. There are only scattered winter records in the interior away from the Salton Sea (exceptionally up to 50 in the Ownes Valley INY 11 Jan 1976). It is an uncommon transient and winter visitor on the Channel Is.

One of our latest shorebirds to arrive in fall, the Dunlin usually begins to appear in mid-September. The last spring stragglers have usually departed the coast by mid-May; spring migration at the Salton Sea is skewed slightly later. There is a puzzling series of records of alternate-plumaged birds in mid-summer. About six June records for the coast presumably pertain to very late spring transients; it has once summered on the coast: 13 Jul-3 Sep 1980 Santa Clara R. estuary VEN. An adult was at Cambria SLO 20 Aug 1980. There are at least four records from June through August at the Salton Sea; two of these (involving three individuals) represent alternate-plumaged birds known to have summered. One on 17 Aug 1974 SESS was probably a very early fall transient (a healthy bird at a well-worked locality where none had been present earlier in summer). An injured bird was present at Furnace Creek Ranch INY 22 May-6 Jun 1971.

CURLEW SANDPIPER
Calidris ferruginea

Two records: a bird in alternate plumage at Salton City IMP 27-28 Apr 1974, and a juvenile at the Santa Clara R. estuary 27-28 Sep 1979.

There are three additional records for northern California; all are of juvenile birds in September.

STILT SANDPIPER
Micropalama himantopus

Uncommon transient and irregular and uncommon winter visitor at the south end of the Salton Sea. Very rare fall transient along the coast, with four spring records and one winter record. Casual transient through District D.

Fall migrants begin appearing at SESS in mid-July; spring passage is primarily from late April to about 20 May (exceptionally to 4 Jun 1978). Maxima in spring include 75 on 17 Apr 1971 and 70 on 15-17 May 1977. Fall maxima include 125 on 14 Aug 1976 and 99 on 31 Aug 1961. The winter maximum of 70 was on 21 Feb 1971. Surprisingly, it is only casual at NESS; there are five fall and three spring records.

In District D this species has been recorded only five times as follows: 28 Aug 1978 Baker SBE; 2 Aug 1979, 6 Aug 1979, and 27-31 Aug 1980 near Lancaster LA; and 24-26 May 1980 Furnace Creek Ranch INY. It is unrecorded in Districts M and R.

A total of about 40 records exist for District C, but the species is unrecorded on the Channel Is. It is a very rare fall transient along the coast from late July through October; earlier records are 29-30 Jun 1980 Santa Maria R. mouth SBA, and 6-16 Jul 1980 Goleta SBA. Most coastal records are for Santa Barbara, Ventura, Orange, and San Diego Cos.; it has also been recorded once in coastal Los Angeles Co. (8 Sep 1976 Playa del Rey) and casually inland in District C (Otay L. and L. Hodges SD, L. Elsinore and vic. Riverside RIV). The latest fall coastal record is 18 Nov 1972 Newport Bay ORA, except for one winter record: 18 Nov 1979-2 Mar 1980 Pt. Mugu VEN. There are four records of spring transients for the coast: 14 Apr 1977 Goleta (2); 26 Apr 1978 Pt. Mugu; 17-21 May 1980 Santa Clara R. estuary VEN; and 1 Jun 1980 Santa Maria R. mouth.

At the Salton Sea Stilt Sandpipers occupy shallow diked ponds and pools; they often associate with dowitchers and peeps. Most records for District C have been at coastal estuaries and adjacent ponds. The majority of birds away from District S have been juveniles.

BUFF-BREASTED SANDPIPER
Tryngites subruficollis

Casual transient in District C; 14 records, nine of which come from 1978 and 1979.

The records are as follows: 14 Sep 1923 Morro Bay SLO; 10-26 Sep 1964 Goleta SBA (2); 16 Sep 1967 Oceanside SD; 5-17 Sep 1971 Palos Verdes Peninsula LA; 30 Aug 1975 Santa Catalina I.; 27 Aug-1 Sep 1978 near Lakeview RIV; 2-3 Sep 1978 L. Hodges SD (2); 10-18 Sep 1978 Imperial Beach SD; 3 Sep 1978 near Pt. Mugu VEN (2); 6 Sep 1979 Santa Clara R. estuary VEN (4); 16-18 Sep 1979 near Oxnard VEN (at least 7); 23 Sep-6 Oct 1979 near Oxnard; 9 Oct 1979 Tijuana River Valley SD; and 12-22 Oct 1979 Tijuana River Valley (2; one of the latest records for North America).

The nine records for 1978 and 1979 represent parts of unprecedented invasions of the Pacific Coast; there were numerous records in Oregon and northern California, including up to 11 birds on Pt. Reyes, Marin Co., California in the fall of 1978.

Buff-breasted Sandpipers have been found on short-grass fields (including cemeteries, airports, and sod farms) and at the margins of shallow freshwater lakes and coastal estuaries. Virtually all records are of juveniles.

RUFF
Philomachus pugnax

Casual fall transient and winter visitant along the coast; two spring records. One record for District D.

There is a total of 31 records for the region: 20 of fall transients (the earliest being an adult female on 10 Aug 1980 Tijuana River Valley SD and a juvenile on 2-7 Sep 1979 Santa Clara R. estuary VEN); nine of wintering birds (involving up to three individuals each); and two of spring transients (possibly involving birds wintering locally—30 Mar 1962 San Diego R. mouth SD and 1 Apr 1978 near Pt. Mugu VEN). Most records are for Santa Barbara (vic. Santa Maria), Ventura, and San Diego Cos. Records from elsewhere are: 22 Dec 1966-25 Jan 1967 and 27 Nov 1967-7 Apr 1968 San Simeon SLO (probably the same individual); 6 Oct 1972 Morro Bay SLO; 6-15 Jan 1975 Playa del Rey LA; 31 Dec 1962 Santa Ana R. mouth ORA; and 26 Sep-11 Oct 1966 Capistrano Beach ORA.

The only interior record is 3 Oct 1979 near Lancaster LA. A significant record just outside the region is for Buena Vista L. KRN 10 Nov 1978.

Ruffs do not appear tied to any particular type of shore habitat; though most birds in the region have been in flooded fields or coastal estuaries, some wintering birds have been on rocky shores and jetties. All but one of the fall records appear to pertain to juveniles.

SHORT-BILLED DOWITCHER
Limnodromus griseus

Common transient along the coast and at the Salton Sea. Rare to locally uncommon transient, mainly in fall, through the rest of the region. Spring and fall passage is earlier than in the Long-billed. Winters only along the coast, where generally scarce, but locally common.

This species is uncommon to rare in winter along most of the coast, but it is common to abundant at this season on San Diego Bay SD and at Newport Bay ORA (and possibly Morro Bay SLO). Note that the bar graph generalizes the winter status on the coast and does not reflect its abundance at places such as San Diego Bay. Small numbers remain through the summer on coastal estuaries, particularly on San Diego Bay, where small flocks occur. The fall passage averages somewhat earlier than that of the Long-billed Dowitcher. It is a very rare transient on the Channel Is., where the majority of records are for fall.

Short-billed Dowitchers are common transients at the Salton Sea, but in general are outnumbered there by Long-billed Dowitchers (numbers may be more or less equal at NESS, and around the barren shoreline of the sea the Short-billed can greatly outnumber the Long-billed in migration). Scattered records exist for summer (June), when this species outnumbers the Long-billed; there are no definite winter records.

Elsewhere in the interior, including District M and the inland portions of District C, it is a rare to uncommon fall transient. Small flocks have been noted in spring in the vicinity of Lancaster LA in the Antelope Valley, including concentrations of up to 15 on 17 Apr 1978 and 25 on 7 Apr 1980. In the eastern part of the region it is mainly a rare but regular fall transient (the majority of records are of juveniles). There is an early fall record for District R north of Bard IMP 1 Jul 1973. Because of the difficulty in separating silent birds from the Long-billed Dowitcher, its status in the interior is not entirely clear; the interior status is also confused by poor coverage early in the migration periods (April, July). A concentration of 17 near Lancaster LA 9 Jul 1980 suggests that numbers may be greater in early fall (a period when adults are moving south) than we have shown.

LONG-BILLED DOWITCHER
Limnodromus scolopaceus

Common transient and winter visitant along the coast and at the Salton Sea. Uncommon to locally common transient and rare to uncommon winter visitant through the rest of the region. A few may summer in Districts C and S.

The majority of migrants pass through later in fall and spring than the Short-billed Dowitcher. It is quite abundant during migration at the Salton Sea, where the period of migration is somewhat longer than on the coast. In the interior portions of District C it is a fairly common to common transient and uncommon winter visitant (flocks may winter locally, e.g. at Chino SBE). It is generally an uncommon to fairly common transient and very rare winter visitant in District D, but it is locally common as a transient in the Antelope Valley LA/KRN, and probably winters there regularly (e.g. 14 on 15 Dec 1979 near Lancaster LA). It may also be somewhat more regular in winter along the Colorado R. There are very few mid-summer (June) records anywhere in the region.

This species is a rare transient and winter visitant on the Channel Is.

Along the coast it is most partial to estuarine borders, river channels, and flooded fields. Unlike the Short-billed, flocks are routinely found a fair distance inland in District C. During migration it occurs by the thousands on mudflats and diked ponds at the Salton Sea.

Observers should exercise caution in delineating the status of our two dowitcher species because there is considerable overlap in their morphological characters. They are always best identified by call notes, which are diagnostic.

COMMON SNIPE
Gallinago gallinago

Fairly common to locally common winter visitant throughout District C; uncommon, bordering on fairly common, winter visitant in Districts S and R. Elsewhere in the interior primarily a fairly common fall transient and uncommon spring transient, with a few birds remaining through the winter. A few breeding records, the most recent of which are from the Owens Valley.

Fall transients appear somewhat earlier in the northern part of District D than on the coast; they are regular there by mid-August. They remain rarely in winter in District D (e.g. Antelope Valley LA). Snipe are not regularly recorded on the coast until September, but they occur exceptionally there and in District R at the end of July and in early August. This species winters regularly in small numbers on Santa Catalina I.; otherwise it is primarily a transient on the Channel Is.

Common Snipe formerly bred in small numbers in District C (San Bernardino and Colton SBE, Gorman LA) and once in District M (Big Bear L. SBE); these breeding records are from the late 1800s and early 1900s. A nest was recently found near Olancha INY (1 egg set taken 22 May 1971); snipe probably still nest in wet meadows in the Owens Valley. They are common summer residents just north of the region in Mono Co.

Snipe inhabit the marshy borders of streams and ponds, as well as flooded fields, ditches, and wet meadows.

PHALAROPODIDAE: PHALAROPES

WILSON'S PHALAROPE
Phalaropus tricolor

Fairly common to common spring transient and common to abundant fall transient throughout. Very rare, but possibly regular, winter visitant at the south end of San Diego Bay SD; five winter records for District S. Two nesting records for the Owens Valley.

This species is most numerous at the Salton Sea, where it is common in spring and abundant in fall. Along the coast it is rather local and borders on uncommon in spring; the largest numbers occur on the salt works at the south end of San Diego Bay SD and at Upper Newport Bay ORA. This phalarope is somewhat more widespread along the coast in fall. Transients occur throughout the interior (fairly common in spring, common to abundant in fall). It is only a casual transient on the Channel Is.

Spring transients may occasionally arrive by late March and may linger into early June; the first fall transients (usually females) arrive by mid-June. Thus, at least at the Salton Sea, the species is almost continuously present through the summer period. Peak fall numbers pass through early (mid-July to late August) and drop off rapidly in September; this species is decidedly rare after the first of October.

Winter records come mostly from the salt works at the south end of San Diego Bay; small numbers (up to 8) irregularly occur here with wintering Northern Phalaropes. Other late fall and winter records for the coast are: 16 Nov 1963 Newport Bay; 27 Dec 1969 Goleta SBA; 5 Jan 1964 San Elijo Lagoon SD; and 3 Mar 1972 Oceanside SD. There are five winter records for SESS: 28 Nov 1970, 20 Dec 1976, 21 Dec 1974, 28 Dec 1968-2 Feb 1969 (2 on 28-29 Dec), and 16-17 Feb 1975 (4). There are no interior winter records away from the Salton Sea. The total number of winter records, while not large, is enough to suggest that the species may be somewhat regular at this season.

The two breeding records are from the Owens Valley: egg sets taken near Olancha INY 22 May 1971 and near Cartago INY 3 Jun 1972; nesting may be more regular than the two records indicate. Outside of the region it nests in small numbers to the north of the Owens Valley in Mono Co.

Wilson's Phalaropes prefer shallow ponds (e.g. salt works, sewage ponds), marshes, flooded fields, mudflats, and grassy shores. Unlike the Red and Northern Phalaropes, they shun marine habitats.

NORTHERN PHALAROPE
Phalaropus lobatus

Common transient coastally, offshore, and at the Salton Sea, particularly in fall. Generally an uncommon spring transient and common fall transient in the remainder of the region. Regular winter visitant at the south end of San Diego Bay SD, but very few winter records elsewhere.

Much of the spring movement of this species takes place off the coast, flocks of thousands sometimes pass just offshore in late April and May. It is generally an uncommon spring transient elsewhere in the region (including the interior of District C); concentrations are occasionally noted. It is rather irregular in spring at the Salton Sea, where most birds are recorded at the south end. Spring concentrations away from the coast and District S include: 250 at Santee SD and 155 at Ramona SD 1 May 1955; 3500 at L. Cuyamaca SD 29 Apr 1978; and 500 near Lancaster LA 16 May 1980 (with numbers present 27 Apr-26 May); it is probably regular at this last locality. The paucity of other spring concentrations for the interior suggests that large numbers normally pass over the interior without stopping in the region. An interesting spring report just north of the region is of 51 birds in the snow in the Greenhorn Mtns. KRN 4 May 1952.

Northern Phalaropes are far more numerous and widespread in fall than in spring. They are common to abundant fall transients along and off the coast and at the Salton Sea; they are also common at this season in Districts D, M, and R and in the inland portions of District C. Fall transients may arrive as early as mid-June. A late fall concentration for the interior was 40 at SESS 11 Nov 1978.

This species is a somewhat regular winter visitant at the salt works at the south end of San Diego Bay SD (up to 100 birds). The only winter records away from here are: 26 Nov 1954 SESS (2); 27 Nov 1970 NESS; "December" 1969 Goleta SBA; 18 Dec 1976 Santa Monica Bay LA; 22 Dec 1975 SESS (3); 1 Mar 1959 SESS; and 25 Mar-2Apr 1978 Pt. Mugu VEN (may have wintered). The late November records may pertain to late fall stragglers.

Northern Phalaropes occur on open water of all types from shallow ponds (e.g. salt works and sewage ponds), coastal estuaries, and marshes to the open ocean.

RED PHALAROPE
Phalaropus fulicarius

Status complex. Irregularly common to abundant late fall and early winter visitant offshore and, to a lesser extent, along the coast; even more irregular as a spring transient along the coast, but occasionally abundant. Of nearly annual occurrence in spring, summer, and fall at the Salton Sea; several fall records for elsewhere in the interior.

Small numbers migrate offshore every fall (August through October). Periodic late fall invasions (late October through January) may sometimes involve thousands of individuals, e.g. 3000 at Imperial Beach SD in late Oct 1963 and "thousands" off southern California in Nov 1969. During the latter invasion, perhaps the largest on record for fall in the region, a few birds appeared inland, e.g. 15 Nov 1969 Hollywood Res. LA, 11 Nov 1969 Salton City IMP (five, with three present on 23 Nov), and 11 Jan 1970 Salton City. A large coastal die-off took place that year; many starved birds were found.

There are relatively few records for late winter and early spring (mid-February to mid-April). An invasion in late winter and spring 1976 did not fit the established pattern: scattered birds turned up in late January, and hundreds were present along the coast by February and March. Large numbers were again seen in mid-April (e.g. 6500 off Goleta Pt. SBA on 17 Apr, during strong westerly gales), and again in late May. It is possible that large numbers of Red Phalaropes winter off our coast in some years and are occasionally driven inshore by storms; in other years they may winter well to the south of the region.

The major spring passage off the coast is in May; the species is irregularly abundant at this time. Concentrations include: 800 at Imperial Beach 6 May 1971; 2320 at Santa Rosa I. 23 May 1976; 15,000 at San Miguel I. 21 May 1976; 7500 off San Miguel I. 17 May 1980; and 30,000+ off Santa Cruz I. 28 May 1980. After the offshore concentrations of May 1980, four late birds were at the Santa Maria R. mouth SBA 15-24 Jun 1980.

Red Phalaropes are casual (recently almost annual) at the Salton Sea; about 20 records extend from 10 May 1980 NESS (4, a high count) to 23 Nov 1969 and 11 Jan 1970 Salton City (both cited above). A few of the records are for mid-summer. There are seven fall records for elsewhere in the interior: 27 Aug and 24 Sep 1978 Baker SBE; 25 Sep 1953 L. Havasu SBE; 16 Oct 1971 Deep Springs INY; 23 Oct 1949 L. Havasu; 26-28 Oct 1974 Furnace Creek Ranch INY; and 11 Nov 1978 Lancaster LA. These records suggest that there may be a very small inland passage in fall. There are also scattered fall records for the inland portion of District C. The only inland spring record away from the Salton Sea is 20 May 1974 El Monte LA.

175

Normally this is the most exclusively pelagic of our phalaropes, although the Northern also migrates over the open ocean. During periodic invasions they frequently enter coastal bays and estuaries. Away from the south end of San Diego Bay SD and SESS this is the only phalarope likely to be seen in winter.

LARIDAE: SKUAS, JAEGERS, GULLS, TERNS

POMARINE JAEGER
Stercorarius pomarinus

Common transient and uncommon winter visitant offshore, remaining rarely through the summer period. Five inland records (all in Districts S and R).

Spring passage peaks in early to mid-May; the largest fall concentrations are in September and early October (occasionally later, e.g. 250 off San Pedro LA 22 Oct 1977). The highest winter concentrations include: 50 on 22 Nov 1968 off San Pedro; 35 on 26 Feb 1978 between Ventura VEN and San Nicolas I.; 25 on 10 Dec 1977 off La Jolla SD; and 14 on 21 Jan 1979 off Morro Bay SLO. Numbers tend to diminish through the course of the winter.

The five inland records are from only two years: 8-12 Sep 1977 NESS (imm.); 11 Sep 1977 NESS (ad.); 24 Sep 1977 NESS (imm.); 3-5 Sep 1977 L. Havasu SBE (2 imms.); and 26 Sep 1950 L. Havasu (specimen). Inland birds should be identified with caution.

The Pomarine Jaeger is, on average, a far more pelagic species than the Parasitic and it is always the dominant jaeger more than about four km offshore.

PARASITIC JAEGER
Stercorarius parasiticus

Fairly common transient and uncommon winter visitant off the coast, mainly within 4-5 km of shore. Rather rare inshore around the Channel Is. Casual in summer. Rare fall transient at the Salton Sea; casual at that season along the Colorado R.

Parasitic Jaegers prefer inshore marine waters. They are only rarely seen well offshore, and then generally in migration. They pirate food mainly from Common and Elegant terns, and thus get scarce more than 4-5 km offshore, the distance beyond which these species generally drop out. They are often seen from shore around feeding concentrations of terns and gulls and are even seen around harbors and estuaries. This jaeger is casual in summer along the coast; while it is perhaps regular in very small numbers at this season, it is definitely less numerous than the Pomarine.

This species is a rare but regular fall transient at the Salton Sea. It has been recorded as early as 30 Aug 1971 and as late as 28 Nov 1976; the great majority of records are from September. The maximum was of eight on 18 Sep 1964; other mid-September concentrations involve 3-6 birds. It is a casual transient in September and October along the Colorado R. where it may prove to be regular on the larger impoundments such as L. Havasu.

LONG-TAILED JAEGER
Stercorarius longicaudus

Rare but regular fall transient well offshore, mainly in September; one spring record for the coast. Four fall records for the interior.

The great majority of records are for mid-September and off San Diego SD, but this is no doubt due in part to the timing and location of pelagic birdwatching trips. Maxima are 9 off San Diego 13 Oct 1971 and 5 off San Diego 3 Sep 1967 and 11 Sep 1976. There are only two fall records prior to September (certainly a function of inadequate offshore coverage in August): 29 Jul 1933 off San Pedro LA and 28 Aug 1937 off San Pedro. The only spring record is of an adult at the south end of San Diego Bay 11 May 1962.

There are four inland records: 24 Aug 1974 NESS (imm., specimen); 4-5 Sep 1977 L. Havasu SBE (2 ad.); 14 Sep 1977 L. Havasu (imm.); and 18 Aug 1977 Pala Indian Reservation n. SD (an exhausted adult grounded after Tropical Storm Doreen).

This is the most highly pelagic of our jaegers; it often works flocks of Arctic Terns. Records are fairly evenly divided between adult, subadult, and immature birds. First year birds should be identified with extreme care, as they closely resemble Parasitic Jaegers and have been inaccurately depicted in some field guides. Because mis-identification was likely, we have dismissed several inshore reports of Long-tailed Jaegers which lack sufficient documentation. It should be noted that the Parasitic Jaeger is almost as rare as the Long-tailed well offshore.

SOUTH POLAR SKUA
Catharacta maccormicki

Uncommon late spring visitant and rare fall transient well offshore.

It has been recorded as early as 30 Apr 1978 off Santa Catalina I. Up to six in a day have been recorded in the period from mid-May to early June. It is casual through summer (July-August). This species is less numerous in fall than in spring, but it is probably regular at least in the northern part of the region. Exceptional fall numbers include eight off San Miguel I. 28-29 Sep 1976, and nine off the southern California coast 9-11 Sep 1975. The paucity of fall records may be due in part to inadequate pelagic coverage in the northern part of the region. There are two records onshore: one found dead at Imperial Beach SD 23 Nov 1975 and one off the mouth of the Santa Maria R. SLO/SBA 19 Oct 1978. The latest fall records are 17 Nov 1979 Davidson Seamount off SLO and 23 Nov 1975 Imperial Beach (see above).

Confusion with dark-phase Pomarine Jaegers and with immature gulls may account for several winter records (November-April); no winter records for the region are documented sufficiently. Recent taxonomic work has shown that *maccormicki*, which breeds in the southern hemisphere, is specifically distinct from the other skuas. Reports in California of other forms of skua from the southern hemisphere are incorrect or insufficiently documented.

LAUGHING GULL
Larus atricilla

Common post-breeding visitant to the Salton Sea, with largest numbers from late June through September. Four recent December and January records. Casual visitant to the coast, with some 14 records. One record each for Districts R and D.

At the Salton Sea peak numbers vary from year to year; the maximum was up to 600 in mid-Aug 1977. The great majority are found at SESS; the species is decidedly uncommon at NESS where flocks seldom exceed about a dozen birds. It generally arrives in late May or early June, and is present in large numbers by mid-July. Numbers diminish in October and it is generally absent after November. Later records are: 19 Dec 1977 North Shore RIV; 2 Jan 1979 NESS; 8 Jan 1966 SESS; and 10 Jan 1976 SESS. It formerly nested at SESS, with breeding birds arriving in mid-April (exceptionally to 3 Apr 1947); the last recorded nesting was in 1957. In recent years it has not been recorded before mid-May.

There is one record for District D: 15 Jun 1975 Daggett SBE (2). It has also been recorded once in District R: 3 Sep 1960 Imperial Dam IMP.

The Laughing Gull is a casual visitant along the coast. The inaccurate portrayal of immature plumages of Laughing and, especially, Franklin's Gulls in the popular field guides has led to the frequent confusion of these two species. As Franklin's greatly predominates on the coast, we have dismissed numerous coastal reports of Laughing Gulls which we feel to be in error. We accept 14 coastal records (six of which are from winter 1979-1980): 23 Mar 1964 San Diego SD (ad.); 1-30 May 1965 San Diego (year-old bird); 16 Feb 1969 Imperial Beach SD; 15 Nov 1969 Pt. Loma SD; 9 Sep 1972 off San Diego (juvenile which followed a boat 50 km toward San Clemente I.); 28 Dec 1976 Imperial Beach (ad.); 30 Dec 1979 off Newport ORA (first-winter); 23 Jan-4 Feb 1980 Oceanside SD (first-winter); 3 Feb 1980 Malibu LA (second-winter); 1-6 Feb 1980 Fiesta Island, Mission Bay SD (two on 1 Feb; first- and second-winter); 12 Feb-1 Mar 1980 Imperial Beach (first-winter); 10 Mar 1980 off San Diego (first-winter); 22 Jul 1976 Santa Clara R. estuary VEN (year-old bird); and 18-19 May 1980 Santa Ynez R. mouth SBA (year-old bird). Other coastal records published in *AFN* and *AB* may be correct, but the authors have elected to take a very conservative approach to underscore the rarity of this species on the coast. Laughing Gulls should be identified with extreme caution away from District S, and standard field guides should not be relied upon. There are several valid records for coastal northern California.

Laughing Gulls are found in the largest numbers around the mouths of the New and Alamo Rivers at SESS, although they also range out into adjacent flooded agricultural fields. Nesting formerly took place on low islets at the sw corner of the sea.

FRANKLIN'S GULL
Larus pipixcan

Generally a rare transient, mostly in fall, but status complex. Most numerous at the Salton Sea. Casual (perhaps regular) winter visitant along the coast.

At the Salton Sea this species is a rare spring and fall transient (probably uncommon in fall, especially October, but coverage is limited at this season); it is also a casual, but almost regular, non-breeding summer visitant there, especially at NESS. Extreme dates at the Salton Sea are: 1 Apr 1978 Desert Shores IMP to 18 Nov 1966 Calipatria IMP (7).

Along the coast it is a rare but regular late fall transient and casual (nearly regular) winter visitant; most records are of first-winter birds. Up to 20 per fall (1964) have been recorded along the coast. Some winter records exist for the interior of District C (e.g. slightly inland at downtown Los Angeles LA 15-19 Jan 1978 and well inland at San Bernardino SBE 3-4 Jan 1971 and L. Hodges SD 10 Nov 1979-5 Jan 1980). It is a casual (possibly regular) spring transient along the coast, with a number of records well at sea (and three May records for the Channel Is.). The pelagic tendency in spring seems surprising for what is generally considered an "inland" gull, but it should be noted that this species winters at sea off South America. It is casual in summer in District C: 21 Jun 1979 Goleta SBA; 1 Jul 1977 Santa Clara R. estuary VEN; 29 Jul 1951 Santa Margarita R. mouth SD; 4 Aug 1974 Santa Ynez R. mouth SBA; and 9 Aug 1974 Playa del Rey LA. Juveniles at Malibu LA 15 Aug 1979 and at NESS 13 Aug 1980 indicate how early fall migrants may arrive.

In Districts D, M, and R it is a rare but somewhat regular transient. A concentration of some 20 adults occurred at Baldwin L. SBE in early May 1972 (with at least one present to 18 June).

Franklin's Gulls are found around mudflats and flooded agricultural fields at the Salton Sea; along the coast they often occur with concentrations of Bonaparte's Gulls.

LITTLE GULL
Larus minutus

Five records as follows: 16-21 Nov 1968 near Mecca RIV (ad.); 22-26 Dec 1969 Redondo Beach LA (ad.); 3 Dec 1972 SESS (ad.); 14-22 Apr

179

1977 Goleta SBA (first-winter bird); and 1-5 Mar 1980 Santa Clara R. estuary VEN (first-winter). All have occurred with Bonaparte's Gulls.
There are six additional records for northern California.

BLACK-HEADED GULL
Larus ridibundus

One record: an adult observed 1 km off Santa Barbara SBA 30 Dec 1978.
There are six additional records for northern California; most have been with large flocks of Bonaparte's Gulls.

BONAPARTE'S GULL
Larus philadelphia

Common to abundant winter visitant along the coast and adjacent inshore waters. Primarily a transient through the interior, being common during spring at the Salton Sea and locally on lakes in the southern portion of District M.

The largest numbers are present along the coast from October through April; it is most numerous along the immediate coast and adjacent inshore waters, but it also occurs irregularly around the Channel Is., particularly as a spring transient. A few occur in the interior of District C. Large concentrations may occur around sewage plants and outfalls.

The Bonaparte's Gull is primarily a transient through the interior. The largest numbers occur in spring when birds move north out of the Gulf of California. It is common at the Salton Sea during spring (exceptionally up to several hundred birds in a day); large numbers occasionally remain into summer (exceptionally up to 250 in Jun-Jul 1977). Few birds remain by the end of summer and large summer dieoffs have occurred. This gull is a fairly common fall transient at the Salton Sea, but it is rare and irregular in winter (often absent, although flocks up to 30 have been found, e.g. winter 1976-1977 SESS). In Districts D, M, and R it is an irregular spring transient; large concentrations occasionally occur on lakes in the San Diego Co. mountains: 490 on L. Henshaw SD 31 Mar 1979 and 300 there on 2 May 1979; 200 on L. Cuyamaca SD 17 Apr 1964 and again 15 Apr 1978; and 300 on L. Henshaw 1 Apr 1978. These concentrations closely fit the pattern of other "coastal" species which come north out of the Gulf of California in spring (Brant, Surf Scoter). Birds occasionally linger into summer (e.g. up to 22 near Lancaster LA, summer 1980). It is a rare to uncommon fall transient in Districts D, M, and R; it is absent from there in winter.

HEERMANN'S GULL
Larus heermanni

Common non-breeding visitant along the immediate coast; only uncommon to fairly common in spring, when breeding takes place in

Mexico. Rare and irregular post-breeding visitant to the Salton Sea; casual elsewhere in the interior (seven records).

Coastal birds begin departing for Mexican breeding colonies in mid-February, becoming increasingly scarce through the spring until the first adults dispersing northward arrive in late May. This species is generally found on the immediate coast, wandering inland as far as the back portions of coastal estuaries and certain lakes on the immediate coast (e.g. Harbor L. LA). It is fairly common at sea and around the Channel Islands. Heermann's Gulls frequently associate with Brown Pelicans and cormorants.

Two pairs attempted to nest at Shell Beach Rocks of Vandenberg AFB SBA in May-Jun 1980; one nest had an egg on 27 May, but both nests were abandoned by July. North of the region, this species also nested (unsuccessfully) at Alcatraz, San Francisco Bay in summer 1980. The closest regular nesting site is on the San Benito Is. off the west coast of Baja California.

There is one record inland in District C: 17 Oct 1979 Otay Mesa SD.

This gull is a rare and irregular post-breeding summer visitant at the Salton Sea, where it is recorded most frequently in July. A major flight in 1969 accounted for ten of the approximately 30 records for District S. The earliest records are: 3 May 1969 NESS, 15 May 1979 SESS (2), and 17-24 May 1969 SESS. The latest records are: 11 Oct 1969 Brawley IMP, 11 Oct-14 Nov 1969 Salton City IMP (3), and 2 Nov 1974 SESS. It has not been recorded at the Salton Sea in many years (e.g. 1970, 1971, 1973, 1977, 1980). All have been along the immediate shoreline of the sea except for birds at Brawley (record cited above) and Seeley IMP 4-14 Jul 1979.

Heermann's Gulls are casual elsewhere in the interior: 13 Jul 1948 Needles Landing, L. Havasu SBE; 14 Jul 1968 Plaster City, extreme w. Imperial Co. (6); 14 Jul 1968 Coyote Wells IMP; 14 Jul 1968 Jacumba SD; 21 May 1972 Desert Center RIV; and unseasonal records 18 Jan 1980 L. Henshaw (ad.) and 7 Apr 1974 Big Bear L. SBE. On the border of the region, was s. of Parker, Arizona 15 Oct 1977 and one was n. of Yuma, Arizona 10 Nov 1978. Unlike the pattern in southeastern California, most records for Arizona are in fall.

MEW GULL
Larus canus

Fairly common to locally common winter visitant along the coast, remaining casually into summer. Wanders rarely to the inland portions of District C; in the true interior, recorded only at the Salton Sea (about 20 records).

It is most numerous along the coast from Ventura Co. north (including the northern Channel Is.); concentrations occur locally farther south (e.g. Los Angeles Harbor LA). The first fall transients normally arrive in late October. Individuals remain casually into early summer along the coast (once in the interior of District C: 7-31 Jul 1976 Hansen Dam, San Fernando Valley LA). There is only one record of a bird remaining into August and September (Goleta SBA, summer 1979 — not graphed). In winter it wanders rarely into the interior portions of District C; up to a dozen per winter have been noted at Hansen Dam, and it is probably of annual occurrence in the San Bernardino/Riverside area.

In the true interior the Mew Gull has been recorded only at the Salton Sea (about 20 records); it has been of annual occurrence in recent years. Extreme dates at the Salton Sea are 14 Nov 1969 Salton City IMP and 8 May 1971 SESS. Most records are from mid-December to early April. The great majority of records from the interior are of first and second winter birds. While it is unrecorded in District R, there is a recent record at Davis Dam along the Colorado R. just north of the region (four birds 19 Mar-1 Apr 1979).

Mew Gulls primarily frequent the outer coast, especially around sewage plants and theor outfalls, river mouths, and harbors. They range uncommonly over the open ocean. Most birds in District S have been on the shoreline of the Salton Sea, but a few have been noted in flooded fields with other gulls.

RING-BILLED GULL
Larus delawarensis

Common to abundant winter visitant throughout District C. Abundant winter visitant in District S and fairly common to common winter visitant in District R. Primarily a transient through the rest of the interior. Summers fairly commonly, primarily along the coast and in District S.

As a winter visitant it is quite common in District C, although total numbers are less than those of the California Gull. In District S winter flocks of thousands occur along the shoreline at SESS and in adjacent agricultural areas. It is fairly common to common in winter along the Colorado R.; flocks of up to about 100 birds are noted. This species is primarily a transient through the rest of the interior; a few non-breeding birds remain through the summer (e.g. Antelope Valley LA). It winters regularly on montane lakes and locally in District D (Antelope Valley, Owens Valley).

Non-breeding birds remain fairly commonly through summer along the coast and at the Salton Sea, with lesser numbers elsewhere. The Ring-billed Bull generally outnumbers the California Gull at this season. Definite fall migrants (juveniles) begin arriving in the region in late July.

This is the least pelagic of our gulls and is no more than casual at sea (only five records for the Channel Is.). In District C it occurs in a variety of situations, from city parks and urban centers to garbage dumps and shorelines.

CALIFORNIA GULL
Larus californicus

Abundant winter visitant throughout District C. from inland valleys to well offshore; small numbers remain through summer. Common transient at the Salton Sea, remaining uncommonly in winter and fairly commonly as a non-breeder in summer. Primarily a transient through the remainder of the interior.

In District C winter flocks often contain thousands of birds. It remains uncommonly along the coast through summer as a non-breeder. Juveniles begin arriving on the coast as early as late July.

It is a common transient in District S. where it remains fairly commonly as a non-breeder through summer. This species is distinctly uncommon there in winter, and is greatly outnumbered at SESS by Ring-billed and even Herring Gulls. It borders on fairly common in winter at NESS and Salton City IMP (a locality which is good in general for wintering gulls).

Elsewhere in the interior it is primarily a transient, although a few non-breeders regularly remain through summer (e.g. Antelope Valley LA). Adults may be fairly common in summer in the northern Owens Valley INY, which is just south of a major nesting area at Mono L. MNO (however, this colony is immediately threatened by water diversions by the City of Los Angeles). This species is very rare in winter through most of District D (except the Antelope Valley, where it can be uncommon). It is generally casual in winter in District R; a wintering flock at Davis Dam along the Colorado R. north of the region probably accounts for winter records in the vicinity of Needles SBE. It is irregularly fairly common in winter in the Big Bear Valley, San Bernardino Mtns.

The California Gull is an opportunistic bird which occupies a broad range of winter habitats. It ranges well out to sea and is common around the Channel Is. Huge flocks feed at garbage dumps in District C, resting on nearby reservoirs; the largest numbers are found during stormy weather. California and Ring-billed Gulls are the common gulls of urban centers in winter.

HERRING GULL
Larus argentatus

Uncommon to fairly common winter visitant in District C (primarily along the immediate coast and offshore waters). Rather common winter visitant at the Salton Sea, but casual elsewhere in the interior.

This species is somewhat locally distributed along the coast; the largest numbers are in the San Diego area, at the Santa Clara R. estuary VEN, and at the Santa Maria R. mouth SLO/SBA. It is uncommon in most other coastal areas, although it is fairly common well offshore (particularly in the northern part of the region). This gull is generally uncommon around the Channel Is., although 300-500 adults were counted on 24

Mar 1973 at San Miguel I. Small numbers regularly visit inland valleys and lakes in District C, such as L. Cachuma SBA, San Fernando Valley LA, and the San Bernardino/Riverside area (where it is fairly common). Some northward movement is evident in spring along the coast in March and April; stragglers occur into May. Extreme dates along the coast are from 23 Sep 1979 San Diego SD to early June, except for three summer records: 22 Jun 1980 Tijuana River Valley SD, and 31 Jul 1980 and 25 Aug 1979 Santa Maria R. mouth. Although it is possibly overlooked in summer, the Herring Gull is certainly very rare at this season.

The Herring Gull is rather common at the Salton Sea, where it is the second most numerous gull in winter (after Ring-billed); high counts generally far exceed those on the coast. Birds may linger here well into May, and there are eight recent records for mid-summer (when it is possibly regular).

In the interior away from the Salton Sea it is a casual winter visitant in District R (considered "uncommon" along the lower Colorado R. by Phillips et al 1964). Elsewhere it has been recorded only at L. Cuyamaca SD 25 Apr 1978 and at L. Palmdale LA 20 Oct 1979. It seems odd that this species is so common at the Salton Sea, yet is virtually unrecorded elsewhere in the true interior of the region. It occurs regularly in the San Joaquin Valley just north of our region.

Along the coast Herring Gulls occupy harbors and estuaries, especially where there are nearby garbage dumps. They are more frequent far off-shore than most of our gulls.

THAYER'S GULL
Larus thayeri

Uncommon winter visitant along the coast and in adjacent offshore waters; extends rarely into the inland portions of District C. Very rare, but probably regular, winter visitant to the Salton Sea; otherwise recorded inland only once (District R).

Along the coast single birds or small groups are found with winter concentrations of the larger gulls, especially at estuaries and dumps. The largest numbers formerly occurred at the now-defunct Otay Pig Farm near Chula Vista SD (up to 50 in a winter); the Santa Maria area SBA currently has the largest concentrations. It is a rare winter visitant to the Channel Is. and it is a rare but regular winter visitant to the interior portions of District C (exceptionally up to 20+ at Hansen Dam, San Fernando Valley LA 28 Nov 1975). This gull has been recorded annually in small numbers in the San Bernardino/Riverside area. In fall Thayer's Gulls first arrive in late October; the latest spring date for the coast is 6 May 1978 off Newport ORA.

At the Salton Sea there are about 15 records. It is undoubtedly regular, and was probably overlooked prior to the first record in 1969; it may prove to be more numerous here than the Glaucous-winged Gull. At present records are from 14 Dec 1964 to 5 May 1978 NESS (exceptionally to 20 May 1977 SESS, the latest record for the region). Most occur from mid-December through February.

There is one record for District R: 26 Nov 1978 Imperial Dam IMP. It has also been recorded on the Arizona side of L. Havasu 13 Dec 1946; there are additional records for Davis Dam on the Arizona/Nevada border.

Thayer's Gulls are most frequently noted at the same areas where Herring Gulls concentrate; there are some pelagic tendencies among winter birds in the region. At the Salton Sea they are noted both on the shoreline of the sea and in flooded fields nearby. Immatures predominate throughout the region. There is frequent confusion with Glaucous-winged Gulls and with Glaucous-winged X Western Gull hybrids; records from the interior should be carefully documented.

WESTERN GULL
Larus occidentalis

Common resident along the immediate coast, breeding locally. Abundant resident on and around the Channel Is. Wanders only a short distance inland on the coastal slope. One record for District R.

Along the coast this species breeds primarily in San Luis Obispo Co., with a few pairs along the w. Santa Barbara Co. coast at Vandenberg AFB. A few pairs also nest at Pt. Loma SD and just off North I., Coronado SD. It formerly nested at La Jolla SD (two pairs in 1935). It is an abundant breeding resident on the Channel Is. The great majority of Western Gulls occurring in the region are of the dark-mantled, southern race *L.o. wymani*; all of our breeding birds are of this race. The paler-mantled *L.o. occidentalis* is fairly common in winter on the northern coast; it decreases in numbers to the south, but is probably regular in limited numbers south to the Mexican border.

There is one acceptable record of a pink-legged Western Gull in the interior: 12 Dec 1946 Parker Dam SBE (*L.o. occidentalis*, specimen). Two probable records for District S are: 17 Jan-13 Feb 1965 and 29 Mar 1969 Salton Sea.

Coastal Western Gulls occur in all marine habitats and are common well offshore. For breeding they require predator-free islands or rocky islets. Those breeding at North I. off Coronado utilize cement pilings for nest sites. They occasionally wander a short distance inland (routinely in the San Diego area), visiting garbage dumps with concentrations of other gull species. Many reports from inland localities (e.g. reports of large numbers on Christmas Bird Counts) are clearly erroneous, however. Several published reports of pink-footed Western Gulls at the Salton Sea (*AFN*) actually pertain to the Yellow-footed Gull, *L.livens*.

YELLOW-FOOTED GULL
Larus livens

Fairly common visitant to the Salton Sea from the Gulf of California, primarily in summer. Three records for the southern coast.

This gull is fairly common and perhaps increasing as a summer visitant to the Salton Sea. First detected in the region in 1966, it has increased so that recent maxima have reached 200 in a day at Salton City IMP (e.g. 19 Aug 1977). The largest numbers are found at Salton City, and it is rarest at NESS. Small numbers have recently occurred at the Salton Sea in winter (up to 15 on 26 Feb 1978 Salton City). It is found primarily along the immediate shore line of the Salton Sea, although birds occasionally range into flooded fields in adjacent agricultural areas.

There are three records for coastal San Diego Co.: 23 Jun 1966 Otay; 7 Dec 1978 Imperial Beach; and 19 Jan 1979 Otay.

The exact relationships of the Yellow-footed Gull are problematical, but most taxonomists now agree that it is specifically distinct from the Western Gull, *L.occidentalis*.

GLAUCOUS-WINGED GULL
Larus glaucescens

Fairly common winter visitant along the coast, bordering on common in San Luis Obispo Co. Rare winter visitant to inland valleys in District C and to the Salton Sea, where most occur in late winter and spring. Two records for District R. A few birds regularly summer along the coast.

The largest numbers are present from mid-November through mid-March. While most occur along the outer coast, a few birds regularly occur a short distance inland (e.g. San Fernando Valley LA) and, casually, as far inland as the San Bernardino/Riverside area. It is an uncommon winter visitant around the Channel Islands.

This gull is a rare but regular visitant to the Salton Sea; there are over 30 records, mostly from late winter and spring. The two records prior to December are 31 Oct 1971 SESS and 23 Nov 1969 Salton City IMP. In spring a few birds have lingered into June, the latest being an adult at SESS 17 Jun 1972. There are two records for District R: 24 Feb 1954 L. Havasu SBE and 17 Nov 1956 north of Imperial Dam IMP. The great majority of interior records are of first-winter birds.

Hybrid Glaucous-winged X Western Gulls are frequently noted along the coast in winter, especially in the northern part of the region. These species hybridize extensively in the Pacific Northwest. Suspected Glaucous-winged X Herring hybrids have been noted, including an adult at SESS 20 Dec 1977.

Glaucous-winged Gulls frequent outer coastal areas and concentrate at harbors and garbage dumps. They occasionally enter major coastal plains and even inland valleys in District C, especially around dumps where large numbers of other "coastal" gulls (e.g. California) concentrate during the day. They range offshore, and are regularly noted on pelagic trips.

GLAUCOUS GULL
Larus hyperboreus

Very rare winter visitant along the coast, mainly from late December through March. Five records for the Salton Sea.

There are over forty published records for the coast, covering all coastal counties; this gull has been recorded almost annually in the last 15 years, with 1-4 birds per winter. Extreme dates for the region are 24 Nov 1915 Hyperion LA to 20 May 1973 Pt. Loma SD. The only other valid May record is for Newport Bay ORA 18 Apr-9 May 1976. There are two records for the Channel Is.: 24 Mar 1973 San Miguel I. and 15 Mar 1979 San Miguel I. (2). It has been recorded once well at sea (31° 31' N, 123° 19' W on 13 Feb 1967); there are a number of offshore records from northern California.

The five records for the interior are all from the Salton Sea: 15 Feb-22 Mar 1969 SESS (specimen); 22 Mar-2 Apr 1969 SESS; 9 Dec 1972 SESS (ad.); 7 Feb 1976 SESS; and 26 Feb-15 Apr 1978 Salton City IMP (second-winter bird).

An adult Glaucous X Herring hybrid was collected at San Diego SD 24 Mar 1969 (present since early March). Immatures that were possibly of this hybrid combination have been noted in the region.

Other gulls, particularly worn Glaucous-winged and albinistic Western and Herring, are frequently misidentified as Glaucous Gulls; we have dismissed numerous unseasonal reports which lack adequate documentation. A number of second-winter Glaucous Gulls reported actually are worn first-winter birds. The only records of birds definitely older than the first year are the two Salton Sea records noted above.

Glaucous Gulls in the region generally occur with flocks of other large species of gull. Most have been noted at dumps (especially) and coastal estuaries.

GREAT BLACK-BACKED GULL
Larus marinus

One record: a third-year bird photographed at Upper Newport Bay ORA 11 Aug 1977.

This record has not yet been reviewed by the California Bird Records Committee. This species has been recorded casually inland in North America as far west as Montana and Colorado, but the present record (the photographs of the bird appear to be conclusive) constitutes the only sighting for the Pacific coast.

BLACK-LEGGED KITTIWAKE
Rissa tridactyla

Irregularly common winter visitant to offshore waters; occurs in numbers onshore during very irregular flight winters, sometimes lingering into summer during these years. Recorded six times at the Salton Sea and once along the Colorado R.

Numbers peak offshore from late November through March and are generally greatest in the northern part of the region. During flight years numbers appear onshore in late winter and spring (the bar graph reflects these inshore flights which peak from late January through April). After invasions birds often linger into summer (exceptionally to 300, Jun-Jul 1976 Redondo Beach LA), and small numbers are occasionally even present into the following fall.

The Black-legged Kittiwake is casual at the Salton Sea; the six records are: 22 Jul 1967 NESS; 24 Nov 1967 SESS; 15 Jun-3 Aug 1968 NESS; 11 May-1 Aug 1969 NESS (5 imms. on 11 May, one thereafter); 16 Sep 1973 NESS; and 27 Dec 1974 NESS.

There is one record for District R: 11-19 Nov 1978 Parker Dam SBE.

Although the Black-legged Kittiwake is essentially a pelagic bird away from its breeding grounds, it is often found in the region in harbors and with flocks of other gulls at coastal estuaries and beaches; in flight years it sometimes wanders a few km inland.

SABINE'S GULL
Xema sabini

Fairly common spring transient and uncommon fall transient offshore; a few non-breeding birds remain regularly through summer. Casual transient through the interior, with most records from Districts S and R.

Spring transients peak offshore in the latter half of May. A few non-breeding birds remain through the summer, with fall transients returning in August. Fall numbers fluctuate; it is fairly common in some years and almost unrecorded in other years. Fall birds are probably most numerous off the northern part of the region, where coverage is scanty. It remains casually into early November and, exceptionally, to 2 Dec 1978 off Santa Clara R. estuary VEN.

This species is casual in the interior. Most birds probably represent either late spring and early summer stragglers out of the Gulf of California or fall transients (all fall records are of immatures). Of the ten records for District S (majority at NESS), six are for September and four are for late spring and summer: 23 Jun 1968 SESS; 24 Jun 1966 NESS; 27 Jun 1968 near El Centro (ad. on freeway); and 15 Jul 1977 NESS. There are six records for L. Havasu SBE between 8 Sep 1948 and 17 Oct 1957 (3). The remaining interior records are: 22-23 Jun 1974 Imperial Dam IMP; 20-21 Sep 1976 Oasis MNO; 27 Sep 1971 China Lake SBE; 18 Oct 1969 Badwater,

Death Valley INY; 3 Oct 1979 Tinnemaha Res.; and, (in the interior of District C; not graphed) 26 Aug 1971 L. Elsinore RIV and 10 Oct 1920 near El Cajon SD. There are two additional spring records from the Arizona side of the Colorado R.

This is the most pelagic of our gulls. It is rarely noted from coastal promontories during migration (especially in spring). While unrecorded in winter in the region, there are three winter records off northern California.

GULL-BILLED TERN
Sterna nilotica

Fairly common summer resident at the Salton Sea, with six late fall and early winter records. Unrecorded in California away from the Salton Sea.

The largest breeding colonies are currently at the southeast corner of the Salton Sea and to the south of Salton City IMP. It arrives at the Salton Sea in late March; the earliest record is 14 Mar 1978 (2 at Salton City). It is rare after early September, but a few occasionally linger through October. The only records after October are: 21 Nov 1979 NESS; 27 Nov 1977 NESS; 1 Dec 1979 NESS; 28 Dec 1978 SESS (4); 31 Dec 1971 SESS; and 20 Jan 1979 NESS (2). There are no records through the rest of the winter.

There are no valid records elsewhere in the region, although there have been several reports. It was recorded 24 May 1959 n. of Imperial Dam IMP (2), presumably in Arizona.

The Gull-billed Tern was first discovered in California in May 1927, when a colony of some 500 nesting pairs was located at SESS; this colony had probably been present for at least several years. Numbers have since declined as the rising sea has flooded nesting islands; the small colonies around the southern shores of the sea should be carefully monitored. This isolated breeding population is the only landlocked one in North America. Colonies are on low islets where there is safety from mammal predation. Foraging birds are found over shallows, mudflats, and agricultural fields bordering the sea.

CASPIAN TERN
Sterna caspia

Fairly common to common transient and summer visitant along the coast, breeding at San Diego Bay SD. Fairly common but local in winter. Very common to abundant transient and common summer visitant at the Salton Sea; formerly bred there. Rare to uncommon transient through the remainder of the region.

Along the coast the largest numbers occur during spring and fall. The only nesting colony is at the south end of San Diego Bay. This species is fairly common in San Diego and Orange Cos. in winter, but is generally rare farther north (small numbers do winter at Pt. Mugu VEN).

189

The Caspian Tern is a very common spring transient, common summer visitant, and abundant fall transient at the Salton Sea; summer numbers (always less than those of spring and fall) may vary somewhat from year to year. Small numbers nested at the Salton Sea until about 1950. It is rare but regular there in winter, approaching uncommon status at NESS (maximum of 14 on 17 Dec 1977).

This tern is an uncommon but local transient through the rest of the interior, including montane lakes. Up to 30 have been noted in a day at L. Henshaw SD. It is quite rare in the northern portion of District D; seven at Tinnemaha Res. INY 1 Jun 1980 was a large number for that area. This species has nested in recent years at Bridgeport and Mono L. MNO, north of the region. In the Antelope Valley LA/KRN it is uncommon to fairly common in spring and fall, with a maximum count of 24 on 27 May 1980. The Caspian Tern is a rare spring transient and uncommon fall transient along the Colorado R.; it has been recorded once there in winter: two at Laguna Dam IMP 19 Jan 1979 (with one present to 27 Feb 1979 at nearby Imperial Dam IMP).

Caspian Terns occupy inshore coastal waters, estuaries, and, particularly in migration, freshwater lakes. They are not found over the open ocean and have not been reliably recorded on the Channel Is. Wintering birds in the San Diego area are usually on freshwater ponds just inland, although elsewhere on the coast wintering birds inhabit coastal estuaries.

ROYAL TERN
Sterna maxima

Fairly common but somewhat local winter visitant along the coast and over offshore waters. More numerous around the Channel Is. and the San Diego area, where numbers of non-breeding birds remain through summer. Has attempted to nest twice in San Diego.

The bar graph reflects status from Santa Barbara Co. south to Orange Co. It is uncommon north of Santa Barbara Co., although it can be fairly common at Morro Bay SLO. That there are very few recent records along the coast north of the region indicates a sharp decline in the northern part of its range in the past two or three decades. This is the predominant tern species around the Channel Is., where, exceptionally, 200 birds have been found in a day. It is only rarely found in summer away from the Channel Is. and San Diego Bay SD. At this season the more numerous Elegant Tern is frequently mistaken for this species.

The Royal Tern has attempted to breed twice in the region at San Diego Bay SD: summer 1959 and summer 1980 (one pair each year).

Royal Terns occur in inshore coastal waters and around the Channel Is.; resting birds may be found on estuaries. The breeding records are from the tern colony at the diked salt works at the south end of San Diego Bay.

ELEGANT TERN
Sterna elegans

Common post-breeding visitant along the coast, primarily from July through October; lingers very exceptionally to late December and January. One nesting colony at San Diego Bay SD where birds arrive in March.

Along most of our coast Elegant Terns arrive from Mexican breeding colonies at the end of June and become common by (variably) early to late July. They arrive much earlier (to 3 Mar 1968) in southern San Diego Co. where a colony of some 200 pairs nests at the south end of San Diego Bay. Flocks are regularly found at coastal San Diego Co. lagoons in spring; graph reflects status north of San Diego Co. Most birds leave by the end of October, although small numbers linger through November and occasionally into December. The latest records are: 30 Dec 1978 Santa Barbara SBA; 31 Dec 1977 Santa Barbara (2); and 13 Jan 1979 Santa Clara R. estuary VEN. There are no records of birds successfully overwintering in the region, although one remained to the north of the region at Princeton Harbor, San Mateo Co., California 17 Dec 1976-25 Jan 1977.

The colony at San Diego Bay is the only one in the United States; it was established in 1959. Birds from this colony forage north to La Jolla SD. Away from the San Diego area there are only a few spring records; most of these are for April, but in the spring of 1980 small numbers were recorded in Los Angeles, Ventura, and Santa Barbara Cos. (remaining until June at Santa Clara R. estuary). All of the spring records

from Los Angeles Co. north have been since 1977; most are of adults, and may portend continued northward expansion. Few records of Elegant Terns existed for the region prior to about 1950; irregular flights of post-breeding birds took place in the 1950s, and such flights are now a regular, large-scale phenomenon.

This species inhabits inshore coastal waters, bays, harbors, and estuaries. It is unrecorded inland and is virtually never seen more than a few km offshore. On the Channel Is. it has been recorded casually, and only at Pyramid Cove at the southern tip of San Clemente I.

SANDWICH TERN
Sterna sandvicensis

One record: an adult was present in the tern colony at the south end of San Diego Bay SD 11-15 May 1980; it unsuccessfully attempted to court Elegant Terns. (Not graphed.)

This represents the only record for California. This species winters regularly off southwestern Mexico, and it is possible that the San Diego bird was caught up in the northward spring movement of Elegant Terns.

COMMON TERN
Sterna hirundo

Common spring and fall transient along the coast, remaining casually through winter in the San Diego area. Common in fall at the Salton Sea and locally along the Colorado R. Rare fall transient elsewhere in the region.

Along the coast spring migrants arrive in mid-April and occur through May; numbers remain locally through summer (up to 100 in summer 1968 on San Diego Bay SD, and 175 there 4 Jul 1962). Fall transients arrive in late July and large concentrations occur in late August and September. This species is still numerous into October and individuals (usually first-year birds) linger well into winter, especially in the San Diego area. Exceptionally, up to 10-15 birds have wintered on San Diego Bay (winter 1974-1975). It is casual after early December north of San Diego Co.

At the Salton Sea it is a rare spring transient and non-breeding summer visitant. It has been recorded as early as 18 Apr 1973; exceptionally early for a concentration was 50 at NESS on 13 May 1967. A few birds regularly appear by the end of May and numbers increase in June and July (apparently non-breeding birds drifting north) until fall transients arrive in an influx at the end of July. Numbers build to a peak from late August through late September. The fall maximum of 715 was on 16 Sep 1976 at NESS. A late fall concentration of 30+ was at NESS 13 Nov 1979 and the latest fall record is 6 Dec 1978 NESS.

The Common Tern is much less numerous along the Colorado R. than it is in District S, but it is still probably a fairly common fall transient on the larger bodies of water, particularly at L. Havasu SBE, where up to 100 were present 14 Sep 1977.

It is a rare fall transient in Districts D and M (somewhat more numerous in the Antelope Valley LA) and in the interior of District C; records are scattered from late July through September.

Common Terns feed in inshore coastal waters and congregate at coastal estuaries. Fall migrants often utilize the same areas as Elegant Terns and occur only infrequently more than about 4 km offshore. They have been recorded only once within 1 km of the Channel Is.: 13 Sep 1975 San Clemente I. This tern is outnumbered over the open ocean by the Arctic Tern (greatly so in fall). In the interior it is numerous only over the large bodies of water noted above, although scattered transients may occur at almost any body of water. This species is often erroneously reported in winter, and we have dismissed numerous unsupported records from that season (especially from Christmas Bird Counts).

ARCTIC TERN
Sterna paradisaea

Common fall transient and uncommon late spring transient well offshore; immatures remain rarely through summer off the coast. Casual in the interior.

Fall migrants arrive by the end of July and peak from late August to mid-September; individuals have lingered well into October. A notable late record was 19-28 Oct 1978 Santa Maria R. mouth SBA/SLO (also one of the few onshore records). The largest reported fall concentration was 400 off Morro Bay SLO 7 Sep 1969. The spring passage of alternate-plumaged adults appears to take place from mid-May to early June, with very small numbers involved; a maximum of 10 was off San Diego SD 19 May 1973. Most spring sightings are from the outer waters of the region. A specimen from Laguna Beach ORA 1 May 1915 (specimen has not been located) would be the earliest spring record for the region. This late passage is in opposition to published reports of large concentrations close to the northern California coast in late April and early May (which we suspect to be in error).

This species is casual in the interior. It has been recorded four times at the Salton Sea: 13 Jun 1976 SESS (3); 4 Jun 1978 SESS; 10 Jun 1979 SESS; and 10 Jun 1979 Salton City IMP (5). In District D it has been recorded at Tinnemaha Res. INY 13 Jun 1975 and near Pearblossom LA 1-3 Jun 1980 (2 at L. Los Angeles). There is also a specimen from just north of the region at Bridgeport MNO 22 May 1973. All interior records are of adults.

Arctic Terns are generally restricted to open ocean waters in the region; they are only rarely observed from shore, and we suspect that many sightings from shore are erroneous and pertain to Common Terns (adults of which also show extensive gray underparts). Pelagic transients are often found perched on floating kelp.

FORSTER'S TERN
Sterna forsteri

Common year-round visitant along the coast, with a breeding colony south of San Diego SD. Rather common summer resident at the Salton Sea (mostly non-breeding), remaining uncommonly through winter. Transient through the remainder of the region, commonest along the Colorado R.

Along the coast the largest numbers in winter occur in the southern counties. It is common along the coast in migration and large numbers of non-breeders remain through the summer. The only breeding colony on the coast is at the south end of San Diego Bay, where up to 500 pairs have nested since about 1962.

This tern is a very common summer resident at the Salton Sea, although most do not breed. A breeding colony has been present at SESS irregularly since 1970 and 200 pairs nested at NESS in 1978. It is uncommon, bordering on fairly common, in winter.

Along the Colorado R. the Forster's Tern is a fairly common spring transient and a rather common fall transient, especially at the larger reservoirs. A few non-breeders remain rarely through the summer. In Districts D and M and in the interior of District C, it is an uncommon transient (more numerous in fall than spring).

Forster's Terns occupy inshore coastal waters and coastal estuaries and harbors; they are very rare over the open ocean (only about six records from the Channel Is.). Nesting colonies are on small, low islands and dikes, or matted reedbeds.

LEAST TERN
Sterna albifrons

Fairly common but local summer resident along the coast, primarily from late April through August. Casual spring and summer visitant to the Salton Sea; four records for District R.

Least Terns arrive about 10 April in the San Diego region (earliest 8 Apr 1978) and somewhat later farther north. Numbers diminish after the first of September; this tern has not been reliably reported after September. The latest records are 20 Sep 1977 Pt. Mugu VEN (2 ad., 4 imm.) and 25 Sep 1921 Carpinteria SBA (adults feeding young, at a time when this species was much more common in the region). In spring transients are rarely noted away from breeding areas along the coast; the Least Tern is more widespread as a post-breeding wanderer in late summer. This species is rarely noted over the open ocean; it is unrecorded from the Channel Is. Breeding is restricted to a few protected beaches, estuaries, and adjacent flat areas from the Santa Maria R. mouth SBA/SLO south to the San Diego area. In 1980, 835 pairs were estimated to be breeding in southern California.

In the interior it has been recorded about 16 times at the Salton Sea, primarily from mid-May to mid-August; extreme dates are 15 Apr 1978 SESS and 29 Apr 1962 SESS to 13 Sep 1976 SESS. It has been recorded four times in District R: 18 Jun 1953 L. Havasu SBE; 30 Jul 1959 Imperial Dam IMP; 1 Jul 1973 Imperial Dam; and 19-20 Jun 1980 s. of Palo Verde IMP. Another interesting inland record is of a bird at L. Cachuma SBA 1 May 1976 (several km inland, over a 1000m ridge). The great majority of interior records are of adults; records at the Salton Sea involve up to three birds together.

The subspecies occurring in the region, *S. a. browni*, is considered endangered in California. Open sandy or gravelly shores (occasionally artificial surfaces) with suitable nearby fishing waters are required for breeding; becuase these sites have suffered from considerable human disturbance this species has declined greatly in the region in the past several decades. Foraging occurs around bays, estuaries, tidal channels, and harbors. In late summer family groups regularly occur over fresh-water ponds and lakes a short distance inland from the coast.

BLACK TERN
Chlidonias niger

Abundant transient and common summer visitant at the Salton Sea. Primarily an uncommon transient elsewhere in the region, and casual in winter along the coast.

Extreme dates at the Salton Sea are 10 Apr 1963 and 14 Apr 1968 (25) to 11 Nov 1967 (3) and, exceptionally, 1 Dec 1979 SESS. Although numbers may be found through summer, there is no evidence that nesting takes place. It is a fairly common fall and uncommon spring transient along the Colorado R.; a few non-breeding birds remain through the summer (mostly at L. Havasu SBE). This tern is an uncommon spring and fall transient elsewhere in the interior, but it can be locally fairly common, e.g. in the Antelope Valley LA/KRN. It is generally a rare transient through the inland portions of District C.

Along the coast the Black Tern is a rare spring transient and uncommon fall transient. Very large concentrations of transients just offshore were cited by Willett (1933), but recent maxima have not exceeded about 25 birds. Coastal migrants have been found at estuaries and over the open ocean. It is casual in winter along the coast. Most of the 10+ winter records come from San Diego Co.; some of these records involve birds known to have spent the entire winter.

Black Terns occupy marshes, estuaries, and adjacent open water. At the Salton Sea they commonly hawk for insects over flooded agricultural fields. This species breeds just north of our region in the San Joaquin Valley.

195

RYNCHOPIDAE: SKIMMERS

BLACK SKIMMER
Rynchops niger

Fairly common summer resident at the Salton Sea; small (but increasing) numbers have recently been resident at the south end of San Diego Bay SD. Sporadic visitant elsewhere along the coast, with one record for District R and one (possibly two) for the interior of District C.

Arrival and departure dates at the Salton Sea vary; birds have arrived as early as mid-April and the species is usually present by the end of April. Nesting does not begin until June or later and it has exceptionally continued into October. Nesting dates are undoubtedly a function of the level of the sea; this factor determines the availability of nest sites. It has remained late into the fall, e.g. 14 present at SESS 20 Nov 1976 and two still present 20 Dec 1976. Skimmers were first recorded at the Salton Sea on 3 Jul 1968 (5 at NESS); occasional birds were noted until 1972 when full-scale colonization and the state's first nesting occurred. Numbers have increased steadily: 500 birds and 100 nests were found in 1977. However, the rising level of the Salton Sea may threaten this species' continued existence there. Colonies have been at SESS, NESS (erratic), and along the west shore south of Salton City IMP.

Along the coast a small group has nested within the tern colony at the south end of San Diego Bay SD since 1976; up to 75 birds were present by the fall of 1979. Unlike the population at the Salton Sea, the birds on San Diego Bay are present all year. Elsewhere on the coast it is a casual visitant, primarily in mid-to-late summer. The records are: 8 Sep 1962 Santa Ana R. mouth ORA (first California record); 6 Sep 1971 Newport Bay ORA; 24 Apr 1972 Playa del Rey LA; 30 Jun 1976 Santa Barbara SBA (2); 16 Jul 1977 Carpinteria SBA; 1 Aug 1980 Santa Ynez R. mouth SBA; 15 Jul 1977 Santa Maria R. mouth SBA/SLO (2); and about fifteen records in spring, summer, and early fall in coastal Ventura Co. (Pt. Mugu, Santa Clara R. estuary).

In District R it was recorded at L. Havasu SBE 1-3 Sep 1977. There is an additional record for the Arizona side of the river: 12 Jun 1977 above Yuma.

There is one record from the interior of District C: 27 Aug 1978 near Lakeview RIV (juv.); a juvenile at nearby L. Elsinore RIV 4 Sep 1978 was possibly the same individual. These sightings suggest occasional dispersal of birds from the Salton Sea to the coast.

Black Skimmers nest on gravel bars, low islets, and (in San Diego) dikes. Foraging takes place over calm, shallow water; at the Salton Sea most feeding is done around the mouths of the rivers and channels which enter the sea. The phenomenal increase of this species in the region, and its establishment as a breeder several hundred km. from its nearest breeding colonies in Sonora, Mexico, is difficult to explain.

ALCIDAE: AUKS, MURRES, AND PUFFINS

COMMON MURRE
Uria aalge

Status complex. Generally an irregular offshore winter visitant; often present in considerable numbers, but in some winters very few occur south of Pt. Conception SBA. Routinely summers off the northernmost coast, but rare farther south at this season. Formerly bred near San Miguel I.

In winter this species is common to abundant north of Pt. Conception SBA and concentrations are present throughout the year. Exceptionally large numbers were present in this part of the region in summer 1980, but little data exists for other years. Concentrations in 1980 include 21,000 off Pt. Sal SBA 1 Aug, with 480 elsewhere off Vandenberg AFB in late July. The bar graph reflects status in southern Santa Barbara Co., Ventura Co., and Los Angeles Co. In these areas Common Murres occur primarily from late November into spring, being uncommon some years and fairly common to common others. Numbers of birds may linger into late spring, and small numbers occasionally summer. Exceptional late concentrations include 20 between Ventura VEN and Anacapa I. 26 May 1974 and 30 off San Pedro LA 8 Jun 1978; in addition, during the anomalous summer of 1980, 1020 were at Pt. Mugu VEN 19 Jul 1980 (with 561 counted there on 28 Jun) and 60+ were in the Santa Catalina Channel 4 May 1980. This species is scarcer south of Los Angeles Co. and only a few birds are normally present in winter; there are very few summer records. A high count of 140+ was made off Pt. Loma SD 21 Dec 1958; 40 were off Torrey Pines State Park SD 29 Apr 1973. Again, the highest summer counts came from 1980: 30 off San Diego SD 20 Apr and 25 off San Onofre SD 18 May.

This species formerly bred in the region; a colony of some 11 pairs was present on Prince Islet off San Miguel I. from at least 1906 to 1912. A pair of birds in alternate plumage on the cliffs at that locality 14 Jul 1976 suggests the possibility of future recolonization.

Common Murres occupy both inshore waters and the open ocean well offshore. During large winter flights they frequently occur close to shore and, occasionally, inside bays and harbors; these last are often sick or oiled birds.

PIGEON GUILLEMOT
Cepphus columba

Fairly common to locally common summer resident around the northern Channel Is. (south to Santa Barbara I.) and on the coasts of San Luis Obispo and Santa Barbara Cos. south to Pt. Conception. A few wander south to vic. Pt. Mugu VEN; casual south of there.

Along the mainland coast the Pigeon Guillemot is especially numerous in the vicinity of Morro Bay SLO, Shell Beach SLO, and Pt. Arguello SBA. It is quite rare farther south, although it has been recorded somewhat regularly in the Santa Barbara Channel southeast to Pt. Mugu. From this area there are spring and summer records of adults, and, especially, post-breeding records of juveniles and adults. The only records south of Ventura Co. are: summer 1977 Pt. Dume LA (2 ad.); Jul 1980 Las Tunas Beach nr. Malibu LA; 11-20 Aug 1980 Redondo Beach LA; 1 Sep 1976 nr. San Clemente I. (2); and Dec 1897 off Santa Catalina I. There is an additional record just south of the region at Los Coronados Is. 6 Jun 1969. A few other records from the southern part of the region published in *AFN* lack supporting details.

The winter status of this species is poorly known; it is probably regular at this season at Morro Bay, but most or all depart the Channel Is. Where the majority of the birds go remains a mystery.

In late winter, spring, and summer Pigeon Guillemots are found on inshore waters and in bays and (at Morro Bay) harbors. For nesting they require cliffs with caves or ledges. They are occasionally found on the open ocean (and perhaps winter well at sea).

MARBLED MURRELET
Brachyramphus marmoratus

Generally a casual visitant to inshore waters, but with occasional invasions. Very few acceptable recent records outside of winter 1979-1980.

Prior to the winter of 1979-1980, it had been recorded as follows: "winter 1885-1886" Santa Barbara SBA ("several specimens"); 30 Jul 1910 Santa Barbara (found dead); 12 Apr 1922 Santa Barbara (found dead); 11 Dec 1955 between Santa Monica and Malibu LA (3, with one off Santa Monica 26 Dec); 2 Jan 1959 Will Rogers State Beach nr. Santa Monica (7); 25 Aug 1966 Cambria SLO; 20 Dec 1967 Morro Bay SLO; 21-24 Aug 1974 Santa Barbara; and 21 Jan 1979 one km off Avila Beach SLO (2).

The winter of 1979-1980 represented an exceptional invasion into the region, with records for all coastal counties except Orange Co. In Morro Bay it was recorded as early as 3 Nov 1979, and the maximum count was 79 on 26 Dec 1979. Farther south it was recorded at the Santa Maria R. mouth SBA/SLO 24 Jan 1980 (2); Goleta SBA 18 Dec 1979; Santa Barbara 17 and 29 Dec 1979 (with 2 on the latter date); Pt. Hueneme VEN 17 Dec 1979 and 6 Jan 1980; Malibu 16 Dec 1979 (3, with one seen on 20 Dec and one on 1 Jan 1980); San Pedro LA 11 Dec 1979; San Diego SD 29 Nov and 3 Dec 1979; and Imperial Beach SD 15-16 Dec 1979 (3). This invasion was coincident with the largest recent invasion of Ancient Murrelets into the region. After the winter 1979-1980 invasion there were several summer records off the coast (the normal status off the northern coast is unknown; better coverage may show the species to be regularly present). They were recorded at Pt. Sal SBA 15 Jul-1 Aug 1980 (1 Pair) and 25 Aug 1980 (9; four were present until 18 Sep, and three were a few km south, off Vandenberg AFB 15 Oct — graphed as one record); nine were at Cayucos SLO 9 Aug 1980.

A few additional records published in *AFN* have been dismissed here; any report of this species in the region should have excellent substantiating details. Marbled Murrelets in the region have been found almost exclusively in inshore waters. This species breeds along forested coasts from central California north.

XANTUS' MURRELET
Endomychura hypoleuca

The northern race, *E.h. scrippsi*, is a fairly common to common breeder on the Channel Is. and is present in the region primarily from March through July. The southern race, nominate *hypoleuca*, is a rare and irregular late summer and fall visitant to souther offshore waters.

E.h. scrippsi is commonest as a breeder on Santa Barbara I. It is rare on Santa Catalina I. and San Clemente I. and absent from San Nicolas I. and Santa Rosa I. It is fairly common to common in waters surrounding the breeding islands. This murrelet arrives on its breeding grounds in March and begins its dispersal by early July. Post-breeding dispersal appears to be northward out of our region; the species occasionally occurs close to the mainland after the breeding season. Late summer and fall records for the region are few; it may be regular off the San Luis Obispo Co. coast at this season (but coverage is poor; it is recorded regularly at this season to the north, at Monterey Bay). It is probably regular in very small numbers in winter, but records are few (again, perhaps due to poor coverage at season).

The "Guadalupe Island" Xantus' Murrelet, *E.h. hypoleuca*, is a rare and irregular late summer and fall visitant to southern offshore waters. Additionally, an adult was found incubating in the *scrippsi* colony on Santa Barbara I. in the summer of 1977 (subspecific identity of mate not ascertained). Outside of a 1976 "invasion," the only records are: 11 and 13 Aug 1928 Santa Catalina Channel LA (specimen each day); 4 Dec 1966 off San Diego SD (two specimens, with three other birds seen believed to be of this race); and 4 Sep 1971 nr. San Clemente I. In 1976 some 17 birds were found off San Diego 11-18 Sep, and single birds were noted off Anacapa I. 18 Aug and 12 Sep.

Xantus' Murrelets are frequently seen inshore around the Channel Is. during the breeding season. For nesting they utilize small caves, burrows, piles of debris, and plant cover. Pairs and famiy groups are frequently seen on the open ocean. It is only rarely seen from shore on the mainland.

Our normal breeding race is *scrippsi; hypoleuca* nests on Guadalupe I. and the San Benitos Is. off Baja California. In the latter area, *hypoleuca*, *scrippsi*, and the Craveri's Murrelet, *E. craveri* appear to coexist with little, if any, interbreeding involving *craveri* and only limited inter-breeding between *scrippsi* and *hypoleuca*.

CRAVERI'S MURRELET
Endomychura craveri

Uncommon to fairly common late summer and early fall visitant off-shore; it appears most regularly and in the largest numbers off San Diego Co.

It has been recorded annually in recent years off San Diego Co.; concentrations include up to 30 on 9 Sep 1972, 45 on 11-18 Sep 1976, and 30 on 10-18 Sep 1977. The earliest record is 11 Jul 1972 (2 off San Diego); the latest record is 13 Oct 1971 (off San Diego), but the lack of coverage after September suggests that this species could be regular into October. It is probably somewhat regular north to the Santa Barbara Channel, but there are few records. The only record from San Luis Obispo Co. is of four off Morro Bay 7 Sep 1969, but coverage is poor in northern waters and the species is irregularly present in Monterey Bay to the north.

Two at Santa Barbara I. 16 and 19 Apr 1977, if correct, would be an unprecedented spring record and would suggest occasional summer residence in colonies of Xantus' Murrelets on the Channel Is.

Until 4 Sep 1966 this species had been unrecorded in the region for 35 years; this hiatus was undoubtedly caused by the understandable ignorance of observers who confused it with Xantus'. It is now clear that *Endomychura* in late summer are most likely Craveri's. While generally seen well at sea, the species has been seen from shore: 28 Aug 1978 Playa del Rey LA and 19 Aug-12 Sep 1980 Corral Beach, Malibu LA.

ANCIENT MURRELET
Synthliboramphus antiquus

Irregular and generally rare late fall and winter visitant just offshore; more regular and numerous off San Luis Obispo Co., where probably occasionally fairly common. A few summer records.

This species generally occurs between early November and late March; the earliest record is 28 Oct 1974 Imperial Beach SD (found dead; not graphed). The only records after early April are: 25 Apr 1904 Pacific Beach SD (found dead; not graphed); 1 Jun 1980 Santa Barbara SBA; 3 Jun 1976 off Oxnard VEN; 23 Jun 1980 nr. Cayucos SLO (2); 17-18 Jul 1980 Pt. Arguello SBA (2); 3 Aug 1980 Pt. Mugu VEN; 26 Aug 1928 off Pt. Loma SD; and 8 Sep 1979 off San Diego SD (possibly a very early fall bird, considering the subsequent invasion). Note that four of these records follow the major invasion of winter 1979-1980.

Major recent invasions have occurred during the winters of 1955-1956, 1965-1966, and 1979-1980. During the first two invasions, concentrations included 33 between Santa Monica and Malibu LA 10 Dec 1955 and 50 off Pt. Dume LA 9 Mar 1966. During the winter of 1979-1980 it was recorded in all coastal counties; records included: 58 vic. Morro Bay SLO 29 Dec 1979 and 40+ there 6 Jan 1980; 17 at the Santa Maria R. mouth SBA/SLO 1-2 Dec 1979; 10+ in the Goleta/Santa Barbara SBA area in Dec 1979 and early Jan 1980; 15+ in Los Angeles Co. in Dec 1979 and early Jan 1980; one at Newport ORA 4 Jan 1980; and 11+ in the San Diego area 10-23 Dec 1979. Two at Pt. Mugu 23 Feb 1980 were the latest of the invasion (excluding the records from the following summer), the largest numbers were present in December. This invasion corresponds to the largest invasion of Marbled Murrelets on record.

In general it is quite rare south of Los Angeles Co.; the 1979-1980 invasion excluded, there are only five records from that area since 1942 (all for San Diego Co., three involving dead birds on shore).

There is an undated specimen from District D at Palm Springs RIV; this species is a casual vagrant to the interior of North America.

In general this species appears to have experienced some decline in the region in recent years; there is also evidence of this decline in northern California. When Ancient Murrelets are found, they may be on inshore or offshore waters and are often seen from shore.

CASSIN'S AUKLET
Ptychoramphus aleuticus

Locally abundant breeder on the Channel Is. Uncommon to fairly com-

mon winter visitant offshore (common from the northern border of the region south to the northern Channel Is.).

This auklet is an abundant breeder on San Miguel I.; small numbers also breed on Santa Barbara I., Santa Cruz I., and, possibly, Anacapa I. It also breeds just to the south of the region on Los Coronados Is. In summer (April through September) this species is quite uncommon well away from the breeding areas; it disperses away from the breeding grounds in late summer. By fall, numbers are augmented by wintering birds arriving from outside of the region. The complex status of this species is difficult to show on a single bar graph; the graph summarizes and approximates its status in the region as a whole.

Cassin's Auklets are normally found well offshore, although they may occasionally be seen from shore (especially during strong blows). Breeding birds may travel some distance away from nesting colonies to feed.

PARAKEET AUKLET
Cyclorrhynchus psittacula

Two records: three "more or less decomposed" birds were picked up on the beach n. of La Jolla SD 28 Jan 1937; and one was found dead on the beach at San Simeon SLO 6 Feb 1955.

While we include this species on the main list, we acknowledge the possibility that these birds had died outside of the region and had been carried by currents for several days before they eventually washed ashore. There are several records, mostly old, for the coast of northern California.

RHINOCEROS AUKLET
Cerorhinca monocerata

Common to abundant winter visitant offshore from the northern border of the region south to the northern Channel Is.; fairly common from there south to the Mexican border. A few non-breeders regularly remain through the summer; may breed off Santa Barbara Co.

Maxima in the northern part of the region (e.g. off Morro Bay) frequently exceed 1000 birds per day; farther south, a maximum of 350+ off San Diego 22 Jan 1972 was exceptional — usually no more than about 25 are encountered in a day in the southern part of the region. The graph reflects the status off the south coast.

Up to 25 were present at Pt. Arguello SBA 17-18 Jul 1980, with several seen entering burrows; confirmation of nesting here should be sought. This species is not known to nest south of the Farallon Is. off San Francisco.

Rhinoceros Auklets generally occur well offshore, but they are frequently seen from shore (especially during strong winds) from Santa Barbara Co. north.

202

TUFTED PUFFIN
Lunda cirrhata

Very rare visitant well offshore, with the majority of records in late spring; formerly bred around the Channel Is. and probably on the San Luis Obispo Co. coast.

Recently it has been recorded primarily from late April to early June. In 1975 an invasion of this species coincided with the largest regional invasion of the Horned Puffin. Fifty-one were noted from the northern border of the region south to San Nicolas I. 7-30 May 1975. Otherwise, it has been recorded recently 14 times as follows: 24 Jan 1965 Santa Cruz I.; 27 Apr 1968 off San Diego SD; 1 Jun 1971 off San Clemente I.; 11 Sep 1971 off Santa Barbara SBA; 11 Sep 1972 Ocean Beach SD (dead on beach; not graphed); 14 Jan 1976 off Santa Cruz I. (7); 6 Apr 1976 off San Miguel I.; 5 Jun 1977 off Santa Barbara I.; 26 Feb 1978 near Anacapa I.; 15 May 1978 near Santa Cruz I.; 28 Jul 1978 Prince Islet, off San Miguel I. (see below); 20 May 1979 between Santa Rosa I. and San Nicolas I. (2); 6 Jan 1980 off Morro Bay SLO; and 1 Jun 1980 near Santa Rosa I.

Formerly it was a fairly common breeder on Anacapa I., Santa Cruz I., and San Miguel I. (including Prince Islet), and possibly Santa Rosa, Santa Barbara, and San Nicolas Is. It was recorded by Willett (1933) as nesting on islets off Pt. Harford SLO; an egg set was taken 5 Jun 1896 off "San Luis" SLO. It appears to have vanished as a breeder in the region in the 1930s and 1940s. A recent sighting of an alternate-plumaged adult at Prince Islet 28 Jul 1978 suggests the possibility of future recolonization.

HORNED PUFFIN
Fratercula corniculata

Irregular late spring visitant well offshore, recorded primarily from mid-May to early June. Few or none recorded most years.

There are only three records prior to 1971: 25 Feb 1933 La Jolla SD (dead on beach; not graphed); 21 Jan 1966 Huntington Beach ORA (caught alive); and 9 May 1955 Morro Bay SLO (dead on beach; not graphed). Since then it has been recorded between mid-May and early June in 1971 (once), 1973 (two records totaling three birds), and 1974 (once, plus a long-dead bird on the beach at La Jolla 28 Aug 1974). In 1975 a large invasion occurred and over 200 individuals were found along the length of the coast between 7 May and 8 Jun; two late birds were off Pt. Piedras Blancas SLO 13 Jul 1975. A smaller invasion in 1976 brought some 64 birds to the region (21 May-8 Jun), mostly off San Miguel, Santa Rosa, and Santa Barbara Is. Two were south of Santa Rosa I. 20 May 1979. One seen 26 Feb 1978 nr. San Nicolas I. and one 8 Mar 1980 vic. Davidson Seamount off SLO represent the only late winter records since 1966.

Invasions of Horned Puffins in the region involve healthy, flying birds; some are adults in full alternate plumage. That there is a sharp decline in numbers in early June suggests a spring passage of transients. It is probable that this species wanders south irregularly in winter very far offshore and swings closer to the coast while northbound in the spring. The recent increase in records in the region may largely reflect increased coverage of offshore waters by birdwatchers in the late spring.

GAVIIDAE: LOONS

RED-THROATED LOON
Gavia stellata

Common winter visitant and transient along the coast remaining rarely in summer. Very rare in winter in the interior of District C; strictly casual in the true interior.

It is a common winter visitant along the length of the coast. This loon is decidedly a species of inshore waters and is the loon most likely to be seen right in the surf. It is the scarcest loon far offshore and around the Channel Is. A common spring transient, its numbers peak in late March and early April, which is earlier than the peak of the Arctic Loon. The fall migration is less pronounced.

Very small numbers summer along the coast, especially in the north; this is the scarcest of our regular loons in summer.

This species is a very rare but regular winter visitant to inland bodies of water in District C; records extend from early January to mid-March.

It is casual in the true interior: 12 Nov 1978 L. Henshaw SD; 25-29 Apr 1978 L. Cuyamaca SD; and 8-15 Jun 1948 L. Havasu SBE. Other records exist for the interior of northern California and from along the Colorado R. outside of the region (L. Mead NV and Bill Williams R. delta AZ). We have discounted other reports from the interior because of insufficient details.

ARCTIC LOON
Gavia arctica

Common to abundant transient and fairly common winter visitant along the coast, including offshore waters. Rare along the coast in summer, and a casual transient and winter visitant in the interior.

This species is generally fairly common along the coast in mid-winter, although it may be common along the north coast and in offshore waters. In spring, Arctic Loons are common to abundant transients along the coast and well offshore from mid-April through late May. Small numbers still pass through well into June; straggling migrants may be seen flying up the coast into early July and should not be mistaken for summering birds. In fall it is quite common well at sea and less numerous inshore. On the coast it remains regularly through the summer, with most birds on the north coast where the species can be locally uncommon or even fairly common.

There are eight inland records for the coastal lowlands: 3-8 Dec 1979, 10 Apr 1980, and 6 Jun-23 Jul 1980 (2) L. Cachuma SBA; 8 Jan 1974 L. Sherwood VEN (found in a flooded field after a severe storm); 27 Apr 1973 Franklin Canyon Res. LA; 31 May 1980 Harbor L. LA; 3 Nov 1973 Whittier LA (found dead); and 17 Apr 1980 Whalen L. SD.

Arctic Loons are casual transients in the true interior, although they may prove to be regular in late fall and early winter along the Colorado R. (three records plus several more from the Arizona side). Two later records for District R are: 17 Feb-17 Apr 1954 L. Havasu SBE and 27 Feb 1979 Senator Wash Res. IMP. There are seven records from the Salton Sea: two of late spring transients (4 Jul 1968 and 2 on 22 Jun 1974), four late fall and winter sightings (27 Nov 1977; 2 at Ramer L. SESS 22 Dec 1975-25 Jan 1976; 19 Feb 1955; and 6-20 Mar 1965), and one bird probably summering (25 Aug 1977). The only records from District D are: 27 May 1980 Little L. INY; 29 Oct-4 Dec 1978 L. Palmdale LA (2); 10 Nov 1979 Lancaster LA; and 27 Oct 1975 Desert Center RIV.

The subspecies *G. a. pacifica* occurs in our area. Some authorities consider this race (the "Pacific Loon") to be specifically distinct from the *arctica/viridigularis* subspecies group (the "Arctic Loon").

COMMON LOON
Gavia immer

Common transient and winter visitant along the length of the coast, remaining rarely through the summer. Uncommon spring and fall migrant inland on deep water lakes, remaining regularly in winter only along the Colorado R. A few summer records from the interior.

Along the coast it is a common winter visitant that favors harbors, protected bays, and inshore ocean waters. A common spring migrant just offshore, it is outnumbered in early spring by Red-throated Loons and in late spring by Arctic Loons. The fall migration is less noticeable because the main passage occurs farther offshore and more evenly over a longer period. It remains rarely in summer along the coast; occasional concentrations are noted, such as nine at Pt. Mugu VEN summer 1979. As with the other loons, summering birds are generally in basic plumage. Most summering birds are on the north coast.

Inland, including the interior portion of District C, the Common Loon is an uncommon spring and fall transient, preferring deep water lakes and reservoirs. Spring dates are generally from early April through mid-May; stragglers occur into early June. Fall dates are from mid-October through November, with birds sometimes lingering into January. Concentrations of transients include: 75 at L. Palmdale LA 11 Nov 1978; 24 at L. Havasu SBE 10 Apr 1954; 19 at Tinnemaha Res. INY 10 Apr 1975; and, in District M, nine on L. Cuyamaca SD 29 Apr 1978. The species winters regularly in District R (e.g. L. Havasu); a few winter elsewhere in the interior, and concentrations have been noted: L. Cachuma SBA winter 1978-79 (up to 12); and L. Palmdale LA Dec 1978-27 Jan 1979 (up to 10). There are some 15 summer records (mid-June through September) from the interior (including District M), some of which involve birds known to have spent the entire summer. The summer maximum away from the coast was eight on L. Cachuma, Jun-Jul 1980.

YELLOW-BILLED LOON
Gavia adamsii

One satisfactory record: 20 Apr 1977 Pt. Dume LA — an alternate plumaged bird flying up the coast with other migrating loons.

A basic-plumaged bird at Pt. Mugu VEN 5-9 May 1976 appears to be correct, but the record has not yet been accepted by the CBRC. There is one record from just south of the region: Los Coronados Is., Baja California 24 Nov 1968. It is recorded almost annually in northern California, principally in the Monterey area, and it is likely to occur in this region again. Extreme caution should be used in separating it from the Common Loon.

COLUMBIDAE: PIGEONS AND DOVES
BAND-TAILED PIGEON
Columba fasciata   Map p. 391

Common resident in oak and oak-conifer woodlands of District M (exclusive of the desert ranges), extending locally into District C. Casual visitant to Districts D, S, and R.

Within District M there is some seasonal movement and, in winter, some consolidation into flocks. In winter there is also some downslope movement out of the mountains; at this season the species becomes more common in oak woodlands in the foothills. Large flocks may even winter below the foothills, for instance in the San Bernardino/Riverside area.

This species is a common resident in District C from inland San Luis Obispo Co. south locally to coastal foothills and ranges of Santa Barbara Co. and then eastward along the coastal foothills of the San Gabriel and San Bernardino Mtns. and locally elsewhere, e.g. the Santa Monica Mtns. (local), vic. Pomona, and San Gabriel Valley LA. It is quite rare away from woodland habitat in District C; records are concentrated from late April to early July and again in September and October, with a few records through the summer season. The lack of winter records away from woodlands in the lower portions of District C is difficult to explain, but it suggests that the species is closely tied to oaks at this season. Its status on the Channel Is. is complex; flocks have wintered in oak woodlands on the larger islands, and the species is a sporadic non-breeding summer visitant on the smaller islands (April to October).

The Band-tailed Pigeon is a casual late spring and fall visitant in the desert regions; records are widely scattered, but are concentrated in the northern deserts. The latest records from the deserts are: 25 Oct 1971 Corn Spring RIV and 3 Nov 1973 Kelso SBE. There is one record from District R: 25 May 1979 Blythe RIV (there are several additional records for the Arizona side of the river). The three records for District S are: 4 Oct 1941 nr. Calexico IMP; 9 May 1974 SESS; and 12-13 Aug 1974 SESS. In the northern desert ranges there are five recent records for Clark Mtn. SBE (18 May-28 Aug); a record for the New York Mtns. SBE 30 Jul 1976, and an unseasonal record of a large concentration in the Panamint Mtns. INY 4 Nov 1962-7 Apr 1963 (up to 81 present on the former date). The recent records for the desert ranges of San Bernardino Co. probably reflect increased coverage and suggest that this species may be regular in summer in this marginal woodland habitat.

Band-tailed Pigeons are closely tied to oaks, whether in pure woodland or mixed with various conifers. They have adapted locally to heavily planted suburban areas, as long as some oaks are present.

WHITE-WINGED DOVE
Zenaida asiatica   Map p. 392

Common summer resident in the Colorado River Valley, with smaller numbers summering in District S and the southern part of District D. Rare visitant to the northern deserts and to District C. A few winter on the coast and very locally in the southern deserts.

In District R the first birds arrive in late March, and numbers decline after late August. Its arrival in Districts D and S is in mid-April (as early as 27 Mar 1980 s. of Palm Springs RIV). It is fairly common in summer in the Borrego Valley SD and the desert canyons of e. San Diego Co.; it is uncommon elsewhere in District D, but it does nest north to the vicinity of Joshua Tree National Monument. This dove is an uncommon summer resident in District S; it becomes more numerous there around the end of summer.

In District D it is rare from the Mohave Desert north; the majority of records are in late spring, with a few in fall. It is somewhat regular in the Death Valley area, but there are only a few records farther north (to Oasis MNO). It is casual in the Owens Valley. In District C (including the Channel Is.) this species is primarily a rare fall transient. There are a few spring records through early June, and three later records: 26 Jun 1975 Claremont LA; 17 Jul 1980 New Cuyama SBA; and 30 Jul 1978 e. of San Diego SD (early fall vagrant). Regularity and numbers generally decrease to the north along the coast; there are only about three San Luis Obispo Co. records and the species is casual north of our region.

The White-winged Dove is very rare in winter; it is more or less annual at this season along the coast. A number of winter records also exist for the Yaqui Well/Agua Caliente SD area on the eastern base of the Laguna

207

Mtns.; this species is probably regular there at this season. It is otherwise unrecorded in winter in District D. There are three winter records for Districts S and R: 22 Feb 1963 SESS (2); 5 Jan-19 Feb 1951 Parker Dam SBE; and 26 Jan 1978 near Palo Verde IMP.

White-winged Doves inhabit wooded groves in the desert, whether they are natural riparian areas or artificial habitats (citrus orchards, eucalyptus, etc.).

MOURNING DOVE
Zenaida macroura

Common to abundant resident through most of the region, occupying a wide range of habitats from arid deserts to open forests.

There is considerable withdrawal from the northern desert regions and the mountains in fall and winter. There is a tendency for aggregation into large flocks in the wintering areas and around water sources on the deserts in spring and summer. This species breeds commonly on the larger Channel Is.; it is a fairly common transient on the remaining islands and transient individuals or small flocks are sometimes also noted over the open ocean.

INCA DOVE
Columbina inca

Very local resident along the Colorado R., primarily from Parker Dam SBE south to Blythe RIV. Casual vagrant elsewhere in the region.

In District R it has been found strictly in association with human dwellings (e.g. trailer parks); numbers are locally fairly large, e.g. in the vicinity of Earp SBE. This species has been recorded north to Needles SBE (where it is possibly resident in very small numbers) and south to the vicinity of Bard IMP (three records; resident across the river in Yuma, Arizona).

It is casual elsewhere in the region: "mid-February" 1928 Palm Springs RIV (two; questioned by Grinnell and Miller only because it was a sight record); 29 Oct-28 Nov 1976 Furnace Creek Ranch INY; and "late September" 1974 near Tecopa INY. There is an additional record for coastal San Diego Co.: 9 Sep-30 Nov 1974 Tijuana River Valley (possibly an escapee). There are also three published reports from the Corona and Whittier areas east of Los Angeles which, while possibly correct, may pertain to Common Ground-Doves.

COMMON GROUND-DOVE
Columbina passerina   Map p. 392

Fairly common resident in the Imperial and Coachella Valleys and along the Colorado R. Local and generally uncommon resident in the southern part of Districts D and C. Vagrant north of breeding range, both along the coast and on the northern deserts.

This species is by far most numerous in Districts S and R, although it is uncommon in the northern part of District R. It is a local and uncommon resident in the southern portion of District D, primarily in the Borrego Valley SD, but also irregularly in the Morongo Valley SBE area (the graph for District D does not include these populations).

It is an uncommon to fairly common (but very local) resident in the southern portions of District C north to ne. Orange Co. and extreme w. Riverside Co. Recent localities include: Tijuana River Valley SD, San Luis Rey River Valley SD, Pauma Valley SD, Valley Center SD, Garden Grove ORA, Yorba Linda ORA, "near Whittier" ORA (on the Los Angeles Co. line), Corona RIV, Sunnymead RIV, and vic. Lakeview RIV. Because of the clearing of brushlands in river valleys this species has declined considerably in District C.

The Common Ground-Dove is a vagrant north of its breeding range. There are about ten records for Death Valley and vicinity (INY), most of which fall between early October and mid-November; the others are 14 Apr 1974 and 9 Jul 1961 Furnace Creek Ranch. It has also been recorded twice in October at Kelso SBE, and once there in spring (7 May 1978). Along the coast it has been recorded casually from Los Angeles Co. north as follows: 28 Oct 1979 San Pedro LA; 23 Nov 1979 W. Los Angeles LA; 2 Oct 1978 Altadena LA; 16-26 Dec 1978 Bouquet Canyon LA; 13 Sep 1974 Santa Clara R. estuary VEN; 20-21 Aug 1947 nr. Santa Paula VEN (two present on the latter date); and 2 Oct 1977 Goleta SBA.

In Districts S and R this dove is partial to orchards, ranchyards, brushy fields, and riparian clearings and edges. Along the coast it is limited to similar growth in river valleys.

CUCULIDAE: CUCKOOS
YELLOW-BILLED CUCKOO
Coccyzus americanus

Presently an uncommon summer resident along the Colorado R., generally arriving in the first week of June. A very few pairs summer in riparian woodlands elsewhere in the region. Very rare transient away from breeding habitat.

A 1977 survey revealed 50 pairs between Needles SBE and Laguna Dam IMP in District R. It has been recorded as late as 26 Sep 1975 Laguna Dam. Elsewhere in the region it summers only in the Owens Valley (a few pairs in the vic. of Lone Pine and Big Pine INY), possibly along the Amargosa R. in the vic. of Tecopa INY (pairs present 1977, 1979, 1980), and along the Santa Ana R. near Riverside RIV (one pair seen 20 Jul 1977). Several pairs also breed just north of the region along the South Fork of the Kern R. near Weldon KRN. A record of three to four birds present near Vista SD 11-12 Aug 1978 suggests that nesting may take place in the adjacent San Luis Rey River Valley.

Transients are recorded very rarely but regularly in the northern portion of District D; these occur primarily at the end of May and in early June, but scattered records exist into early summer (e.g. 5 Jul 1972 and 1 Jul 1976 Kelso SBE). Some of these records (Ft. Piute and Morongo Valley SBE) are from localities where suitable nesting habitat exists. Fall transients have been recorded at Furnace Creek Ranch INY 3 Sep 1972 and 24 Sep 1977. There are two recent records for District S: 5 Jul 1974 Finney L. SESS and 10 Jul 1977 near Niland IMP. In the last twenty years there are only nine coastal records away from suspected breeding areas: 30 Jun 1963 Montecito SBA; 22 Jun 1967 Santa Barbara SBA; 24 May 1970 Sespe VEN; 5 Jul 1970 Rialto SBE; 14 Jun 1971 Santa Barbara; 5 Oct 1976 Santa Catalina I.; 23 Jun-4 Jul 1979 Santa Clara River Valley, extreme e. VEN; 4 Jul 1979 Quatal Canyon VEN (in pinyon woodland); and 8 Aug 1980 Los Osos SLO. An additional record near Oceanside SD 23 Aug 1969 was near the San Luis Rey River Valley where breeding is suspected.

The Yellow-billed Cuckoo was formerly much more common and widespread, particularly in District C, where it nested widely in the lowlands (e.g. vic. San Luis Obispo SLO, nr. Hueneme VEN, much of the lowlands of coastal Los Angeles Co., San Bernardino Valley SBE, vic. Temecula RIV, and vic. Anaheim and Santa Ana ORA). Most egg sets were taken in the region prior to 1940. It persisted along the San Gabriel R. near El Monte LA until at least 1952. Birds breeding along the coast arrived much earlier than the present interior populations (probably as early as late April, as newly hatched young were taken in Los Angeles Co. 10 May 1901). It was also possibly more common and widespread on the deserts in former years (e.g. summer records for Death Valley INY, vic. Yermo SBE).

In California the Yellow-billed Cuckoo requires dense riparian groves, particularly with a dense understory of willow or mesquite. Suitable habitat has been largely eliminated from the coastal lowlands and severely decimated along the Colorado R. and elsewhere in the interior. This type of habitat is clearly in urgent and immediate need of preservation in the region. The California Yellow-billed Cuckoo (*C.a. occidentalis*) is officially designated as rare by the California Department of Fish and Game.

GREATER ROADRUNNER
Geococcyx californianus

Uncommon to rather common resident through most of the region, although primarily absent from District M and now somewhat local in District C. Greatest numbers occur in Districts S and R and in the southern portions of District D.

In the interior it is generally uncommon on the Mohave Desert, where the range extends north to the head of the Owens Valley (scarce), the

Deep Springs Valley, and the Death Valley region (fairly common). Coastal populations have diminished with urbanization and the clearing of brushlands, but the species is still found in all coastal counties. It is absent from the Channel Is.

Roadrunners are characteristic birds of open desert and brushland habitats. They reach peak abundance where weedy fields and brushy riparian growth border on agricultural areas, but they are certainly found in desert scrub habitats as well. In District C it is found locally in open chaparral, coastal sage scrub, and brushlands of river valleys. It is found in mountains up to the lower border of District M, where it reaches its highest altitudes in the arid woodlands of the desert ranges and the desert slopes of the coastal mountains.

GROOVE-BILLED ANI
Crotophaga sulcirostris

Two records, both in fall in the interior of District C: 4-16 Nov 1974 nr. Lakeview RIV and 13-17 Sep 1978 nr. Anaheim ORA.

There is also a record for southern Nevada; this species is an irregular wanderer to southeastern Arizona.

TYTONIDAE: BARN OWLS
BARN OWL
Tyto alba

Rather common resident at lower elevations through much of the region, including the Channel Is.

It can be locally quite abundant (for an owl) in agricultural regions with scattered ranchyards and groves of trees (e.g. in the Antelope Valley LA/KRN), and in other areas where grasslands intermix with groves, cliffs, or buildings. Few records exist from the e. Mohave Desert north, except in the Owens Valley, where it is fairly common. It occurs locally in unforested sections of the lower portions of District M. This owl is resident on all of the Channel Is. except San Nicolas I., where it is unrecorded. In District C it is widespread in suburban residential areas.

STRIGIDAE: TYPICAL OWLS
FLAMMULATED SCREECH-OWL
Otus flammeolus

Rather rare summer resident in conifer and oak-conifer woodlands in District M, arriving primarily in May. Very few records of transients. One mid-winter and one early spring record suggest occasional wintering in the region.

This owl is quite local as a summer resident and it is apparently absent from large tracts of suitable habitat. The Flammulated Screech-Owl is undoubtedly overlooked to an extent, and it is probably locally of uncommon to fairly common status. Localities of summer occurrence include: Mt. Pinos, San Gabriel Mtns. (Buckhorn Flat, Mt. Waterman, Big Pines), San Bernardino Mtns. (vic. Big Bear), San Jacinto Mtns. (Tahquitz Valley), and Mt. Palomar SD. It also occurs locally in the northern desert ranges: Clark Mtn. SBE, Kingston Mtns. SBE (21 Jun 1977), Argus Mtns. INY (juv. found 11 Aug 1931), and possibly the White and Inyo Mtns. (but no supporting summer records). It arrives primarily in May; there are few acceptable late April reports; the earliest is 28 Apr 1973 Pippet Flat, San Jacinto Mtns. The latest bird recorded in suitable breeding habitat was 5 Oct 1962 Running Springs, San Bernardino Mtns.

There are very few records of transients: the Pippet Flat record mentioned above (below suitable breeding habitat), plus 18 May 1977 Deep Springs INY; 26-27 May 1977 Cottonwood Canyon, e. base of White Mtns. INY; 4 Oct 1977 Westmorland IMP; and 10 Oct 1962 on a boat in San Diego Bay. There is one mid-winter record: a specimen from the San Bernardino Mtns. 18 Jan 1885. A bird was tape-recorded at Tecopa INY during early Mar 1979 (not on graph), and one was calling just outside the region at the Bill Williams R. delta, Arizona 9 Mar-18 Apr 1979. These dates are exceptionally early for spring transients and may pertain to birds having wintered locally.

For breeding, this species utilizes open Jeffrey and Yellow Pine forests with intermixed California Black Oaks, White Firs, etc. (generally from 1750-2500m). The birds on Clark Mtn. use a mixture of pinyons and White Firs, and the Argus Mtn. specimen was taken in pure pinyons.

COMMON SCREECH-OWL
Otus asio   Map p. 392

Generally an uncommon to rather common resident in woodlands through much of the region. Most numerous in mature live-oak woodlands in the northern coastal counties; absent from the central and western Mohave Desert, from developed portions of the coastal lowlands, and from the most heavily forested parts of District M. Limited seasonal movement.

Several subspecies occur in the region, with habitat preferences differing somewhat among them. In the interior it is fairly common in riparian woodlands in the Owens Valley INY, and uncommon and local in Joshua Tree and pinyon-juniper woodlands from the White Mtns. south through the ranges of the e. Mohave Desert. It also occurs south locally through riparian groves and wooded desert washes to the Mexican border, e.g. Morongo Valley SBE, the length of the Colorado R. (where common), and the east side of the Algodones Dunes IMP. This owl nested as recently as 1948 in groves of trees in the Imperial Valley and Coachella Valley, but it now appears to have been largely or completely extirpated there. The only recent records for District S are SESS 6 Sep 1977; and Brawley IMP 17 Dec 1979. It is widespread along the coast in oak and oak-riparian woodlands. In District M it is primarily restricted to the lower portions where oaks are numerous. This species is unrecorded on the Channel Is.

That there is some seasonal movement is indicated by scattered fall and winter records away from nesting habitat, e.g. Deep Springs INY 6 Sep 1970 and the two recent records for District S cited above.

GREAT HORNED OWL
Bubo virginianus

Common resident through much of the region; scarce only in agricultural portions of the Imperial Valley and in the most heavily forested portions of District M. Absent from the Channel Is.

This ubiquitous but very sedentary species occupies a wide variety of habitats, but it requires cliffs or some tall trees with old hawk or raven nests for breeding. It is a common bird in suburban areas.

NORTHERN PYGMY-OWL
Glaucidium gnoma   *Map p. 392*

Uncommon resident in oak, oak-conifer, and riparian-conifer woodlands, with a general decrease in abundance from north to south. No convincing reports outside of suitable breeding habitat.

This species occurs uncommonly on the northern coastal slope in oak-sycamore woodlands of canyons in San Luis Obispo Co. south to the vicinity of Santa Barbara SBA, where it is found in most foothill canyons and on forested mountains in the interior. It is also resident in closed-cone pine forests around Cambria SLO. South and east of the Santa Barbara region its status borders on rare. It occurs on Mt. Pinos, locally elsewhere in the higher portions of Ventura Co., and in the San Gabriel, San Bernardino, and San Jacinto Mtns., both in montane forests and foothill canyons. This owl is decidedly rare in the Santa Ana Mtns. and in the mountains of San Diego Co., where it is generally confined to the higher forests in the Palomar, Laguna, and Cuyamaca Mtns.; there are, however, nesting records for 1895 and 1896 near Escondido in the San Diego Co. lowlands. It has also been recorded as nesting in the Piute Mtns. KRN on the northern border of the region. It has recently been recorded in pinyons in the Inyo Mtns., and there is an old record for the Panamint Mtns. (30 Sep 1917 Jackass Springs). The status of pygmy-owls in these desert ranges is unclear, but they appear to be absent from the mountains of e. San Bernardino Co. It is unrecorded on the Channel Is.

The Northern Pygmy-Owl is largely resident in the region with little, if any, seasonal movement.

ELF OWL
Micrathene whitneyi

Very rare summer resident in the Colorado River Valley; now virtually extirpated from the region. Arrives in late March (earliest date 18 Mar 1972 Corn Spring RIV).

Extensive recent surveys revealed a maximum of 10 pairs in 1978 and four to six pairs in 1979 in riparian habitat n. of Needles SBE (two birds were noted there in 1980); one calling bird was 35 km n. of Blythe RIV in 1978. The habitat n. of Needles was almost totally eliminated by 1979. This extensive clearing of mesquite-cottonwood-willow associations for agriculture along the Colorado R. seriously and immediately imperils the continued existence of this species in California.

West of the Colorado R. one or two pairs bred at Cottonwood Springs, Joshua Tree National Monument RIV from 1946 until 1970, when they were finally eliminated by the removal of cottonwood trees by the National Park Service. It was present at Corn Springs, Chuckwalla Mtns. RIV from 1972 to 1976 (possibly eliminated by human disturbance).

The Elf Owl was probably found along the length of the Colorado R. in the early part of this century; published records extended south to vic. Bard IMP (to 1915).

In California Elf Owls inhabit riparian woodlands along desert watercourses or at desert springs; some taller trees (cottonwoods, willows) with a shrub understory seem to be required. Preservation and protection of such desert riparian habitats is vital if this species is to survive within the state.

BURROWING OWL
Athene cunicularia

Resident in open areas of the lowlands over much of the region. Common in the Imperial Valley, and rather common in agricultural areas within District R; elsewhere generally scarce and decreasing.

It is quite scarce on the northern deserts from the e. Mohave Desert north through Inyo Co. This species is greatly reduced in numbers and is now quite local in District C, where it is found primarily in agricultural and grassland areas of interior and coastal valleys, and, to a lesser extent, on bluffs along the immediate coast. It is resident on some of the Channel Is. and an occasional transient on the remaining islands.

While it is largely resident in the region, there is some winter movement of more northerly birds into the southern and coastal parts of the region. From just outside the region comes an odd record of a transient at sea 100 km s. of San Clemente I. 20 Oct 1964.

The Burrowing Owl reaches peak abundance in agricultural areas in the Imperial Valley; the banks of irrigation ditches provide suitable nesting sites. Open desert scrub is widely but sparsely inhabited.

SPOTTED OWL
Strix occidentalis

Map p. 392

Uncommon and local resident in oak and, especially, oak-conifer woodlands in District M, foothill canyons, and the coastal ranges.

It breeds locally from sw San Luis Obispo Co., south and east through the foothills and mountains of Santa Barbara Co. and Ventura Co. (Mt. Pinos area, Upper Agua Blanca Ck., Santa Paula Canyon, etc.). It also breeds in the San Gabriel, San Bernardino, and San Jacinto Mtns. south to the Santa Ana Mtns. ORA, Mt. Palomar SD, and the Cuyamaca and Laguna Mtns. SD.

This owl is normally generally quite sedentary, but it has been recorded away from nesting habitat as follows: 30 Nov 1960-early Jan 1961 Barnsdall Park in Los Angeles LA; 31 Dec 1977 to mid-Jan 1978 Hope Ranch, Santa Barbara SBA (a few km from breeding habitat); 19 Nov 1973 San Diego SD; and Nov 1973 "Cottonwood Canyon" RIV. It was found nesting "near Oceanside" SD 24 Mar 1894; this is well away from current breeding localities.

The preferred habitat of the Spotted Owl consists of steep-walled canyons that are densely wooded with mixtures of oaks and conifers (even pure live oaks in the northern coastal counties). It ranges well up into mixed coniferous forest in the southern mountains, but it always requires some dense stands of oaks.

LONG-EARED OWL
Asio otus

Uncommon resident, with some seasonal movement (discussed below); occurs primarily in riparian groves and plantings of larger trees in District D. Now quite rare coastally, and virtually eliminated there as a breeder.

This species occurs virtually throughout District D, but it is quite local there. It is probably most numerous in the northern portion (Owens Valley, Fish Lake Valley); it also nests in the Antelope Valley LA, the Mohave R. drainage, around Morongo Valley SBE, near Yaqui Well SD, and on the east side of the Algodones Dunes IMP. It undoubtedly also nests in numerous other wooded washes and oases through District D. Winter roosts involving up to 20 birds have been found regularly in District D (e.g. Yaqui Well, Afton Canyon SBE, and Antelope Valley); maxima are 75 reported together at Klinefelter SBE 28 Mar 1977 and 40+ at Harper Dry L. SBE during February 1980. These roosts reflect in part a winter influx from outside the region. Scattered fall transients have been noted in District D away from breeding areas.

In general it is absent from District M, although there are old nesting records at 2150m in the San Bernardino Mtns., 2750m in the San Jacinto Mtns., and 3000m in the White Mtns. It does nest in oak canyons in the New York Mtns. SBE.

This owl is casual in Districts S and R; there are four winter records for SESS and several records for District R, including one of three family groups near Needles SBE 17-26 May 1979.

The Long-eared Owl is now a very rare transient and winter visitant along the coast. It is more numerous and regular as a transient and winter visitant on the Channel Is.; most records are for the smaller, more barren islands (e.g. Santa Barbara I.) where birds are more easily located. A few summer records exist for the Channel Is.; it has nested on Santa Catalina I. (1909). The only recently recorded nestings in District C are for 1973 near Oceanside SD, 1973 along San Juan Ck. w. of Santa Margarita SLO, and 1975 in Santa Barbara Canyon SBA. Individuals at Upper Agua Blanca Ck. VEN (mid-Jun 1980) and Barka Slough, Vandenberg AFB SBA (16 Jul 1980) were in suitable nesting habitat. It was formerly a much more numerous resident in District C, where it nested in dense willow thickets. This owl was even termed "abundant" in the 1800s in oaks and willows of the Santa Clara River Valley by Willet (1933). The decline of this species along the coast is largely tied to the destruction of lowland riparian habitat.

The habitat has been outlined above. Plantings of elms, cottonwoods, conifers, and tamarisks around desert ranchyards have locally proven an adequate substitute for natural desert riparian woodland. Dense groves of such trees are occupied for winter roosts.

SHORT-EARED OWL
Asio flammeus

Uncommon and local winter visitant in District C (where it formerly nested), including the Channel Is. Generally a rare fall transient and winter visitant in Districts D, S, and R, although occasional concentrations have been noted; one nesting record for District D.

In District C it winters primarily in coastal estuaries and, to a lesser extent, in agricultural fields and grasslands. Wintering localities include Morro Bay SLO, Goleta SBA, Pt. Mugu VEN, Newport Bay ORA, and the Tijuana R. estuary SD. The Short-eared Owl is somewhat irregular at these localities, and is quite rare away from them. Until recently it wintered at the Sepulveda Basin, Encino LA. It probably winters with some regularity near Lakeview RIV in the interior of District C. There are scattered older summer records for District C; nesting was recorded at Newport ORA 25 Apr 1928 and San Diego Bay SD 10 Apr 1906. The most recent summer record for the coast was 10 Jul 1947 Huntington Beach ORA. Note that the bar graph does not reflect these older summer records.

The Short-eared Owl is an uncommon transient and winter visitant on the Channel Is. They have been recorded from 12 Sep to 29 Apr (earlier and later than the respective extremes on the coast of the mainland). It is most frequently encountered on Santa Barbara I.

This species is rare throughout the interior. It is an irregular winter visitant in small numbers to Districts S and R (but not of annual occurrence). A high count was eight at SESS 30 Jan 1970; an unseasonal record for SESS was 7 Aug 1971. It is probably largely a rare fall transient through District D; recent maxima include: four s. of Kelso SBE 27 Oct 1978 and 20+ at Cronese Dry L. SBE 19 Nov 1978 (an exceptional number for anywhere in the region). Early fall transients in District D were at Saratoga Springs SBE 1 Sep 1968 and Furnace Creek Ranch INY 30 Aug 1969. There is one nesting record for the interior: up to 12 birds at Harper Dry L. SBE Apr-May 1980, with three active nests found (this record not graphed); nesting probably takes place here irregularly, following wet winters.

NORTHERN SAW-WHET OWL
Aegolius acadicus

Uncommon and very local resident in montane coniferous forests, the northernmost coastal ranges, and the Channel Is. Very rare but probably regular transient and winter visitant in the lowlands (primarily in the interior).

This species breeds on Figueroa Mtn. and Big Pine Mtn. SBA, Mt. Pinos VEN/KRN, vic. Big Bear L. in the San Bernardino Mtns., Round Valley and L. Fulmor in the San Jacinto Mtns., and Mt. Palomar SD. Curiously, it is unrecorded in summer in the San Gabriel Mtns., where there appears to be much suitable breeding habitat. It has also bred at 2500 m along Wyman Ck., White Mtns. INY (1954, but possibly overlooked since then). In District C it has recently nested east of Morro Bay SLO at Cerro Alto and may nest locally elsewhere in w. San Luis Obispo Co. It is also resident on Santa Cruz and Santa Catalina Is.

This owl is a rare, but probably regular, transient through District D, and a very rare winter visitant in the southern deserts. Records, from north to south, are: 20 Nov 1971 Mesquite Spring INY; 11 Jun 1974 near Furnace Creek Ranch INY (very odd date); 1 Sep 1974 Kelso SBE (mummified specimen, not on graph); 22 Apr 1974 Joshua Tree National Monument RIV; 23 Jan 1934 Twentynine Palms SBE (dessicated specimen, not graphed); 29 Jan 1974 Cottonwood Springs, Joshua Tree National Monument, 26 Mar 1932 near Corn Spring, Chuckwalla Mtns. RIV (long dead, not on graph); 23 Jan-11 Mar 1971 Mecca Beach, Salton Sea (probably present for at least one month when found, based on pellet accumulation); 18 Oct 1969 SESS; 3 Feb 1950 SESS; and 4 Feb 1978 Regina, e. side of Algodones Dunes IMP. The paucity of records may in part reflect the secretive nature of this nocturnal species outside of the breeding season.

There are also three records from District C that are well away from breeding localities: 28 Jan 1928 near Santa Paula VEN; 10 Jan 1960 Manhattan Beach LA; and 22 Oct 1972 Duarte LA. It was also recorded 14 Apr 1948 at 1000m in Big Tujunga Canyon LA; this locality is in the foothills of the San Gabriel Mtns., where the species is not known to be resident.

Saw-whet Owls breed in the greatest numbers in dense oaks that are intermixed with conifers. In the higher ranges (San Bernardinos, San Jacintos) more open coniferous forest is also occupied. Live oaks are occupied at the site in San Luis Obispo Co. and live oaks and (especially) eucalyptus groves are occupied on the Channel Is. Birds wintering on the southern deserts have been found where there is heavy tree and shrub cover.

CAPRIMULGIDAE: NIGHTJARS
LESSER NIGHTHAWK
Chordeiles acutipennis

Uncommon to locally common summer resident; most numerous on the Colorado Desert and through Districts S and R, with smaller numbers north through the remainder of District D and locally in District C. Scarce fall transient away from breeding areas; casual in winter in the southern lowlands.

As a breeder it reaches peak abundance in Districts S and R (concentrations of over 100 birds are not unusual in late summer in District S). This species is uncommon from the Mohave Desert north through the Owens Valley; it is also scarce west to the Antelope Valley. Its range extends north to the Fish Lake Valley MNO in the extreme northeastern part of the region. The species is locally fairly common on the northern deserts, e.g. Furnace Creek Ranch INY.

The Lesser Nighthawk nests very locally within District C, particularly in situations such as desert-like gravel washes. It occurs north to Chalome SLO, from the San Fernando Valley LA east locally through the San Gabriel and San Bernardino Valleys, and from there south very locally (away from the immediate coast) to southern San Diego Co. Much needs to be learned about the breeding distribution of this species in the coastal lowlands; it has probably declined as a breeder on the coast since the 1930s and 1940s.

In District C (away from breeding areas) it is primarily a fall transient; dispersal begins as early as late July. Occasional concentrations may occur in September and October, such as 29 in the Tijuana River Valley SD 7 Oct 1977 (with smaller numbers present there all fall). It is rare north of San Diego Co. Transients have been noted in spring and summer on the Channel Is.

This nighthawk is casual in winter. There are about eight coastal records prior to March; all are from Los Angeles Co. and Riverside Co. south. There are also several records from the southern deserts (including Districts S and R) in winter; it appears to be regular at least to December in District R. Up to six were found 3-4 Feb 1978 near Regina

IMP. It is possible that it is regularly present in small numbers through the winter on the southern deserts but is largely inactive.

Lesser Nighthawks range widely over arid, open habitats. Open gravelly areas (including dikes and levees) are utilized for nesting.

COMMON NIGHTHAWK
Chordeiles minor

Very local summer resident; uncommon to fairly common (or even common) where found. Arrives very late; the earliest record is 22 May 1980 Baldwin L. SBE (2). Casual transient in District C.

This species is almost restricted to the extreme northeastern part of the region, where it summers in the higher valleys: upper Owens Valley INY (common), Deep Springs Valley INY (scarce), and Fish Lake Valley MNO (rather common). It also summers in the Big Bear L. area of the San Bernardino Mtns., where it is fairly common, and ranges over much of the eastern portion of these mountains. A record of 10+ birds at Big Pines in the San Gabriel Mtns. 28-29 Jul 1978 may represent wanderers from the San Bernardino Mtns. population, a previously unknown breeding population in the San Gabriels, or extremely early fall transients. In the San Jacinto Mtns. it has been recorded once in summer at 2600m, 23 Jun 1893 (specimen).

There are three records in spring from the lower valleys of the northern deserts; it is possibly a regular spring transient there. The records are: 30-31 May 1975 Furnace Creek Ranch INY; 28 May 1977 Mesquite Spring INY; and 29 May 1977 Furnace Creek Ranch.

There are only six acceptable records elsewhere in the region: 16 Oct 1924 n. of Bard IMP (specimen); 27 Oct 1896 Pasadena LA (specimen); 5 Jun 1975 Pt. Loma SD; 25 Sep 1976 Imperial Beach SD; 3 Jun 1979 Pt. Mugu VEN (4); and 3 Aug 1980 Ojai VEN (probably early fall transients). We have dismissed other, undocumented records of transient Common Nighthawks because of likely confusion with the much more widespread Lesser Nighthawk. Especially questionable are spring reports prior to late May.

Common Nighthawks forage over a variety of habitats from open coniferous forest to sagebrush plains, and are frequently seen foraging over or drinking from open bodies of water. Some open, gravelly substrate is required for nesting. The species is virtually unknown outside of its limited breeding areas.

COMMON POORWILL
Phalaenoptilus nuttallii

Fairly common to common breeder in desert scrub, brushlands, and open woodlands throughout much of the region. There is probably considerable withdrawal in winter, but winter status imperfectly known.

Poorwills are absent as breeders from only the Channel Is., the agricultural areas of Districts S and R, and the highest and most heavily-forested portions of District M. They are most numerous in the arid scrub of District D, where they occur from the sagebrush regions of Mono and Inyo Cos. south through the Mohave and Colorado Deserts. In District C they are found in hills and foothills, and are locally rather common in open chaparral.

The status in winter is complex and imperfectly known. There are many winter records for District D (particularly in the southern portion), and numerous records from the length of the coast in District C. The species is undoubtedly present in some numbers in both areas (perhaps even rather common), but the tendency to be inactive and the ability to undergo prolonged torpor in cooler weather makes this species difficult to find in winter. Note that the bar graphs indicate detectibility through the year and show an increase in vocalizing by late March; in an absolute sense this species is probably not rare in winter in District C — it is only rarely detected. In District D there is a clear gradient in the timing of the onset of spring vocalizing; it may begin up to a month later in the extreme northern portions. There is undoubtedly some movement of breeding birds out of the region in winter, particularly by birds leaving the mountains and the northern interior. Transients have been recorded away from known breeding areas in District S, along the immediate coast, and on the Channel Is. (mainly in fall in these areas). Small numbers winter on the larger Channel Is.

WHIP-POOR-WILL
Caprimulgus vociferus

Rare summer resident in arid woodlands of District M (Clark Mtn., and very locally in the San Gabriel, San Bernardino, and San Jacinto Mtns.). Casual transient and winter visitant in the lowlands.

This species has apparently colonized California within the past 20 years. It has been present at L. Fulmor and vicinity in the San Jacinto Mtns. since at least 1968 (reported by local residents for about 10 years prior to then). It has been known from Clark Mtn. SBE since 1974, from the San Bernardino Mtns. since 1975 (found that year at Arrastre Ck.; present near Camp Angelus since 1977), and from Big Pines in the San Gabriel Mtns. since 1977. Two other records also come from possible breeding areas: 8 Jul 1971 near Julian SD and 2 Jun 1976 Ojai VEN (only summer record for District C; in marginally suitable nesting habitat). No definite breeding evidence has yet been obtained in the region; based on vocalizations, summering birds represent *C.v. arizonae*, a race which has been expanding its range north and west in recent years. Summering birds arrive at the end of April or early May.

There are five records of transients and wintering birds: 14 Nov 1970 Pt. Loma SD (netted and banded; thought to be *C.v. vociferus*, which would represent the only record of this eastern race in the region); late Dec 1971-25 Mar 1972 Coronado SD (ssp. unknown); 26 Sep 1973 Long Beach LA (*arizonae*, specimen); 23 Aug 1975 SESS (*arizonae*, specimen); and 10-28 Jan 1976 Riverside RIV (ssp. unknown).

In California Whip-poor-wills have been found summering on steep mountain slopes and canyon sides where there is a mixture of oaks and conifers. On Clark Mtn. a mixture of White Fir and pinyons is inhabited.

APODIDAE: SWIFTS

BLACK SWIFT
Cypseloides niger

Rare and very local summer resident in mountain foothill canyons, with most arriving after early May. Rare and irregular transient (mainly in spring) away from breeding areas, principally west of the deserts; large flocks have been noted.

Known nesting localities include Santa Anita Canyon in the San Gabriel Mtns., Fallsvale in Mill Creek Canyon in the San Bernardino Mtns., and Tahquitz Ck. (and probably the north fork of the San Jacinto R.) in the San Jacinto Mtns. It nests at a few other localities in these ranges. Foraging birds range widely within the mountain ranges where nesting occurs, and they occasionally descend into District C (Arcadia LA. San Jacinto L. RIV) and District D (vic. Big Pine INY, e.g. 10 on 30 Jul 1974, probably representing birds ranging from breeding areas in the nearby Sierra Nevada). Birds at Owens L. INY 2-12 Jun 1891 may also have been foraging birds from the Sierra Nevada (or possibly spring transients).

Away from breeding localities, the Black Swift is generally a rare and irregular transient through Districts C and M, with most records for spring; transients were especially widespread in 1971 and 1980. It has been found primarily from Los Angeles Co. north. One in Goleta SBA 20-23 Apr 1980 and another in Santa Barbara 23 Apr 1980 are the earliest documented records by almost two weeks. Early transients occasionally arrive in the first week of May otherwise, e.g. 3-7 May 1964 Doheny State Beach ORA (1-2) and 4 May 1972 Goleta (50, an exceptional concentration for so early in the season). There are few other valid records before mid-May, and we have rejected numerous unsupported early records (most published in *AFN*). The great majority of flocks have been in late May, and migrants pass through until mid-June. Nesting birds arrive as early as the earliest pure transients. Notable spring concentrations include: 300-400 in the Santa Barbara area 27 May-1 Jun 1971; 300 at Carlsbad SD 29 May 1948 and 40 there 21-24 May 1980 (both especially impressive because there are only about six San Diego Co. records); and 200 at Sierra Madre LA 27 May 1898. Records of late spring transients on the coast include one at Encino LA 10 Jun 1971 (with up to 40 there the preceding ten days), and four there 9 Jun 1976.

Fall migration generally begins in late August; one at Corona del Mar ORA 10 Aug 1941 probably represents an extremely early fall transient. The majority of fall records are in September; a few occur into early October. It is recorded irregularly and much less frequently in fall than in spring. Fall concentrations include: 60 near Santa Maria SBA 24 Sep 1967; "fair numbers" in Santa Barbara 17-19 Sep 1967; and 50 in Hollywood LA 23 Sep 1968 (incorrectly published as 23 Oct in *AFN*). Notably late concentrations are of ten birds in Sespe Canyon VEN 4 Oct 1972 and six at Lebec KRN 5 Oct 1972.

There is one record for the Channel Is.: 25 Jul 1976 Anacapa I.

There are very few records of transients in the interior: 4 May 1969 Finney L. SESS; 22 May 1980 Desert Hot Springs RIV (10); 24 May 1980 near Pearblossom LA; 26 May 1978 near Cartago INY (3); 18 Aug 1977 Gilbert Pass INY (14); 26 Aug 1973 near Big Pine INY (4; this and the preceding record possibly pertain to wanderers from the Sierra Nevada); and 2 Nov 1974 Furnace Creek Ranch INY (by far the latest record for the region, and probably the latest anywhere north of Mexico). It has been recorded in San Gorgonio Pass on the extreme western edge of the desert 19 May 1962 and 15 May 1978.

For nesting, waterfalls in steep canyons are favored. Transients are most frequently noted during overcast weather.

CHIMNEY SWIFT
Chaetura pelagica

Rare but regular summer visitant in District C; most records are from Los Angeles Co., but also recorded in coastal Santa Barbara, Ventura, and San Diego Cos. Arrives in late May. Casual transient in the interior and on the Channel Is.

Some more or less consistent summering areas include the San Gabriel and San Fernando Valleys LA. Most records involve two to six birds; an exceptional concentration of 55 birds was present through the summer of 1978 at Burbank LA and was thought to be a non-breeding aggregation; smaller numbers were present there in the summers of 1979 and 1980. There is a suggestion of a peak in late May and early June, with fewer records through the remainder of the summer. There is one certain nesting in the region: 13 Jun-1 Oct 1976 Ventura VEN (three young found on 2 Aug). Nesting is to be watched for at other coastal localities. It is now clear that *Chaetura* present in summer in the lowlands are likely to be Chimney Swifts rather than Vaux's.

This species is casual in the interior: 6 May 1930 Laguna Dam IMP (specimen; an unusually early date); 30 May 1971 Saratoga Springs SBE; 20 May 1972 Oasis MNO; 23 Jun 1974 Laguna Dam; and 5 Jul 1977 Big Pine INY.

It has also been recorded once on the Channel Is.: 25 May-7 Jun 1975 Santa Barbara I. (probably more than one bird).

Chimney Swifts are often found with flocks of Cliff Swallows; they are especially likely to occur in the summer fog belt on the coastal slope and are most often observed under overcast conditions.

VAUX'S SWIFT
Chaetura vauxi

Fairly common spring and fall transient through most of the region; rare and irregular winter visitant, primarily along the coast. Very few acceptable mid-summer records.

Concentrations of up to several hundred transients are often seen, particularly during overcast conditions. The species tends to be noted only in a few strong waves each season, rather than passing through in consistent numbers. This swift is particularly common at NESS, where thousands have sometimes been noted; it is quite uncommon in the remainder of District S. Spring birds arrive after about 10 Apr (earliest 7 Apr 1980 n. of Pearblossom LA); spring concentrations are normally noted from mid-April through early May, with lesser numbers occurring through the end of May (to 31 May 1971 Encino LA). Other later records published as Vaux's Swifts may, in fact, pertain to the Chimney Swift; these include: 13 Aug 1955 Trabuco Canyon ORA (3); 29 Jun-15 Jul 1959 and "May-June" 1960 San Diego (small numbers both years); "all summer" 1964 Santa Barbara SBA (one pair); 31 Jul-22 Sep 1943 S. Pasadena LA (4); and 30 Jul 1944 Pasadena LA.

This species is, in general, an uncommon transient through District M. There are two recent summer records for the San Bernardino Mtns.: 27 Jul 1976 Green Valley and 22 Jul 1978 Big Bear L. (2-3). Summering and nesting is to be watched for in these mountains.

Fall migration normally begins in force after the first week of September. There is an unusually early record of "hundreds" over the Los Angeles R. LA 28 Aug 1947. In general concentrations in fall involve fewer birds than in spring. It is rare after early October. Few fall transients are noted in the interior away from the Salton Sea, Colorado R., and other large bodies of water. Fall coastal transients are most often noted during overcast weather. It is a rare to uncommon fall transient on the Channel Is. (exceptionally up to "several hundred" 28 Sep 1968 Santa Cruz I. and 100 on 7 Oct 1951 Santa Rosa I.).

The Vaux's Swift is a rare and irregular winter visitant (this species normally winters from w. Mexico south). It is most consistent in the vicinity of Oceanside SD, (where 208 were recorded on 22 Dec 1979 and up to 100 were noted 30 Jan-17 Mar 1968 and 31 Mar 1970). Other winter concentrations include 50 at Pt. Mugu VEN 16 Nov 1961; 35 at Gibraltar Res. SBA 2 Jan 1977; 11 at Huntington Beach ORA 21 Feb 1975; and 6 in

Beverly Hills LA 11 Jan 1974. Scattered singles or small groups have been noted elsewhere in the coastal lowlands in winter, and once in the interior: 12 Feb 1969 SESS (2). Any winter *Chaetura* in the region is almost undoubtedly this species.

Transient Vaux's Swifts may be noted anywhere in the region, but concentrations are most often noted during overcast weather (particularly during storms). This species breeds in mature forests south very locally to the Sequoia region, just north of our area.

WHITE-THROATED SWIFT
Aeronautes saxatalis

Fairly common to common resident throughout, although only a rather scarce transient and winter visitant in the Imperial Valley; it largely withdraws from the higher portions of District M and from the colder deserts (e. Mohave north) in winter.

This species appears more irregularly and in lesser numbers in most areas in winter, although large concentrations may still be found in some coastal and desert areas. Its winter range includes Districts S and R, and locally on the southern deserts. It is resident on most of the Channel Is.

White-throated Swifts forage over a variety of habitats; the tremendous distances over which foraging birds range make exact delineation of their status difficult. For nesting, natural cliffs are generally required, although artificial surfaces such as buildings are often substituted.

TROCHILIDAE: HUMMINGBIRDS

BROAD-BILLED HUMMINGBIRD
Cynanthus latirostris

Casual fall transient and winter visitant from the southeast; twenty records.

There are seven records of fall birds between mid-September and early November; these come from Santa Barbara SBA (2), Big Sycamore Canyon VEN, Cabazon RIV, and the Tijuana River Valley SD (3). Wintering birds (some of which arrived in fall) are from Gaviota SBA, Ventura VEN, Los Angeles Co. (3), Redlands SBE, Riverside RIV, Blythe RIV (2), Agua Caliente SD, and San Diego SD (3).

There is an interesting hiatus in records. The first four records (involving five individuals) occurred between 1962 and 1964; there have then been 16 records since 1976. The only females recorded in the region have been one with a male in the Tijuana River Valley 9 Nov 1963 and a wintering bird at Gaviota 10 Oct 1979-3 Feb 1980. Most records of wintering birds are from feeders.

VIOLET-CROWNED HUMMINGBIRD
Amazilia violiceps

One record: a bird present at a feeder near Santa Paula VEN from 6 Jul through late Dec 1976 and again 29 Jun-5 Jul 1977.

For a discussion of this record and the bird's validity as a genuinely wild vagrant; see Johnson and Ziegler *Western Birds* 9: 91-92, 1978.

BLACK-CHINNED HUMMINGBIRD
Archilochus alexandri   Map p. 392

Common summer resident in riparian woodlands (and other woodland types) in coastal lowlands, foothills, and canyons; and also locally on the deserts. Primarily present from early April (earlier in District R) through mid-September. Only two credible winter records.

Away from District C it breeds uncommonly to fairly commonly in the Owens Valley INY, Kelso SBE, Morongo Valley SBE, Brock Ranch IMP, and perhaps elsewhere on the deserts. It is a rather common summer resident along the Colorado R. Birds arrive in District R significantly earlier than along the coast; they are common by mid-March and have been recorded exceptionally to 20 Feb 1979 near Blythe RIV. This species is an uncommon transient in District S; it generally occurs around extensively planted ranchyards, where it breeds locally. Spring transients generally arrive on the coast in early April; the earliest spring records from the coast are 17 Mar 1976 near San Diego SD and 25 Mar 1978 Pt. Mugu VEN.

The Black-chinned Hummingbird departs breeding areas by mid-August; adult males have generally departed the region by this date. Females and immatures may linger well into September and they may be fairly common as transients along the coast (especially in stands of tree tobacco). Post-breeding birds and/or fall transients may also wander upslope into District M. The latest fall record is 9 Oct 1978 Tijuana R. Valley SD. The only credible winter records are of females or immature males carefully identified by voice and plumage at Balboa Park, San Diego SD 14 Dec 1974 (not present before or after this date) and 15 Dec 1979-2 Feb 1980. A published record for 29 Jan 1970 Palos Verdes LA is possibly correct. The 27 Dec 1903 Palm Springs RIV record cited by Grinnell and Miller (1944) is in error (the specimen is a Costa's). Black-chinned Hummingbirds are reported almost annually on Christmas Bird Counts by observers unfamiliar with this species' winter status. We feel that all such reports (other than those cited above) represent misidentifications. Any acceptable winter record must be carefully documented by vocal characteristics as well as by plumage.

Black-chinned Hummingbirds are most numerous as breeders in canyon and lowland riparian woodland dominated by willows, sycamores, and cottonwoods. They also utilize oak woodlands (especially where riparian growth is near) and suburban plantings of exotic flowering shrubs. Transients are widespread, but concentrate in coastal willow thickets and clumps of tree tobacco. Surprisingly, they are unrecorded from the Channel Is.

COSTA'S HUMMINGBIRD
Calypte costae

Common late winter and early spring breeder on the southern deserts (including District R); later and less numerous on the northern deserts. Fairly common to common breeder in District C, north at least through Santa Barbara Co. Uncommon to locally fairly common in winter in District C; also winters rarely on the southern deserts.

In the southern portions of District D and along the Colorado R., it arrives by late January or early February and is common by the end of February. Nesting takes place in March and April; most birds depart the southern deserts with the onset of high summer temperatures in late spring. It breeds uncommonly to fairly commonly north through the e. Mohave Desert and Owens Valley to the lower slopes of the White Mtns. These birds on the northern deserts arrive in March and breed well into June (a few birds undoubtedly remain well into summer). Extreme dates on the e. Mohave Desert are 6 Mar-28 Jul. It is largely absent from District S, where it is a rare transient and casual (possibly regular) winter visitant; its scarcity there is due to the lack of suitable habitat — it breeds rather commonly in desert washes just outside of the Imperial and Coachella Valleys. Along the Colorado R. this species occurs primarily in desert washes away from the taller riparian woodland. It generally departs the desert regions in winter, although small numbers may winter locally around exotic plantings (e.g. Palm Springs RIV, Borrego Valley SD).

In District C this hummingbird is primarily a fairly common to common summer resident, north at least through Santa Barbara Co.; it is especially numerous in drier, more desert-like washes. By mid-summer this species generally departs coastal sage scrub and chaparral for the immediate coast and the exotic plantings of residential areas. In winter it is uncommon and largely restricted to such plantings of exotic flowering shrubs; it occurs in residential areas and parks on the immediate coast and in coastal valleys and foothills. In some coastal localities it is fairly common in winter; thus, there is no seasonal shift in abundance. It is rather rare north of Los Angeles Co. in winter. Post-breeding birds and fall transients are occasionally noted upslope in District M.

The Costa's Hummingbird is an uncommon transient on the Channel Is.; most records are for May and June, but it has been recorded from 26 Jan to 8 Oct. It has bred once (Santa Barbara I.).

Hybrid Costa's X Anna's Hummingbirds have been noted in the coastal lowlands (especially on the Palos Verdes Peninsula LA).

On the average, Costa's Hummingbirds occupy a more arid habitat than our other regular hummingbirds. Most nest in desert washes and riparian edge, taking advantage of the bloom of such plants as *Chilopsis* (desert-willow), *Beloperone* (chuparosa), and ocotillo. Coastal birds occur in the drier washes dominated by *Yucca* and in chaparral, coastal sage scrub, and riparian edge. Throughout the year, but especially in winter, coastal birds take advantage of exotic shrubs such as bottlebrush. This species breeds from below sea level (Death Valley INY) to about 2000m on some of the desert mountain ranges.

ANNA'S HUMMINGBIRD
Calypte anna

Common to abundant resident throughout the coastal slope, breeding primarily in winter and early spring (late November through March). Breeding range extends well up into District M. Primarily a winter visitant on the deserts, but breeds locally.

This is generally our commonest hummingbird west of the deserts; it is the only common wintering hummingbird in most of the region. It ranges fairly commonly through much of District M west of the deserts, occurring locally up to nearly 2500m. It generally departs the higher portions of its range in winter, though small numbers may remain where feeders are provided in the lower portions of District M.

In Districts R and S and in the southern portions of District D, this species is primarily an uncommon to fairly common winter visitant, especially where extensive exotic plantings (bottle brush, eucalyptus, etc.) occur. It breeds sparingly along the Colorado R. (e.g. Parker Dam SBE, Blythe RIV) and in the Borrego area at the eastern base of the mountains of San Diego Co. It has nested at Brock Ranch IMP and it also nests locally elsewhere on the western deserts (e.g. Morongo Valley SBE — a site with numerous affinities with District C). This hummingbird is fairly common in winter around Joshua Tree National Monument, but it does not winter farther north in District D. It is a very rare transient in the remaining desert lowlands. It is also a scarce visitant from spring through late fall in the mountain ranges of the northern deserts (e.g. New York Mtns., also recorded in the White Mtns.). It may breed in some of these ranges.

The Anna's Hummingbird is resident on Santa Cruz and Santa Catalina Is.; it is an occasional transient on the remaining islands.

Anna's Hummingbirds inhabit a wide variety of habitats from coastal sage scrub and chaparral through open coniferous forests. They are very common in suburban and urban situations.

CALLIOPE HUMMINGBIRD
Stellula calliope

Fairly common but local summer resident in District M. Rare to uncommon spring transient through the lowlands; very few records of fall transients.

This species nests on Reyes Peak and Frazier Mtn. VEN, Mt. Pinos (e.g. around Iris Meadow), the north side of the San Gabriel Mtns. (rare), the San Bernardino Mtns. (primarily the north and east slopes), the San Jacinto Mtns. (rare), and perhaps the Santa Rosa Mtns. (female present 22 Jul 1979). Farther south, a male and female were on Hot Springs Mtn. SD 4 Jun-22 Jul 1980. In the northeastern part of the region it breeds in the White, Panamint, and (one record) Kingston Mtns. There is also a late June record from the New York Mtns., and a displaying male was on Clark Mtn. 21 May 1977.

This species is generally an uncommon spring transient through District C and the southern deserts (including Districts S and R) from late March (exceptionally early March) to early May. The earliest records are: 2 Mar 1976 Riverside RIV, 5 Mar 1976 San Diego SD, and 6 Mar 1937 Azusa LA. The largest passage is 10-20 Apr. Late was one 20-21 May 1980 Pt. Loma SD. It is rather irregular in numbers in District C. There are two spring records for the Channel Is.: 3 May 1974 San Clemente I., and 9 May 1975 Santa Barbara I. (2). It is a rare spring transient in the lowlands of the northern deserts; records extend to 20 May 1972 Scotty's Castle INY (3) and 20 May 1972 Furnace Creek Ranch INY.

The only fall record from the lowlands is 19 Aug Los Angeles LA (specimen, year unknown). The paucity of fall records may be due in part to the difficulty of identifying females and immature males. Most adult males have departed by mid-July.

Calliope Hummingbirds breed along meadow borders and in streamside thickets (especially willows) within arid mixed coniferous forest. Coastal migrants may occur in chaparral and coastal sage scrub, and around exotic flowering shrubs. Transients noted in the southern deserts and along the Colorado R. have been at plantings of exotic shrubs.

BROAD-TAILED HUMMINGBIRD
Selasphorus platycercus

Fairly common summer resident in the higher ranges of the northern deserts. Casual summer visitant and transient elsewhere in District M and casual transient through the northern deserts. Recorded twice along the coast, including the only winter record for the region.

This species breeds in the White, Panamint, and Grapevine Mtns. south to the Kingston and Clark Mtns. There are also spring records (to 30 May) for the New York and Providence Mtns. Farther south it has been recorded three times in spring and summer in District M: 13 May 1972 Arrastre Ck., San Bernardino Mtns.; 10 Jun 1971 Green Valley, San Bernardino Mtns.; and 11-12 Jul 1978 Mt. Palomar SD (adult male, probably an early fall transient). Transients have also been recorded in District D adjacent to the northern mountain ranges: 17 Apr 1977 n. of Cima SBE; 3 May 1977 n. of Goffs SBE; 20 Apr 1973 and 24 May 1975 Scotty's Castle INY; 26 May 1975 Kelso SBE; and 28 May 1972 Big Pine INY. Far from any breeding area was a transient in District R at Earp SBE 12 Apr 1975. The latest fall record from the breeding range is 4 Sep 1971 Tollhouse Spring, White Mtns. (ad. males leave earlier). In fall in District M an immature male was recorded 1 Sep 1967 Pine Cove RIV, which is outside of its known breeding range.

There are two records for District C: 4 Nov 1972-20 Jan 1973 San Pedro LA (imm. male or female; tail feathers kept) and a spring transient 15-23 Apr 1974 San Pedro (ad. male).

The Broad-tailed Hummingbird is at the western extreme of its range in our desert mountains; it inhabits canyons and slopes and favors riparian shrubs (such as *Garrya*) and annuals (such as penstemon) within arid pinyon-juniper and pine-fir woodlands.

RUFOUS HUMMINGBIRD
Selasphorus rufus

In general a common transient and probably a rare but regular winter visitant. Spring passage is primarily coastal; fall transients are most numerous in the mountains.

In District C it is a fairly common to common spring transient; the earliest birds arrive in the first week of February. Spring migration peaks in late March and early April, and late spring transients may occur into the first third of May. The first fall transients begin appearing in late June (e.g. 22 Jun 1970 Pt. Loma SD). It is less numerous in the coastal lowlands in fall than in spring. This species is a rare spring transient on the Channel Is.

In District M the Rufous Hummingbird is primarily a common to abundant fall transient; the first birds arrive in late June. It is most numerous from mid-July through late August. This hummingbird is rather uncommon in the mountains in spring, when most birds are on the lower mountain slopes and in the vicinity of feeders.

In Districts D, S, and R it is an uncommon spring transient and fairly common to common fall transient. Spring transients are most numerous on the southern deserts. In spring it has been recorded on the e. Mohave Desert as late as 16 May 1977. In fall it has been recorded as late as 22 Oct in Joshua Tree National Monument.

In both spring and fall adult males are the first arrivals. The great majority of adult males have departed the region by the end of July. Limited banding evidence indicates that after mid-August *Selasphorus* over most of the region are usually Rufous, and that virtually all transients through the interior are Rufous.

The Rufous Hummingbird is casual in winter, although it is most likely regular locally in District C around stands of flowering eucalyptus. Although most winter birds cannot be separated in the field from Allen's, there are at least six winter records of adult males or netted birds which have proven to be Rufous. Counts of up to a dozen *Selasphorus* have been made in winter in the San Diego area; many or most of these birds are probably Rufous. There is only one winter record of a *Selasphorus* from the interior: 26 Dec 1977 below Parker Dam SBE. Based on locality, we feel that the record probably pertains to Rufous. Note that only records from November through late January are likely to pertain to wintering individuals.

In their spring passage Rufous Hummingbirds are particularly fond of flowering eucalyptus trees and other exotic plantings. They are also numerous around native chaparral plants. In fall, birds along the coast are partial to flowering tree tobacco. The bulk of the fall passage is through the mountains, where large numbers of *Selasphorus* occur in mountain meadows, taking advantage of a late summer bloom of penstemon, columbine, etc. On the deserts, flowering *Zauschneria* and other plants are utilized.

ALLEN'S HUMMINGBIRD
Selasphorus sasin

Common resident on the Channel Is. and the Palos Verdes Peninsula LA.

Also breeds along the immediate coast south to Ventura Co. Common spring transient elsewhere in District C; fairly common fall transient through the mountains. Probably a transient in very small numbers through the deserts.

The subspecies *S. s. sedentarius* is a common resident on all of the Channel Is. except San Nicolas I. and Santa Barbara I. (where an occasional visitant), and on the Palos Verdes Peninsula LA. Nominate *sasin* breeds along the immediate coast from the northern border of the region south through Ventura Co. This species has occurred in the breeding season at Malibu LA (bred in 1978; seven territorial birds were at Malibu Lagoon 25 May 1979); nests were found 22 and 24 May 1980 at Marina del Rey LA; and a nest was found in Newport ORA 19 Apr 1980. While the Malibu birds are likely nominate *sasin*, the subspecific identity of the Marina del Rey and Newport birds is problematical. The nominate race migrates rather commonly through the remainder of the coastal slope, with the first birds arriving extremely early (mid-January). The spring passage is largely over by mid-March, although there are scattered records away from nesting areas through the rest of the month (the latest being an adult male specimen from the Jurupa Mtns. RIV 1 Apr 1950). It borders on rare in the far interior of District C. Fall migration begins in late June (exceptionally to early June, e.g. two netted at Pt. Loma SD 4 Jun 1970), and is largely over by the end of August.

Starting in late June it is a fairly common fall transient through District M west of the deserts. Elsewhere in the interior it is probably a regular fall transient in very small numbers through the desert mountains and a casual spring transient through the lower deserts. Specimen evidence, however, is lacking and, because of the similarity of all plumages with those of the Rufous Hummingbird, the exact status of this species on the deserts (and in the region as a whole) is unclear. Specimens or netted birds are needed to clarify this situation. A specimen (not located) from Lost Palm Canyon in the Little San Bernardino Mtns. 22 Oct (year?) is the latest for fall in the region (outside of the range of *sedentarius*) and the only specimen for District D.

In winter, outside of the known range of *sedentarius*, the status is uncertain (see also Rufous Hummingbird). There are records of adult males from Santa Barbara south to San Diego, with most coming from the former area. Whether these records pertain to overwintering *S.s. sasin*, or to *sedentarius*, is not known (these records are not graphed). There are seasonal shifts in abundance of *sedentarius* on some of the Channel Is., and it is possible that some birds move to the mainland in winter.

Hybrid Allen's X Anna's Hummingbirds have been noted on the Palos Verdes Peninsula (e.g. 29 Dec 1976).

The habitat of this species in winter and migration is much like that preferred by the Rufous Hummingbird. On the mainland, breeding birds occur in coastal sage, willows, and oak-riparian woodlands, as well as in gardens and eucalyptus groves. They are very widespread on the Channel Is.

ALCEDINIDAE: KINGFISHERS
BELTED KINGFISHER
Ceryle alcyon

Uncommon to fairly common winter visitor to aquatic habitats, with the greatest numbers occurring along the coast and in District R. Primarily a transient in District M and over much of District D. Rare breeder, mainly on the coastal slope.

This species is local through District D, where little suitable habitat is available. Most depart the colder desert areas in winter, but it has been recorded through the winter in the Owens Valley INY. In District M there are records in winter from Big Bear L. in the San Bernardino Mtns. It is uncommon at this season in District S.

The Belted Kingfisher is a very rare breeder. Most definite records are old: coastal San Luis Obispo Co. (1909), Nojoqui Creek SBA (1924), Santa Paula VEN (1904), Sespe Creek VEN (1946), Whittier LA (1895, 1944), Oceanside SD (1916), and San Diego SD (1905). There are also old mid-summer records for the Owens Valley. In recent years it has nested at L. Silverwood SBE (June 1975), Ventura R. mouth VEN (1979), and the Santa Ynez R. SBA (1979, 1980). There are many other recent mid-summer records on the coastal slope; a pair in suitable nesting habitat along the Santa Ana R. near Barton Flats in the San Bernardino Mtns. in June 1975 suggests nesting in District M. The paucity of recent definite nesting records may in part be due to habitat loss, but it undoubtedly also reflects the diminished efforts by birders to find and publish nesting localities. Non-breeders occur uncommonly virtually year-round on the rocky coasts of the Channel Is.

Kingfishers occur at coastal lagoons, estuaries, rocky coasts, lakes, ponds, and streams. Earth banks are required for nesting.

PICIDAE: WOODPECKERS
LEWIS' WOODPECKER
Melanerpes lewis

Irregularly fairly common winter visitor in the interior portions of District C, the lower portions of District M, and in the northern deserts. Has nested rarely and sporadically, primarily in the northern part of the region.

Movements into the region are very erratic; in some years large numbers are noted and the species may even spread into the southeastern deserts, while in other years the species is almost entirely absent from the region. Fall invasions may start in early September and larger numbers may be present by late September and early October. Individuals along the immediate coast and the Channel Is. are generally noted in fall, although birds winter irregularly on the wooded portions of the Channel Is. The largest fall concentration on the immediate coast was of 105 over West Los Angeles LA 22 Sep 1978. The largest recorded winter concentration in the region was 200 at Furnace Creek Ranch INY winter 1972-1973. Farther south up to 20 have been noted at L. Cuyamaca SD (winter 1965-1966) and Santa Ysabel SD (winter 1977-1978). Wintering birds frequently linger through the end of April, and, exceptionally, to the end of May (e.g. 24-31 May 1975 Furnace Creek Ranch).

This species is casual in the southeastern part of the region (including Districts S and R), although multiples have been noted in major flight years (up to nine in a winter in District S).

The Lewis' Woodpecker nests (irregularly?) in the upper Salinas River Valley in north-central San Luis Obispo Co. It has also nested at Ft. Tejon KRN, in the San Bernardino Mtns. (southeast of Big Bear L. in 1968, and near Pioneertown in 1979), and at Big Pine INY (many in summer 1975; summers more regularly just north of the Owens Valley, outside of the region).

Lewis' Woodpeckers occupy a variety of woodland habitats. In most of District C they are partial to oaks, and in the mountains they occupy a mixture of oaks and conifers. On the desert they inhabit riparian groves, shade trees (elms, etc.), and orchards (especially date orchards at Furnace Creek Ranch). Nesting birds in San Luis Obispo Co. occur in oaks and Digger Pines; nests in the Owens Valley have been in riparian groves.

RED-HEADED WOODPECKER
Melanerpes erythrocephalus

One record: an adult was present in a small grove of eucalyptus near Niland IMP 17 Jul-22 Aug 1971.

A mummified bird found in Pasadena LA 20 May 1962 was possibly not a natural vagrant. The Niland record is the only certain one for California.

ACORN WOODPECKER
Melanerpes formicivorus   Map p. 393

Common resident in oak, oak-conifer, and oak-riparian woodlands in Districts C and M and also on some of the larger Channel Is. Rare and sporadic wanderer away from breeding areas.

In District C it is widespread except on the immediate coast south of Los Angeles Co., an area in which suitable oak habitat is scarce. This species is noted rarely and erratically in fall away from breeding areas; there are infrequent minor irruptions (e.g. 1972, 1978). It has occasionally wintered along the coast away from oaks, and spring transients were noted on the Palos Verdes Peninsula LA 6-14 May 1976 and on Pt. Loma SD 4-6 Jun 1979.

This species is widespread in District M west of the deserts, although it is generally absent from high elevation forests where oaks are rare. It has been recorded twice in summer in the desert mountains (no evidence of nesting): 19 Jul 1974 Clark Mtn. and 2 Aug 1978 Surprise Canyon, Panamint Mtns.

The Acorn Woodpecker is a casual, but nearly regular, spring and fall visitant in the desert areas, primarily from the Mohave Desert north. The only summer record for the desert lowlands is 15 Jun 1978 Harper Dry L. SBE. It is apparently regular in small numbers in winter in an isolated grove of live oaks at the Mt. Whitney Fish Hatchery near Independence INY, and is possibly resident here (these birds not graphed). On the southern deserts it has been recorded only as follows: 24 Oct 1971 Picacho Res. IMP; 4 Nov 1973 SESS; 20 Oct 1976 Chuckwalla Dunes RIV; and 4 Oct 1977 SESS. It has also been recorded at least twice in Joshua Tree National Monument (fall). There are several records for the Arizona side of the Colorado R.

On the Channel Is. it has been resident since 1930 on Santa Cruz I., and since at least 1955 on Santa Catalina I. This woodpecker is otherwise a very rare visitant.

Acorn Woodpeckers are characteristic birds of oak woodlands; they reach their peak abundance in mature live oak woodlands and where live oaks are mixed with riparian trees (especially sycamores), deciduous oaks (valley oaks, California Black Oaks), and conifers.

GILA WOODPECKER
Melanerpes uropygialis
Fairly common resident in District R; a few are also resident very locally around Brawley in District S. Two old records for District C.

In District R riparian groves (cottonwoods, etc.), date palms, and plantings of shade trees are occupied. Saguaros, which form ideal habitat for this species east of the region, are too scarce and local in California to be an important habitat. In District S a few pairs are resident in date palm groves and ranchyards in the vicinity of Brawley IMP; others are occasionally noted at ranchyards elsewhere in the Imperial Valley. It is irregularly present at Brock Ranch IMP between Districts R and S, but it is otherwise absent from District D.

This species was formerly even more numerous in the Colorado River Valley and it was common in the Imperial Valley; there is even a record to the north in the Coachella Valley, 1 Sep 1963 near NESS. The decline may be tied partially to the clearing of woodlands in the southeastern part of the region, and possibly also to nest-site competition with starlings.

There are two old records for District C: 2 Jan 1927 Griffith Park, Los Angeles LA (and present for about a month thereafter); and 20 May 1951 near Ontario SBE. We suspect these records are correct because they come from a period when the species was much more numerous in the region. An additional record from Jacumba SD 17 Oct 1952 is suspected to be in error.

YELLOW-BELLIED SAPSUCKER
Sphyrapicus varius

The "Red-naped Sapsucker", *S.v. nuchalis*, is a fairly common to common fall transient in the northern desert areas, and uncommon to fairly common winter visitant in the interior and the southernmost part of District C (increasingly rare to the north in District C). Breeds in the White Mtns. The eastern "Yellow-bellied Sapsucker", *S.v. varius*, is a casual late fall and early winter visitant, with about 25 records (mostly of immatures).

While a few *nuchalis* winter throughout District D, this subspecies is primarily a fall transient in the northern and eastern portions, where it can be common. In District R it is fairly common (in some years common) in winter around deciduous trees. It is a rare to uncommon fall transient and rare winter visitant in District S.

In District C *nuchalis* is an uncommon fall transient and winter visitant in coastal San Diego Co., where it occurs in about the same numbers as the Red-breasted Sapsucker. Farther north it is a rare fall transient and winter visitant in coastal Orange and Los Angeles Cos. east through the San Bernardino and Riverside Valleys. It is strictly casual north of coastal Los Angeles Co.: one record for southeastern Ventura Co., five records for Santa Barbara Co. (four specimens), and one record for San Luis Obispo Co. (7 Nov 1976 San Luis Obispo). There are six winter records for the Channel Is.

This race breeds only in the higher portions of the White Mtns., primarily in aspen groves (e.g. Cottonwood Creek MNO).

Birds appearing intermediate between *nuchalis* and *ruber/daggetti* have been noted on the deserts and in the Cuyama Valley SBA/SLO.

The "Yellow-bellied Sapsucker", *S.v. varius*, is a casual late fall and early winter visitant, though recently it has proved to be of regular occurrence. There are about 15 records for District D south to Morongo Valley SBE and Whitewater RIV; all fall between 21 Oct (several records) and 24 Jan 1973 Furnace Creek Ranch INY. It has been recorded twice in District R and once at nearby Brock Ranch IMP. It has also been recorded once at Santa Ysabel SD in the mountains bordering District C, 11 Nov 1975. There are five records from the mainland of District C: Pasadena LA 19 Jul 1950 (mummified adult female that had probably died the previous winter; not graphed); Tijuana River Valley SD 20 Dec 1969; Refugio State Beach SBA 20 Oct-9 Dec 1978 and 3-30 Nov 1979; L. Cachuma SBA 5 Dec 1979-10 Feb 1980; and Garden Grove ORA 5 Jan 1980. The two records for the Channel Is. both pertain to adult males: 1-4 Jan 1976 Santa Catalina I., and 13 Jun 1976 San Nicolas I. (the only record of a spring vagrant). The only other records pertaining to adults are 27 Oct-7 Nov 1978 Kelso SBE (female), and the Tijuana River Valley, Pasadena, and Refugio State Beach records noted above.

The following records are of birds showing characters intermediate between *varius* and *nuchalis* (though field identification of such hybrids must remain tentative): 5 Feb 1931 Bard IMP (specimen); 4 Feb to early Mar 1978 Regina IMP; and 1 Jan 1979 Oceanside SD. Some authorities have considered *nuchalis* to be specifically distinct from *S. varius*.

RED-BREASTED SAPSUCKER
Sphyrapicus ruber

Fairly common breeder in District M west of the deserts; uncommon to locally fairly common winter visitant in District C. Very rare winter visitant on the deserts.

This species breeds in the Mt. Pinos area, the San Gabriel Mtns., San Bernardino Mtns., San Jacinto Mtns., and, in very small numbers, Mt. Palomar, to the Cuyamaca Mtns. and possibly the Laguna Mtns. Most depart the higher portions of District M in winter. It is fairly common in winter in the foothills of District C and the northern coastal area, but it is generally uncommon in the coastal lowlands from Los Angeles Co. south. It is an uncommon transient and winter visitant on the Channel Is. (mainly on the larger islands). East of the mountains, it has been recorded very rarely in migration and winter in the Owens Valley and the Death Valley area south to the Colorado R. and Brock Ranch IMP. On the deserts, birds that are intermediate in appearance between *S. ruber* X *S. varius nuchalis* may be nearly as frequent as pure Red-breasted birds.

All breeding birds and the great majority of transient and wintering Red-breasted Sapsuckers in the region are of the southern race *daggetti*. The northwestern race *ruber* is probably a casual fall transient; birds showing the characteristics of this race have been recorded as follows: 9 Nov 1957 near Lakeside SD (specimen); 16 Oct 1976 Furnace Creek Ranch INY; and 6 Nov 1977 Kelso SBE.

Red-breasted Sapsuckers breed in coniferous forests where there is an admixture of deciduous trees (willows, alders, Black Cottonwoods, etc.). Wintering birds are generally found in deciduous groves, orchards, and shade trees (peppers, poplars, etc.).

Recent taxonomic studies have shown *S. ruber* to be specifically distinct from the *S. varius/nuchalis* complex.

WILLIAMSON'S SAPSUCKER
Sphyrapicus thyroideus

Uncommon to fairly common, but local, resident in the higher mountains west of the deserts. More widespread in District M in winter, but casual in the lowlands.

This species breeds in the higher portions of the San Gabriel Mtns. (scarce), the San Bernardino Mtns., the San Jacinto Mtns., and Mt. Pinos (rare; nesting evidence needed). An adult accompanied by two juveniles was on Pine Mtn. VEN 30 Jul 1980. The greatest concentration of breeding birds is in the San Bernardino Mtns. on the north-facing slopes behind Big Bear L. and in the vicinity of Mt. San Gorgonio.

In winter it is found at lower elevations throughout the breeding ranges, where it descends into the Yellow Pine belt. It is also a rare but regular winter visitant in the mountains of Santa Barbara Co. (Figueroa Mtn.) and San Diego Co. from October (perhaps mid-September) to early April.

This species is a casual winter visitant elsewhere in the region, although a few birds of the *nataliae* race of the Great Basin and Rocky Mountains may winter regularly in the mountains of the e. Mohave Desert, in Joshua Tree National Monument, and probably elsewhere on the deserts. Other areas of occurrence in District D include Death Valley National Monument INY, Oasis MNO (and the adjacent White Mtns.), and Morongo Valley SBE. There is one record for District S: 5 Oct 1955 near Mecca RIV. There are no records for the California side of the Colorado R., but the species has been recorded on the Arizona side. About ten fall and winter records exist for District C, even as far from breeding areas as the Palos Verdes Peninsula LA and Bonita SD. There are no records for the Channel Is.

Williamson's Sapsuckers breed at high elevations in coniferous forests dominated by lodgepole pines and firs (down to the upper border of the Yellow/Jeffrey Pine belt). They are much less restricted to the vicinity of deciduous trees than the Red-breasted Sapsucker. In winter a wider variety of conifers may be occupied, including pinyons.

LADDER-BACKED WOODPECKER
Picoides scalaris   Map p. 393

Fairly common resident in desert woodlands from the n. Mohave Desert south. Vagrant north to northern Inyo Co. and to coastal San Diego Co. (one record).

This species is resident north to the Inyo Co. line (Coso, Argus, Kingston Mtns. and probably vic. Tecopa INY), but it is replaced in riparian woodlands in the Owens Valley by the Nuttall's Woodpecker. It occurs northeast to the Walker Pass area KRN (just outside the region) and from there south and west to the Kelso Valley KRN, vic. Palmdale LA; east along the northern slopes of the Transverse Ranges to Morongo Valley SBE, vic. San Gorgonio Pass RIV; and south to the eastern base of the Santa Rosa and Laguna Mtns. It occurs eastward uncommonly through District S, where most native woodland has been cleared, and rather commonly along the length of the Colorado R. In District M it may occur on the higher slopes of some of the desert ranges and in pinyon-*Yucca* associations to at least 1700m on the northeast side of the San Bernardino Mtns.

The Ladder-backed Woodpecker is a vagrant north to Death Valley and the Panamint Valley INY, areas from which there are eight records in fall and winter. Farther north it has been recorded at Cottonwood Canyon on the east slope of the White Mtns. INY 7 Mar 1976, and at Deep Springs INY 12 Aug-3 Sep 1977 and 24 Aug and 26 Oct 1979. It is undoubtedly resident in pinyon-*Yucca* woodland in adjacent Nevada (vic. Lida).

There is one recent record in District C: 9 Oct 1974 Tijuana River Valley SD; this species is resident a short distance south in Baja California. It has been noted west of San Gorgonio Pass to San Timoteo Canyon 22 Aug 1979 and (historically) in the vicinity of Valle Vista in the San Jacinto Valley RIV 29 Aug-5 Sep 1908 (6-7 birds, three specimens) and at Riverside RIV Apr 1895. Although these records are technically within District C, they are not graphed.

Various types of desert woodlands are inhabited by the Ladder-backed Woodpecker; it is perhaps most numerous in wooded desert washes (palo verde, ironwood, mesquite) and in riparian groves and oases. It also ranges widely over Joshua Tree woodland, and less commonly into pinyon-juniper associations (where some Joshua Trees are present). It marginally overlaps the Nuttall's Woodpecker and some hybrids are known (see under that species).

NUTTALL'S WOODPECKER
Picoides nuttallii   Map p. 393

Common resident in woodlands in most of District C and in the lower and middle portions of District M; also resident locally in the northern and western portions of District D. One record for District S.

The Nuttall's Woodpecker is most closely associated with oak woodlands and, especially, a mixture of oaks and riparian trees. In the southern parts of District C this species replaces the Downy Woodpecker in riparian woodlands. In District M a mixture of oaks and conifers is occupied, within and below the Yellow Pine belt. It is resident in the northern and western portions of District D as follows: Owens Valley INY (riparian woodlands); vic. Walker Pass KRN (riparian woodlands); the north base of the San Gabriel and San Bernardino Mtns. where it follows some wooded creek bottoms well out onto the desert floor, as along Big Rock Ck. near Pearblossom LA; Morongo Valley SBE; San Gorgonio Pass near Banning RIV; and the eastern flank of the San Diego Co. mountains (but not onto the Anza Borrego Desert). It has occurred along the Mohave R. drainage out to Barstow SBE, and at ranchyards in the Antelope Valley LA/KRN (where Ladder-backs are also occasionally noted). It is absent from the Channel Is.

There is one record for District S: 3 Sep 1973 at Westmorland IMP.

Where the range of the Nuttall's Woodpecker extends onto the deserts in riparian corridors, there is marginal overlap with the related Ladder-backed Woodpecker. Where the two overlap, Nuttall's appears to predominate in riparian woodlands, while the Ladder-backed occurs in more xeric woodland (e.g. Joshua Trees). A very few hybrids and introgressants are known from the vicinity of Victorville SBE and west of Walker Pass KRN (just outside the region). Apparent introgressants are known from other parts of the region. Additional work to determine the extent of interbreeding of these species is needed.

DOWNY WOODPECKER
Picoides pubescens   *Map p. 393*

Fairly common resident in the northern part of District C, extending uncommonly and very locally south to extreme n. San Diego Co. Possibly resident in the Owens Valley INY, but casual elsewhere on the deserts.

This species is a fairly common resident in District C south to Ventura Co. and w. Los Angeles Co.; it may be locally common in San Luis Obispo and Santa Barbara Cos. It is uncommon from s. and e. Los Angeles Co. east through the Santa Ana R. drainage of w. San Bernardino Co. and locally through w. Riverside Co. (possibly to the vic. of Temecula) and Orange Co. It occurs south to the San Luis Rey R. drainage in n. San Diego Co.; farther south it nested in San Clemente Canyon near La Jolla SD in the early 1960s and along the San Diego R. until 1949. It has occurred as a vagrant south to the vicinity of Otay and the Tijuana River Valley SD.

The Downy Woodpecker is probably a rare resident in the Owens Valley, but nesting has not been documented; it may occur there mostly in winter. It is strictly casual elsewhere on the deserts; most records are of transients, but coverage is limited in mid-winter. It has been recorded four times in the Death Valley INY and Fish Lake Valley MNO areas between 8 Sep 1976 Furnace Creek Ranch INY and 28 Nov 1976 Oasis MNO (these records likely pertaining to the Rocky Mtn. race *P. p. leucurus*). Farther south it has been recorded five times in the Mohave R. drainage SBE and the Antelope Valley LA (20 Oct 1979 Holiday L. LA (2) to 17 Apr 1977 Afton Canyon SBE), once at China Lake KRN/SBE (16 Dec 1978), once in Palm Springs RIV (late Dec 1903 or early Jan 1904), and once at NESS (4 Apr 1977).

This woodpecker is generally absent from District M, although occasional birds have been noted to 2000m in the San Bernardino Mtns. It is unrecorded on the Channel Is.

Downy Woodpeckers inhabit deciduous woodlands (especially willows) or a mixture of deciduous growth and oaks, conifers (occasionally), orchards, and suburban plantings. Two hybrids between Downy and Nuttall's Woodpeckers have been taken along the San Diego R.

HAIRY WOODPECKER
Picoides villosus   Map p. 393

Fairly common resident in a wide variety of coniferous and mixed forests through most of District M, locally in foothill canyons and the north coast, and occasionally elsewhere in the coastal lowlands. Slight influx in winter into the coastal lowlands; casual in the desert lowlands.

The breeding range includes the White, Panamint, and Grapevine Mtns. in addition to the major ranges west of the deserts. There are recent summer records for the Kingston Mtns. (21 Jun 1977) and Clark Mtn. (29 May 1979); it formerly nested in the latter range. It also nests fairly commonly but locally in coastal and foothill canyons in District C (San Luis Obispo, Santa Barbara, and Ventura Cos., and the base of the Transverse Ranges). It is fairly common in the lowlands of w. Santa Barbara Co., and it occasionally nests in the coastal lowlands farther south (e.g. Santa Ana R. in the vicinity of Riverside RIV).

In winter there is a slight influx into the coastal lowlands from August through May. This species is generally casual in the desert lowlands, although it is regular along the Mohave R. and the Owens Valley INY, where it may breed locally. The only record for the southeastern part of the region is 18 Mar 1980 near Palm Springs RIV. It is unrecorded on the Channel Is.

Hairy Woodpeckers are relatively broad in their habitat tolerances. They occupy mixed and pure coniferous woodlands and forests from the live oak/*Pseudotsuga* belt up through Yellow Pine and Lodgepole Pine/ White Fir zones, and locally into pinyons on the drier slopes. Locally they follow riparian woodlands down into the coastal lowlands for breeding. On the north coast they breed in closed-cone pine forests and mixed oak/riparian woodlands.

WHITE-HEADED WOODPECKER
Picoides albolarvatus

Fairly common resident in pine forests of the major ranges west of the deserts. Casual in the coastal lowlands; in addition there are two records for District D and one for District S.

The breeding range includes the Piute Mtns., Mt. Pinos region (including Frazier Mtn., Mt. Abel), San Gabriel Mtns., San Bernardino Mtns., San Jacinto Mtns., Santa Rosa Mtns., Mt. Palomar, and the Cuyamaca/Laguna Mtns. (uncommon). It also breeds west into w. Ventura Co. (Reyes Peak, Pine Mtn.), e. Santa Barbara Co.(Big Pine Mtn.) and possibly on Figueroa Mtn. SBA (where reported mainly in winter.)

This species is quite sedentary; it is only casual outside of District M. Records for the coastal lowlands are: Santa Barbara SBA 23 Jan 1920 and 2 Oct 1975; Hollywood Res. LA 24 Oct-27 Dec 1970; Pt. Fermin, Palos Verdes Peninsula LA 19-29 Sep 1972; Palos Verdes Peninsula 18 Dec

1972; Alhambra LA 5 Jan-5 Apr 1941; and Redlands SBE 27 Oct 1940. There are three records from Districts D and S: 8 Apr 1973 Furnace Creek Ranch INY; late Nov 1915-24 Feb 1916 Palm Springs RIV; and 28 Nov 1955 near Indio RIV.

White-headed Woodpeckers are found in mixed conifer forests dominated by large-coned, prolifically-seeding pines such as Coulter, Sugar, Jeffrey, and Yellow Pines; they range only marginally up into associations dominated by firs and Lodgepole Pines.

COMMON FLICKER
Colaptes auratus

Common resident in Districts C and M, with numbers augmented in winter. Primarily a common winter visitant and transient in Districts D, S, and R, although it breeds locally in District D and the "Gilded" form breeds along the Colorado R.

Nearly all birds in the region are of the "Red-shafted" type (*cafer* group). In winter they are common throughout (including District M and the northernmost portions of District D), but during the breeding season they occur primarily in Districts C and M. This form breeds fairly commonly in riparian groves in the Owens Valley INY and in small numbers in the Joshua Tree woodlands of the e. Mohave Desert. It breeds commonly on Santa Cruz and Santa Catalina Is.; it is otherwise a transient and winter visitant on the Channel Is.

The southern "Gilded" subspecies (*chrysoides* group) is an uncommon resident along the Colorado R., especially from Blythe RIV north. It was formerly more numerous and widespread in District R; the decline is certainly attributable to the loss of riparian woodland. A very few birds are also resident in the Joshua Tree woodlands of the e. Mohave Desert (vic. Cima SBE), but they are probably declining there and are possibly being replaced by red-shafted birds. Gilded birds have been found twice in District S at SESS: 1 Mar 1969 and 20 Jan-24 Mar 1973. Another was collected exceptionally far west at Riverside RIV 21 Nov 1941.

The eastern "Yellow-shafted" form (*auratus* group) is a rare fall transient and winter visitant, especially at the northern desert oases (fall) and along the length of District C (fall and winter). In the interior it has wintered at Furnace Creek Ranch INY and in Districts S and R. This form is rarely noted before mid-October. A few spring transients are noted along the coast and in the northern portion of District D. The latest records for the region are 11 Apr 1968 Pasadena LA and 12 Apr 1917 Furnace Creek Ranch. This form has been recorded as a casual transient on the Channel Is.

Numerous introgressant flickers, displaying characteristics of both red-shafted and yellow-shafted birds, are recorded annually; in fact, introgressants may be as likely to occur as "pure" yellow-shafted birds.

241

Flickers occupy a variety of woodlands and forests; transients and winter birds can occur in quite open areas. The rather more restricted habitat of the Gilded subspecies is noted above.

TYRANNIDAE: TYRANT FLYCATCHERS

OLIVE-SIDED FLYCATCHER
Contopus borealis   *Map p. 393*

Fairly common summer resident in District M and locally in foothill portions of District C; otherwise an uncommon spring and fall transient in lowlands throughout (including the Channel Is.). Two acceptable winter records.

This species breeds in all major ranges west of the deserts, and in the White Mtns. It also breeds in well-wooded canyons in the foothills of the major ranges, and it even breeds close to the coast from Santa Barbara Co. north. Singing birds are occasionally noted in the lower portions of District C south of Santa Barbara Co., which suggests that nesting may occur locally where enough tall trees are present.

Away from breeding areas, it is best termed an uncommon transient. Spring migration is protracted — the first birds arrive in mid-April (earliest is 9 Apr 1976 Ventura VEN) and the last stragglers are still passing through in early (exceptionally middle) June. Birds breeding on the northern coast are generally the earliest arrivals in the region. A bird at Kelso SBE 5 Jul 1972 is difficult to explain. Fall transients have generally departed by late September; stragglers occur casually to mid-October. One at Oasis MNO 18-19 Oct 1975 establishes the latest fall record for the region, and is especially unusual for so northerly an inland locality.

The only adequately documented winter records are of a bird near Monrovia LA 29-30 Dec 1971 and one present in Griffith Park, Los Angeles LA 28 Nov 1979-29 Mar 1980. This species normally winters from Panama south.

Olive-sided Flycatchers breed primarily in open coniferous forests, but also descend wooded canyons well into the foothill portions of District C. Planting of tall trees (e.g. conifers and eucalyptus) form a marginally acceptable breeding habitat locally within District C. The density of migrants is always rather low, but individual transients may be conspicuous because of their habit of perching on the tops of tall, bare-tipped trees.

GREATER PEWEE (COUES' FLYCATCHER)
Contopus pertinax

Casual winter visitant; 14 records fall between 29 Sep 1965 Brock Ranch IMP and 10 Apr 1968 Hollywood LA (wintering bird).

Coastal records are all from Los Angeles Co. south: Los Angeles Co. (4); Riverside RIV (1); Orange Co. (1); and San Diego Co. (3). Interior records come from Brock Ranch IMP (2); the Colorado R. (2); and SESS (1).

All but two records have been since 1968. Most birds have spent much or all of the winter; a bird at Parker Dam SBE was present two consecutive winters (1977-1978, 1978-1979).

WESTERN WOOD-PEWEE
Contopus sordidulus   Map p. 393

Common summer resident in District M and in hills and foothill canyons through much of District C. Common spring transient and fairly common to common fall transient in lowlands throughout. Unrecorded after October.

This species breeds in woodland and open forest habitats; it reaches its peak abundance in mixed oak-riparian and conifer-oak-riparian woodlands. It breeds in all major mountain ranges, including the White and Panamint Mtns., and, recently, other desert ranges (Kingston, Clark, and possibly New York Mtns.). The Western Wood-Pewee also breeds in lowland riparian groves of District C, but it is generally scarce along the immediate coast south of Los Angeles Co.

Away from breeding habitat this flycatcher is a common spring transient through District C (including the Channel Is.), and a common to abundant spring transient through the interior. The species generally arrives on the coast around the third week of April; the earliest birds arrive in mid-April. Exceptionally early records are 3 Apr 1978 Topanga LA and 4 Apr 1969 Pt. Loma SD. Migrants in the interior arrive somewhat later than along the coast. On the deserts, where it is strictly a transient, the spring peak is quite late (mid-to-late May), and late transients are recorded into mid-June. Late concentrations include 100 at Deep Springs INY 10 Jun 1964 and 16 at the Salton Sea 13 Jun 1976. The latest recorded spring transients were at Laguna Dam IMP 23 Jun 1974 (3).

This species is a fairly common to common early fall transient throughout. Birds have largely departed their breeding areas by mid-August, and transients are widespread from early August through early September (e.g. 20 at Morongo Valley SBE 8 Aug 1964). Numbers diminish in District M earlier than in District C. Fall migration is virtually complete by the end of September; stragglers are noted very rarely to mid-October. There are only five reliable records after mid-October: 17-23 Oct 1978 Pt. Fermin LA; 27 Oct 1978 Big Sycamore Canyon VEN; 30 Oct 1971 San Diego SD; and 30-31 Oct 1976 Panamint Springs INY. These late records may best be treated as *Contopus* sp.; there are two additional late October records of birds showing characters more typical of the Eastern Wood-Pewee (see supplemental list).

Winter reports published in *AFN* (mostly from Christmas Bird Counts) lack documentation and are undoubtedly in error. This species normally winters only in South America.

WILLOW FLYCATCHER
Empidonax traillii

Fairly common to common transient; the largest numbers pass through the deserts. Breeds in riparian woodlands, but virtually extirpated from the region. One winter record.

This species is a fairly common spring and common fall transient through the deserts, and an uncommon spring transient and fairly common fall transient along the coast, on the Channel Is., and in the lower portions of District M. This is one of our latest spring transients; it virtually never arrives before 10 May and in recent years it is unrecorded in April. Spring migration peaks in late May; sizeable numbers are still passing through in the first third of June and stragglers are recorded to about 20 June. The first fall transients arrive at the very end of July in the interior, where migration peaks from mid-August to early September. Along the coast it is less numerous and occurs slightly later in fall. After September this species is quite rare anywhere in the region. The latest record of a fall transient is 27 Oct 1978 Santa Maria R. mouth SBA.

The only winter record for California was a bird studied carefully by numerous observers in Arcadia LA from 2 Nov 1979 to 29 Apr 1980.

The Willow Flycatcher has been virtually extirpated as a breeder. A thorough survey of riparian habitat in the summer of 1978 revealed only two singing birds, both in coastal San Diego Co. Two territorial males were along the Santa Margarita R. near Fallbrook SD in summer 1980, and it summered near Otay L. SD in 1975. A pair nested in the Owens Valley in 1979 (not graphed) and raised cowbirds. This species was formerly considered a common summer resident in lowland willow thickets and up into mountain canyons (Willett 1933). Its decline, among the most serious of any bird in the region, can be linked to habitat destruction and to brood parasitism by cowbirds. There is evidence that the major decline began shortly after the large-scale invasion of the coastal lowlands by the Brown-headed Cowbird in the 1920s. Prior to 1933 Hanna noted that it was "now difficult to find a nest near Colton SBE that does not contain at least one egg of the Dwarf (Brown-headed) Cowbird." This decline has also been noted in the lowlands of northern California.

Willow Flycatchers nested in willow thickets in floodplains and the broader canyons. Migrants can often be found in apparently suitable breeding habitat well into June; these should not be assumed to be breeding birds. In northern California the largest numbers of breeding birds remain in montane willow thickets where cowbird pressure is less severe. When the species bred commonly in the region, spring birds arrived as early as late April.

Inadequate portrayal of this species in field guides has resulted in frequent confusion with other species, particularly the Western Wood-Pewee.

LEAST FLYCATCHER
Empidonax minimus

Casual transient, although probably more regular than the 23 records indicate; the majority of records are for fall.

Of the 23 records, 17 are for fall, four are for spring, and two are for winter. Fall transients have been noted between the dates of 11 Sep 1974 Pt. Conception SBA and 28 Oct 1974 Furnace Creek Ranch INY; an exceptionally late bird was at Emigrant Ranger Station INY 28 Oct-24 Nov 1974. All fall records are from the coast, except the two above. Of the four spring records, two are from the northern deserts and two are from the Channel Is.

The two winter records are: 26 Nov 1978-17 Feb 1979 Brock Ranch IMP and 5 Nov 1978-3 Mar 1979 near Fillmore VEN.

While Least Flycatchers clearly reach southern California with some regularity, identification in the field should be attempted only by those thoroughly familiar with *Empidonax* flycatchers. All records save one are since 1974.

HAMMOND'S FLYCATCHER
Empidonax hammondii

Fairly common spring transient and uncommon fall transient; probably a casual winter visitor, but specimen evidence is lacking.

In spring this species borders on common along the southern coast and in the interior, but is quite uncommon from Ventura Co. north. Spring transients can occur rarely by late March, but the bulk of the passage is from mid-April into early May. Numbers are reduced in fall; it is decidedly uncommon at this season and the majority occur in the interior. Most fall birds are found from mid-September through early October. Stragglers have been noted as late as the first half of November; the latest record is 16-17 Nov 1974 Mission Gorge SD (specimen). It is an uncommon spring transient on the Channel Is.; there are two fall records.

The Hammond's Flycatcher is probably a casual winter visitor, although specimen evidence is needed. While some wintering birds have been identified as Hammond's by experienced observers, most should be treated as Hammond's/Dusky. There is a winter specimen for the Bill Williams Delta on the Arizona side of the Colorado R., and a December specimen for northern California.

This species breeds as far south as the forests of the central Sierra Nevada; none has been found in summer in our mountains.

DUSKY FLYCATCHER
Empidonax oberholseri

Fairly common summer resident in open montane forests. Rather rare transient through the lowlands, with most occurring in the interior. Casual winter visitor.

This species breeds in the major mountain ranges (Mt. Pinos, San Gabriel Mtns., San Bernardino Mtns., San Jacinto Mtns., Santa Rosa Mtns.) south sporadically to the Laguna Mtns. (pairs nested in 1974 and 1978; present in 1976), the Cuyamaca Mtns. (present summer 1979 and 1980), and Hot Springs Mtn. (single bird 3-4 Jun 1980). It also nests on some of the ranges in the northern deserts (White, Kingston, Clark, and New York Mtns.).

The Dusky Flycatcher is a rather rare spring and fall transient through the deserts; it is uncommon on the northern deserts and distinctly rare on the southern deserts. The migration in spring is later than that of Hammond's; very few occur before late April, and some late spring transients pass through the northern interior into early June.

Along the coast (including the Channel Is.) it is a casual spring transient and rare, but probably regular, fall transient; its status is imperfectly known. Most certain records come from banding stations at Pt. Loma SD. It is outnumbered in all districts in migration by the Hammond's Flycatcher, particularly in spring.

There are two winter specimens (not checked by us): 24 Feb 1908 Sierra Madre LA and 19 Feb 1910 Needles SBE. It has also been collected at Cibola on the Arizona side of the Colorado R. 16 Dec 1978. Several other winter records of Hammond's/Dusky flycatchers may pertain to this species.

Dusky Flycatchers breed in open montane pine and fir forests; they are most common where there is an adjacent growth of chaparral (manzanita, mountain mahogany, serviceberry, etc.).

GRAY FLYCATCHER
Empidonax wrightii

Fairly common summer resident in arid woodlands of the desert mountain ranges and locally on the arid slopes of the Transverse Ranges. Uncommon spring and fall transient and rare winter visitant on the deserts; very rare transient and winter visitant in District C.

The greatest numbers breed in the White, Inyo, and Panamint Mtns.; singing birds have been noted in late May on Clark Mtn. It breeds locally on the desert slope of the San Bernardino Mtns. A specimen was taken 10 Jun 1966 near Wrightwood SBE in the San Gabriel Mtns. One in the Santa Rosa Mtns. 22 Jul 1979 suggests the possibility of nesting south of the San Bernardinos.

246

This species is an uncommon spring and fall transient and rare but regular winter visitant in the interior; in winter it has occurred casually as far north as Death Valley. There is only one recent winter record for District S (22 Feb 1976 SESS); it was formerly more regular at this season. Along the coast it is presently a very rare but regular fall and spring transient and winter visitant. In spring it occurs casually to late May. Most records are from Los Angeles Co. and to the south and east. It is a very rare transient on the Channel Is.; most records are for spring. The Gray Flycatcher appears to have declined greatly as a winter visitant to District C. Willett (1933) considered it a "fairly common" winter visitant to valley and foothill portions of the district and cited numerous specimens. There appears to have been a distinct decline even since the 1960s. On the other hand, the breeding range presented here is more extensive than that known to Grinnell and Miller (1944).

Gray Flycatchers are closely tied to pinyon-juniper-sagebrush associations, but do breed locally in other arid conifer associations (e.g. Bristlecone Pines in the White Mtns.).

WESTERN FLYCATCHER
Empidonax difficilis   Map p. 394

Fairly common to common summer resident and common transient in District C (including the Channel Is.) and the lower portions of District M. Fairly common to common spring transient and uncommon to fairly common fall transient through the interior. Casual, but perhaps regular, winter visitant in District C.

While it is widespread as a breeder throughout canyons in District C, the largest numbers are in the northern part of the district. It also breeds in woodlands on Santa Cruz, Santa Rosa, Anacapa, Santa Catalina, and San Clemente Is. Breeding birds are present on territory by mid-to-late March (exceptionally even by early March). Late spring transients pass through regularly into early June.

This species is less common as a transient in the interior, but it is still fairly common (bordering on common) in spring, and uncommon (bordering on fairly common) in fall. In the interior, spring transients have been recorded well into June, exceptionally to 22 Jun 1971 Bard IMP. There is a specimen from 27 June 1954 from the White Mtns., where it is not known to breed. The first fall transients appear in the interior by late July.

In fall individuals may linger quite late, but the species is probably best termed casual in winter (although it is nearly regular). In recent years it has possibly even been more numerous and regular in winter than the Gray Flycatcher. All winter records are from Los Angeles Co. south except: 3 Dec 1918 near Santa Barbara SBA (probably a late fall straggler), 23 Feb 1980 Lompoc SBA, 28-29 Jan 1979 and 24 Nov 1979-14 Feb 1980 Carpinteria SBA. The only winter record from the interior possibly

247

pertains to a late fall straggler: 27 Dec 1974 Brock Ranch IMP. Winter records do exist for the Arizona side of the Colorado R. We suspect that some published winter records of this species are in error; all winter *Empidonax* should be carefully documented.

Western Flycatchers breed in canyon bottom woodlands of alders, sycamores, or willows, especially where they are surrounded by oak woodlands. This species is common in these habitats; it is scarcer in the woodlands of coastal plains, and in deciduous groves within coniferous forests in the lower part of District M. Birds wintering along the coast have generally occurred in riparian woodland and heavily planted garden and park-like settings.

EASTERN PHOEBE
Sayornis phoebe

Rare but regular fall transient and winter visitant; about 70 records for the region, mostly from mid-October to early April.

Early and late dates for this species are 14 Oct 1972 Furnace Creek Ranch INY and 6 Apr 1968 San Clemente ORA (wintering), except for one exceptionally early fall transient 19 Sep 1970 Goleta SBA, and one spring vagrant 21 May 1973 Furnace Creek Ranch. A spring transient was at Scotty's Castle INY 26-30 March 1979. Winter records come from Districts C, S, and R. There are also two winter records from the lower border of District M at L. Henshaw SD: 15 Oct-26 Dec 1949 and 6 Feb-14 Mar 1979. It is unrecorded on the Channel Is.

Many published records of this species are questionable; some of them clearly pertain to Willow Flycatchers. We have rejected numerous records lacking details and lying outside the established seasonal pattern. Records prior to mid-October and after March require careful documentation.

Wintering Eastern Phoebes are often found near ponds, streams, and ditches that have riparian groves or brush bordering on open areas.

BLACK PHOEBE
Sayornis nigricans

Fairly common to locally common resident in lowlands through much of the region; numbers augmented in winter. Mainly a winter visitant in the southern part of District D, in District S, and along the Colorado R.

This species is generally a rare breeder on the deserts, where little suitable habitat exists; it may be locally numerous in localities such as Morongo Valley SBE and the Owens Valley INY. It is primarily a winter visitant in District S and along the Colorado R.; small numbers remain to breed. This species breeds in suitable habitat in the lower portions of District M. It nests commonly on most of the larger Channel Is., where it is otherwise a transient and winter visitant.

Black Phoebes are closely tied to the vicinity of water, whether rivers, lakes, coastal lagoons, or small streams, ponds, and ditches. The species is thus limited in suitable habitat over much of the region, being widespread only in the coastal lowlands and canyons. Habitat tolerances are broader on the Channel Is. and among birds wintering on the mainland.

SAY'S PHOEBE
Sayornis saya

Fairly common resident throughout the desert regions, with numbers augmented in winter. Fairly common winter visitant in District C, remaining to breed very locally in the interior of the district.

The Say's Phoebe is widespread in the lowlands (including the Channel Is.) in winter; birds wintering in the interior are most numerous in agricultural regions. Transients and winter visitants occur up into the lower portions of District M. It breeds fairly commonly throughout the desert regions, although it is uncommon in District S, where it breeds in the more arid portions away from agricultural activity — e.g. Salton City IMP. This species formerly nested throughout the interior of District C (e.g. Chalome SLO, Shandon SLO, Painted Rock SLO, vic. Cuyama Valley SBA/SLO/VEN, Sespe VEN, Simi Valley VEN, Whittier LA, Colton SBE, L. Elsinore RIV, San Jacinto Valley RIV, Escondido SD, vic. Encinitas SD, and "near San Diego" SD). A few still nest in the most arid interior portions of District C, particularly near the border of District D (e.g. Carrizo Plain SLO, Cuyama Valley, vic. Agua Dulce LA).

Wintering birds arrive in September and generally depart by mid-March; they sometimes linger into April.

In winter Say's Phoebes are widespread in open, lowland habitats: grassy coastal bluffs, fields, arid scrub, grasslands, and agricultural areas. For breeding, they occupy sparse desert scrub, very arid woodland, and broken grassland with banks, cliffs, or artificial structures for nest sites.

VERMILION FLYCATCHER
Pyrocephalus rubinus

Rare and local resident along the Colorado R., also breeding sporadically farther west (regularly at Morongo Valley SBE). Rare fall and winter visitant to lowlands of Districts C, D, and S.

This flycatcher is quite local along the Colorado R., where most occur in the vicinity of Blythe RIV. There have been sporadic, small, local breeding populations to the west of the Colorado R.; the only currently well-established one is at Morongo Valley SBE.

In the interior this species winters regularly in very small numbers north to Furnace Creek Ranch INY and China Lake INY/SBE. It also winters in very small numbers along the coast, where it occurs primarily in San Diego Co. and irregularly north to Santa Barbara Co. Wintering birds are also found along the Colorado R. and in District S. Fall vagrants have been noted at most of the areas above, and a few spring transients have been recorded on the deserts. The northernmost records for the region are: 24-25 May 1976 and 28 May 1979 Deep Springs INY, and 19 Aug-2 Oct 1976 Oasis MNO. It has been recorded once on the Channel Is.: 29 Sep 1974 San Nicolas I.

The Vermilion Flycatcher was formerly more widespread as a breeder in the interior; it occurred throughout District R and in the Imperial and Coachella Valleys (at least to the late 1950s in the latter area). Nesting was also recorded early in this century in the upper Mohave R. drainage. It formerly bred (at least sporadically) in coastal San Diego Co. (1958 to the mid-1960s). It has recently been recorded in summer along the Santa Clara R. near Castaic LA (1970) and at Frazier Park KRN (1977) (no evidence of breeding).

Vermilion Flycatchers breed near water in both riparian groves and mesquite which have bordering fields (especially irrigated fields).

DUSKY-CAPPED (OLIVACEOUS) FLYCATCHER
Myiarchus tuberculifer

Late fall vagrant and winter visitant from the subtropics; four records: 23 Nov 1968 Furnace Creek Ranch INY; 29 Nov 1975-4 Jan 1976 Furnace Creek Ranch; 9-14 Nov 1977 "Walters Camp" RIV on the Colorado R. (specimen probably taken on the California side of the river); and 30 Dec 1979-10 Feb 1980 Irvine ORA.

There is one northern California record: a bird wintering in Monterey Co.

ASH-THROATED FLYCATCHER
Myiarchus cinerascens

Common summer resident at lower and middle elevations through much of the region; casual in winter along the coast, though probably regular at that season in District R and the southern portions of District D.

This species breeds throughout Districts C, D, and R; it also breeds fairly commonly in open forests in the lower portions of District M. It is primarily a transient in District S, although small numbers remain to breed (especially in the Coachella Valley RIV). This flycatcher is primarily a transient on the Channel Is.; it definitely breeds only on Santa Cruz I. Spring birds arrive by early March along the Colorado R. and in the southernmost deserts; on the northern deserts and in Districts C and M, the arrival is later (mostly mid-April, with the first birds appearing in early April).

250

Fall transients appear away from known breeding localities by mid-July, and the main fall passage takes place in August. Individuals may be met with through September and October and exceptionally into early November. There are enough winter records for District C to justify a casual status; however, this species is frequently erroneously reported at this season. There is one winter record for the Channel Is.: 3 Jan 1980 San Clemente I. Ash-throateds appear to be more regular in winter in the wooded washes of the Colorado Desert and District R, although they are still quite rare. There are no winter records for the northern part of District D.

The breeding habitat of the Ash-throated Flycatcher is varied; it occupies a variety of woodlands, chaparral, desert scrub, and open coniferous forest.

GREAT CRESTED FLYCATCHER
Myiarchus crinitus

Fall vagrant along the immediate coast; this eastern North American species has been recorded seven times: 26 Sep 1970 Pt. Fermin LA; 27 Sep 1974 Goleta SBA; 20 Oct 1974 Pt. Loma SD (one of the latest records for California); 19 Sep 1975 Pt. Loma; 6 Oct 1978 Pt. Loma; 13-14 Oct 1979 Santa Barbara SBA; and 30 Sep 1979 Montana de Oro State Park SLO.

There are 13 additional records for the coast of Northern California and the Farallon Is.

BROWN-CRESTED (WIED'S CRESTED) FLYCATCHER
Myiarchus tyrannulus

Fairly common summer resident in District R; also breeds at Morongo Valley, and possibly very locally elsewhere. Unrecorded west of the deserts.

This species is a fairly common summer resident along the length of the Colorado R., although the clearing of riparian woodlands there has reduced its numbers. To the northwest of District R, one or two pairs also breed at Morongo Valley SBE. A pair present May-Jun 1978 near Mecca RIV and a single bird there 28 Apr 1980 were possibly indicative of breeding, and one along the Mohave R. near Victorville SBE 27 Jul 1978 was also in suitable breeding habitat. The earliest reliable record is 24 Apr 1965 Morongo Valley; it is rare before the first week of May. It is generally gone by the first week of August and is unrecorded after early September.

As a vagrant it has occurred north to Furnace Creek Ranch INY 23 May 1973.

Brown-crested Flycatchers occupy riparian groves of cottonwoods, mesquite, willows, etc., and range into adjacent desert scrub and plantings of tamarisks.

SULPHUR-BELLIED FLYCATCHER
Myiodynastes luteiventris

Fall vagrant from the subtropics; three records: 22 Sep-5 Oct 1974 Big Sycamore Canyon, Pt. Mugu VEN; 6-9 Oct 1978 Goleta SBA; and 7 Oct 1979 Pt. Loma SD.

TROPICAL KINGBIRD
Tyrannus melancholicus

Rare but regular fall and early winter visitant along the immediate coast, with a few records of birds successfully wintering. Casual in spring and in the interior.

Along the coast this species arrives around 20-25 September; the first birds and the majority of all fall records are from San Diego Co. The earliest record for the coast is 12-16 Sep 1962 Coronado SD. Visitants continue well into winter (late December). Records of birds known to have wintered are: 1 Dec 1971-3 Apr 1972 Santa Barbara SBA; 8 Feb-3 Apr 1972 Goleta SBA; 14 Jan-30 Mar 1974 Santa Barbara; 7 Feb-8 Mar 1977 Goleta; 12 Jan-29 Mar 1980 Pt. Mugu VEN; and 1-25 Mar 1980 Whittier Narrows LA. There are other December and early January records of late fall stragglers which have remained for up to a few weeks

before disappearing, and some additional early spring records of birds known not to have wintered locally. There are two unseasonal late spring records for the coast: 17 Apr 1977 Goleta and 15 May 1977 San Pedro LA. It has been recorded only four times in the interior of District C: 30 Sep 1973 Ontario SBE and 21-25 Sep 1976, 15 Sep 1979, and the 1-25 Mar 1980 record cited above, Whittier Narrows LA.

This species is casual in the true interior; the five records are: 1 May 1977 Afton Canyon SBE; 22 Mar 1957 near Palo Verde IMP; 1 Oct 1947 Beal Slough, n. of Topock SBE; 1 Oct 1978 Finney L., SESS; and 23 Oct 1976 Niland IMP.

It has been recorded twice on the Channel Is.: 20 Oct 1974 San Nicolas I. and 13 Oct 1976 San Clemente I. One was also found at sea south of Anacapa I. 17 Oct 1975.

Birds reaching the coast in fall are immatures; this pattern of northward fall vagrancy (or migration) continues into northern California, British Columbia, and (one possible record) Alaska. Tropical Kingbirds dispersing into the region in fall are generally along the immediate coast at promontories such as Pt. Loma SD, or on coastal plains (e.g. Tijuana River Valley). It has wintered where taller trees are mixed with open agricultural fields or parkland.

CASSIN'S KINGBIRD
Tyrannus vociferans   Map p. 394

Fairly common but local summer resident in District C; also breeds locally in the more arid mountain ranges and at oases on the northern deserts. Very few records for the southeastern portion of the region. Small numbers winter along the coast (may be fairly common in winter in San Diego Co.).

In District C it occurs patchily as a summer resident along the coast (e.g. Goleta SBA, Pt. Mugu VEN, Pt. Dume LA, and vic. Santee SD), and in the drier interior valleys and foothills from San Luis Obispo Co. south. In District M it also breeds uncommonly in the eastern part of the San Bernardino Mtns. (Baldwin L.) and uncommonly to fairly commonly on ranges in the e. Mohave Desert (Kingston, Clark, New York, Providence, and Granite Mtns., and higher valleys). This species breeds very locally at oases on the northern deserts (Oasis MNO, Deep Springs INY, Kelso SBE, Morongo Valley SBE, and possibly Furnace Creek Ranch INY).

The Cassin's Kingbird is absent from large portions of District D, especially in the south. It is a casual transient and summer visitant in District R; it does not nest. It has been recorded as a transient and winter visitant in District S as follows: 29 May 1971 SESS; 3 Aug 1968 Salton City IMP; 14-21 Aug 1976 Niland IMP; winter 1910-1911 Brawley IMP; and winter 1910-1911 Mecca RIV. There are two records for nearby Brock Ranch IMP: 9 Sep 1976 (2) and 11 Oct 1976. We list these individual records to underscore the rarity of this species in the south-eastern part of the region.

In fall birds start dispersing from breeding areas in late July and early August; small concentrations of transients are noted in the southern coastal areas between mid-August and early October (e.g. in the Tijuana River Valley SD, where fairly common). It is quite rare as a fall transient north of Orange Co. In winter this species borders on fairly common locally in the southern part of District C (e.g. San Luis Rey River Valley SD). It is decidedly rare in winter north of Orange Co., although records extend north to Morro Bay SLO.

It is a rare transient on the Channel Is. and has been recorded once at sea: some 25-30 km off San Diego 11 May 1951.

Cassin's Kingbirds breed in broken woodlands and around groves of eucalyptus or other tall plantings which border on open areas. On the desert ranges they breed in pinyon-*Yucca* associations. Wintering birds along the southern coast are usually in broken woodlands of the broader river valleys. On the whole, the habitat of this species is less open than that preferred by the Western Kingbird.

THICK-BILLED KINGBIRD
Tyrannus crassirostris

Vagrant from the subtropics; six records. Four records in late fall and early winter in District C: 19 Oct 1965 Tijuana River Valley SD; 3 Dec 1966 Pt. Loma SD; 26-27 Dec 1966 Bonita SD; and 18-23 Oct 1967 Pt. Loma. In District R an adult was present near Blythe RIV 5-16 Aug 1978 and one was n. of Blythe 20-23 Dec 1979.

There are two additional records from the Arizona side of the Colorado R., and two coastal records to the north of our region (San Francisco, Vancouver Island).

WESTERN KINGBIRD
Tyrannus verticalis

Common spring transient and summer resident in lowlands virtually throughout the region, extending locally into open areas of District M. Only one acceptable winter record.

This kingbird breeds nearly throughout Districts C,D,S, and R. It is scarce only in the immediate coastal area, especially from Ventura Co. north, an area of the coast in which it is generally absent. It is a summer resident very locally in open areas within District M (e.g. Baldwin L. in the San Bernardino Mtns.). This species is a rather rare transient on the Channel Is.; it does not breed.

Spring transients appear regularly by 20-25 Mar, occasionally by mid-March; the earliest is 9 Mar 1976 San Marcos SD. This species is much

254

less numerous as a fall transient; fall birds pass through the region early, and the species occurs only rarely into early October. It is casual into late October in the southern coastal areas. The latest record for the region is 3 Nov 1963 Tijuana River Valley SD.

Despite numerous published winter records (*AFN*, Christmas Bird Counts) there is only one acceptable record for this species in the region: 28 Jan 1962 Carlsbad SD.

Western Kingbirds breed almost anywhere in the region where scattered tall trees border agricultural areas, open grasslands, or scrub. In the deserts it is largely restricted as a breeding bird to irrigated areas, and it may be quite abundant in habitats such as the agricultural portions of District S.

EASTERN KINGBIRD
Tyrannus tyrannus

Rare but regular late spring and fall transient in the interior; casual late spring and summer vagrant and very rare but regular fall transient along the coast.

Spring transients through the interior occur mainly in the northeastern portion of the region. An unusually high record fitting the pattern in District D is of a bird at 3000m in the White Mtns. 28 May 1972. This species has not been reliably recorded before 18 May in the region. Vagrants are reported casually through the summer season. Fall transients occur primarily from mid-August to mid-September; stragglers have occurred later: 1 Oct 1973 Shoshone INY and 17 Oct 1978 Vallecito SD. This kingbird has been recorded four times in District S: 4 Jun 1973 SESS, 4 Aug 1968 SESS, 4 Aug 1977 SESS, and 13 Sep 1964 "Salton Sea". It is unrecorded on the California side of the Colorado R., but there is a record at nearby Brock Ranch IMP 20 Jun 1970.

In District C and on the Channel Is. this species is a casual late spring and summer vagrant (unrecorded before mid-June) and a very rare but regular fall transient (mainly from mid-August through late September). There are scattered fall records into early October; the latest record for the region is 20 Oct 1971 Goleta SBA. It has been recorded in all coastal counties.

A pair at Tinnemaha Res. INY 12 and 24 Jun 1978 suggests the possibility of nesting in the region; other summer records exist for the northeastern part of the region, and this species nests in northern Nevada and has nested in northeastern California. In comparison with the eastern part of the continent, the lateness of occurrence of spring birds in the region suggests that, at the tail end of spring migration, we may be receiving birds spreading south and west from their major breeding areas.

SCISSOR-TAILED FLYCATCHER
Tyrannus forficatus

Casual visitant; about 40 records for the region, concentrated in spring and fall. Most spring records are for the interior in late May; fall records are concentrated along the coast. Recorded every month of the year except August.

While most records are for Districts D and C (recorded in all coastal counties), this species has also been found on the Channel Is. (5 records, all for late spring and summer), in District R (4 records), and in District S (26 Mar 1974 near Calexico IMP and 14 Jul 1976 Dos Palmas Spring nr. Mecca RIV). It was recorded once at 2200m at Westgard Pass in the White Mtns. 4 Jun 1978.

The earliest spring record is 3 May 1962 Furnace Creek Ranch INY. Earlier records, which apply either to wintering birds or exceptionally early spring vagrants, are: 3 Jan 1947 and 11 Dec 1947-early Feb 1948 La Mirada LA; 30-31 Jan 1976 Chiriaco Summit RIV; 6 Jan-3 Feb 1980 near Chino SBE; 22 Feb-3 Apr 1965 Tijuana River Valley SD; 4-8 Apr 1976 Ventura VEN (probably a very early spring vagrant); "April" 1947 Anaheim ORA and the Calexico bird above.

Vagrants have been recorded well into summer in the interior and along the coast. The only interior fall records are: 3-8 Oct 1977 Palo Verde IMP; 11-13 Oct 1971 Morongo Valley SBE; and 25 Oct 1948 near Indio RIV.

One attempted to nest in the region. A female present at Needles SBE 26 May through July 1979 constructed a nest and laid five eggs; this nest failed and a second was attempted. The mate was apparently a Western Kingbird.

ALAUDIDAE: LARKS
HORNED LARK
Eremophila alpestris

Common resident in the interior lowlands, common transient and winter visitant in District C (remaining to nest locally), and common summer resident in open areas of District M. Numbers in the interior lowlands are greatly augmented in winter by birds from outside the region.

In the mountains it breeds in open grasslands (e.g. around L. Henshaw and Baldwin L.) and above tree line (in the White Mtns. and on Mt. San Gorgonio in the San Bernardino Mtns.). This species is a common transient in montane grasslands, where it remains irregularly in winter when conditions permit.

Along the coast it breeds where open fields and grasslands remain. It is also an abundant resident on the Channel Is.

In the interior in winter, the Horned Lark may be extremely abundant in grasslands and agricultural regions; interior birds breed in open desert habitats.

HIRUNDINIDAE: SWALLOWS
PURPLE MARTIN
Progne subis

Rather rare and very local summer resident in woodlands of the foothill portions of District C and in District M; also a rare transient, primarily in District C and at the Salton Sea.

Current breeding localities in District C include: Nojoqui Park SBA, O'Neill Park and vic. ORA, and near San Onofre SD; it also nested in 1973 at Monrovia LA. In District M breeding localities include Frazier Park KRN (to 1973); Chilao, San Gabriel Mtns. (at least to the mid-1970s); San Bernardino Mtns. (locally, as near L. Arrowhead, to at least the mid-1970s); the San Jacinto Mtns. (above L. Hemet RIV); and the mountains of San Diego Co. (Mt. Palomar, Cuyamaca Res., Pine Valley).

This species is now a rather rare spring transient along the coastal slope; a recent maximum was of 20 in the Tijuana River Valley SD 15 Apr 1967. Coastal transients are not normally found until mid-April. Spring arrival was earlier (mid-March) when the species bred in greater numbers in District C; a recent record for 11 Mar 1975 at Nojoqui Park suggests that the few remaining coastal breeders arrive early. The earliest record for the region is 2 Mar 1974 Pt. Mugu VEN. The three records for the Channel Is. are all in spring. Fall transients are quite rare and are most often encountered on the immediate coast; they are annual in small numbers at Pt. Loma SD.

The Purple Martin is even scarcer as a transient through the interior, where records are widely scattered. In spring in the interior this species is most regular at the Salton Sea, where migrating swallows in general are more abundant. About two-thirds of the some 27 lowland interior records away from the Salton Sea are from spring. An early fall transient was at SESS 24 Jul 1979. Sixty-five on 6 Aug 1979 at Mt. Palomar were probably fall transients. Fall birds have largely passed through the region by the end of September. Later records are: 21 Oct 1978 L. Henshaw SD and 29 Oct 1977 Furnace Creek Ranch INY (3).

Purple Martins have greatly declined in the region over the last several decades, particularly since the late 1950s. Willett (1933) termed the species a fairly common summer resident, and indicated that by the early 1930s it had actually spread into certain lowland areas where it nested around buildings (e.g. Pasadena and Long Beach LA, and Newport ORA). Its great decline can be linked convincingly to the explosive increase in the regional population of European Starlings. In recent years the spread of starlings into woodlands and forests in District M has threatened the few remaining colonies of Purple Martins in the region. For nesting martins utilize old, tall sycamores, pines, etc., often within oak woodland or open coniferous forest. They have not adapted well to artificial nest houses in the region.

TREE SWALLOW
Tachycineta bicolor

Common spring transient and uncommon to fairly common fall transient through most of the region. Abundant transient and common winter visitant in Districts S and R; also an uncommon winter visitant in District C. Now breeds only rarely and very locally in District C.

The first spring transients arrive in late January; spring migration averages earlier on the coast and the southern deserts. Transients may occur into early June on the northern deserts. Fall transients may linger into early December away from wintering areas. It is always common in winter in Districts R and S, although numbers vary somewhat from year to year. This swallow is an uncommon winter visitant in District C, where it occurs primarily from Orange Co. south (locally farther north, e.g. Pt. Mugu VEN, Santa Maria R. mouth SBA/SLO). It may remain casually through summer in District S.

The Tree Swallow is a rare spring and fall transient on the Channel Is.

It was formerly a common breeder in lowland and foothill riparian groves in District C (e.g. Santa Monica LA, El Monte LA, Riverside RIV, and L. Hodges SD). This species is now a very local summer resident; nesting is now known only from Morro Bay SLO, near the mouth of the Santa Maria R. SLO/SBA, Vandenberg AFB SBA, the Santa Clara R. estuary VEN, L. Henshaw SD, the San Luis Rey R. near Bonsall SD (1978), and near San Diego (1980). It probably breeds at L. Cachuma SBA and it nested at Pt. Mugu until the early 1970s. The decline of this species as a breeder in the region may be tied to the destruction of riparian groves and to competition with starlings for nest cavities.

Winter birds occur primarily around marshes, rivers, and estuaries.

VIOLET-GREEN SWALLOW
Tachycineta thalassina Map p. 394

Very common summer resident through District M and locally in foothills and along the northern coast; also nests near Parker Dam in District R. Generally a common spring transient and uncommon fall transient through the lowlands. Sporadic winter visitant in District C, sometimes in large flocks.

This species breeds throughout District M, including the desert ranges south to the Granite Mtns., and in adjacent foothills of District C. It also breeds locally near the coast from the Santa Monica Mtns. north; it is generally absent as a breeder from the southern coastal sections. An isolated breeding colony exists on the cliffs below Parker Dam SBE in District R; these birds, not graphed, arrive in mid-January and depart by early June. It may nest very locally around cliffs on the deserts (e.g. two

258

at Ft. Piute SBE 3 Jun 1979). Breeding birds may wander widely while foraging.

This swallow is a very common spring transient through District C, where it occurs mainly away from the immediate coast. One of our earliest spring arrivals, the first transients appear in late January and early February. Like other swallows and swifts, migrants are most conspicuous during inclement weather. It is much less numerous and consistent as a fall transient through District C; the fall passage is primarily in mid-October. It migrates rarely past the Channel Is. (mostly in spring).

In the desert districts the Violet-green Swallow is a fairly common spring transient and uncommon and sporadic fall transient. Spring birds arrive later (occurring into April) on the northern deserts. Except for the Purple Martin, this is the least common swallow in District S.

This species largely withdraws from the region in winter, although it winters sporadically along the coast (usually in foothills), primarily from Ventura Co. north (but records south to San Diego Co.). It is occasionally met with in large numbers, e.g. 225 at Gibraltar Res. SBA 2 Jan 1977 and 200 at L. Cachuma SBA winter 1978-1979. It also winters regularly on the coast of central California. There are two winter records in the interior, both for NESS: 31 Dec 1971 and 17 Dec 1977.

The Violet-green Swallow is generally a forest or woodland bird, and is the most numerous swallow over montane forests. Tree cavities (locally crevices in cliffs) are required for nesting. The largest numbers of migrants are encountered over bodies of water during storms.

ROUGH-WINGED SWALLOW
Stelgidopteryx ruficollis

Common summer resident in Districts S and R and fairly common summer resident in District C; fairly common transient and uncommon summer resident in District D. Casual in District C in winter, but irregularly fairly common after mid-December in Districts S and R.

Among our earliest transients, the first birds arrive on the coastal slope by late January. Although it is largely a transient through District D, this species remains to breed locally along river drainages (e.g. fairly common in the Owens Valley). It is largely a transient through District M, although it breeds very locally in the lower portions (e.g. L. Henshaw SD). It is a rare spring and fall transient on the Channel Is.

In Districts S and R this swallow is irregularly fairly common by mid-to-late December: there is no evidence of concentrations there through the fall (mid-September to mid-December). It is strictly casual on the coastal slope after early September; there are about a dozen records between late November and late January, all from Pt. Mugu VEN south.

Birds have generally departed from breeding sites by late July.

Rough-winged Swallows usually nest in the vicinity of watercourses, requiring earth banks (or artificial cavities in walls) for nest sites. Unlike the Bank Swallow, this species is not highly colonial.

BANK SWALLOW
Riparia riparia

Fairly common spring and fall transient through the interior, and very uncommon spring transient and rare fall transient along the coast. Casual in winter, with most records from District S. Only one nesting known in recent years; formerly widespread and numerous as a breeder.

Spring migrants usually arrive after the first week of April (very rarely by late March), and peak in late April and early May (with some transients through the end of May). The fall migration through the interior peaks from mid-August to early September. Migrants along the coast occur in small numbers and are generally mixed in with other swallows; they are best found during inclement weather. It is a rare spring transient on the Channel Is.

This swallow is casual in winter, with the majority of records for the Salton Sea; there are six records between the dates of 9 Nov 1963 and 8 Feb 1964 for SESS. Winter records away from the Salton Sea are: 21-22 Dec 1968 Imperial Beach SD; 26 Jan 1976 San Diego SD; 16 Feb 1974 Imperial Dam IMP (2); 23 Dec 1977 Earp SBE; 1 Mar 1978 Earp; and 5 Jan 1980 Pt. Mugu VEN. A few scattered November records probably pertain to late fall stragglers. A bird in the Tijuana River Valley SD 4 Mar 1973 may have been a very early spring transient.

Non-breeding birds occur casually in June in District S; the first fall migrants appear in early July.

Bank Swallows have been virtually extirpated as a breeder in the region. Willett (1933) considered them a "fairly common" summer resident in suitable habitats; they arrived in March, which is earlier than they now arrive. Former breeding sites included: Santa Barbara SBA (sea cliffs), Sespe VEN (irregularly common), San Pedro LA, Whittier LA, Huntington Beach ORA, Newport ORA, and near Oceanside SD. A colony also existed along the Owens R. near Big Pine INY. The recent record is of one or two pairs that bred at the Santa Clara R. estuary VEN in 1976. The reasons for the disappearance of this species as a breeder are unclear.

CLIFF SWALLOW
Hirundo pyrrhonota

Common to abundant summer resident in all districts, although numbers are much less in the desert regions where suitable habitat is restricted. Abundant and widespread transient. Only five records between late October and mid-January.

The first spring transients arrive in the interior at the end of January (slightly later along the coast). This species is fairly common by the end of February in the interior and by early March along the coast. It is a rare spring transient on the Channel Is.

Although it is quite common at the Salton Sea all through spring and summer, most birds appear to be non-breeders. Breeding was not proven at the Salton Sea until 1977, when 25 nests were found at SESS. Birds summering in District M arrive later than those in the adjacent lowlands.

This species departs very early in fall; it is quite uncommon after late August, and only very rare stragglers occur into October. The only later records are: 2 Nov 1974 and 23 Nov 1977 Furnace Creek Ranch INY; 4 Dec 1971 SESS; 15 Dec 1973 San Diego SD; and 11 Jan 1964 Pt. Mugu VEN. Note that late January birds on the coast are undoubtedly spring transients rather than wintering birds.

Cliff Swallows forage over a wide range of habitats; for nesting they require a source of mud for nest construction and suitable substrate for nest placement (such as eaves or ledges of buildings, highway bridges, rocky cliffs, and even locally the trunks and larger branches of trees — e.g. Yellow Pines in the vicinity of Baldwin L. in the San Bernardino Mtns.).

BARN SWALLOW
Hirundo rustica   Map p. 394

Common transient throughout, breeding locally, especially on the northern coast and around the Channel Is. Casual in winter in the southern lowlands.

One of our commonest migrating swallows, the Barn Swallow often passes through in very large flocks. The first spring arrivals occur in mid-February (exceptionally late January), with the peak spring passage in late April and early May. Stragglers occur as late as mid-June. Birds breeding locally arrive by mid-March. The fall passage is also protracted; the first birds arrive in late July and the last straggle through in November.

This species breeds fairly commonly along the coast south to Pt. Mugu VEN and around most of the Channel Is. It is local farther south on the mainland, breeding at Leo Carillo State Beach, Marina del Rey, and Long Beach LA, Pt. Loma SD, La Jolla SD, and probably in coastal Orange Co. It also breeds in small numbers in the Owens Valley, Antelope Valley, and, recently, very locally at SESS. It does not summer along the Colorado R.

Although it is casual in winter, there are at least 20 records; these are about evenly divided between the southern coastal slope (from Pt. Mugu south) and SESS. There is also a record from Imperial Dam IMP 18 Dec 1973.

Along the coast Barn Swallows nest primarily along the immediate waterfront, either along seacliffs or around waterfront structures. In the interior they breed mainly in culverts on bridges over canals and rivers. Foraging takes place over a wide variety of habitats, including inshore ocean waters.

CORVIDAE: CROWS AND JAYS

STELLER'S JAY
Cyanocitta stelleri Map p. 394

Common resident in woodlands and forests throughout District M (including the White Mtns., but exclusive of the remaining desert ranges). Also resident in the coastal forests of northern San Luis Obispo Co. Rare, but somewhat regular, winter visitant to the coastal lowlands; casual visitant to the desert lowlands.

This species breeds in all major ranges west of the deserts from the Piute Mtns., the area of Mt. Pinos, and the forested mountains of Santa Barbara and Ventura Cos. south through San Diego Co. (exclusive of the Santa Ana Mtns.). It breeds locally down wooded canyons into the foothills of District C (e.g. Santa Anita Canyon LA and Waterman Canyon in San Bernardino SBE). Exceptionally it has even nested lower in groves of planted conifers, eucalyptus, etc. (e.g. Altadena, Pasadena, and Griffith Park LA). It has also summered on the Palos Verdes Peninsula LA. The species breeds in coastal closed-cone pine woodlands in San Luis Obispo Co. south to the vic. of Cambria, Montana de Oro State Park, and Cuesta Summit.

The Steller's Jay is quite rare, but somewhat regular, in the coastal lowlands in winter, particularly in areas adjacent to breeding mountains (especially within Los Angeles Co.). It is casual in the coastal lowlands of Orange and San Diego Cos.

This bird is a casual visitant to the desert areas. It has been recorded at Deep Springs and the Saline Valley INY (fall 1972); Morongo Valley SBE (winter 1971-1972); L. Havasu and Parker Dam SBE (winter 1960-1961); Blythe RIV (23 Feb 1935); and Palo Verde IMP (8 Nov 1950). Most of these records involve several individuals. This jay is rather irruptive in nature; most true interior records come from major corvid flight years and probably pertain to subspecies from the Great Basin (coastal records do not fit this pattern).

BLUE JAY
Cyanocitta cristata

Two records: 30 Oct 1963-20 Apr 1964 Igos, Mill Creek Canyon, San Bernardino Mtns.; and 24 Oct 1973 Panamint City INY.

There are seven additional records for northern California, most of which also fit a recent pattern of fall and winter dispersal through the west.

SCRUB JAY
Aphelocoma coerulescens Map p. 394

Very common resident through District C and in brushlands and arid woodlands of District M. Irregular fall and winter visitant to Districts D, S, and R.

The Scrub Jay is widespread in chaparral, open woodlands, and residential and urban areas. It also breeds in pinyon-juniper habitat from the White Mtns. south through the desert ranges of San Bernardino Co. (including the Little San Bernardino Mtns.), Eagle Mtn. RIV, the desert slopes of the Transverse and Peninsular Ranges, and extreme sw Imperial Co. A distinctive subspecies, *A. c. insularis*, is a common resident on Santa Cruz I.; the species is unrecorded on the other Channel Is.

It is an irregular fall and winter visitant to Districts D, S, and R. The appearance of these birds, which represent interior subspecies, is somewhat correlated with major corvid flights. In District R it is not present some years, but it is of uncommon status other years. Unseasonably late records for birds outside of the breeding range are: 1-27 May 1976 Tecopa INY; 23 Apr 1979 near Tecopa; and 26 May 1979 Scotty's Castle INY.

PINYON JAY
Gymnorhinus cyanocephalus

Fairly common resident in arid woodlands of the desert ranges and locally in similar habitat in the major ranges west of the deserts. Very rare and irregular visitant elsewhere in District M and to District C; casual on the deserts.

This jay breeds in the White, Grapevine, Inyo, Coso, Argus, Panamint, New York, Providence, Granite, and Little San Bernardino Mtns., and very locally farther west: Piute Mtns., ne. San Bernardino Mtns., and San Jacinto Mtns. (primarily in the Garner Valley). Small groups have also been noted in pinyon-juniper habitat around Mt. Pinos, but generally only in fall and winter.

It is a very rare and irregular visitant on the coastal slope and in the mountains outside of the breeding range; its occurrence is almost strictly tied to major corvid invasions. Important flight years on record include: 1876-1877, 1914-1915 (including a March flock of 75 at San Onofre SD, the largest recorded on the coast), 1955-1956, and 1972-1973. Coastal records extend from Paso Robles SLO south to San Diego Co. It has been recorded once on the Channel Is.: 13-28 Sep 1976 Santa Catalina I. (2 on 13 Sep).

The Pinyon Jay is casual on the deserts well away from the breeding range. It has been recorded once on the California side of the Colorado R.: 23 Nov 1978 Parker Dam SBE (6). Two were on the Arizona side near Imperial Dam 8 Oct 1955. Other desert records are: 22 Nov 1955 Essex SBE, 3 Sep 1972 Furnace Creek Ranch INY, and 6 Sep 1970 nw Death Valley Junction INY. Foraging birds often range onto sagebrush deserts adjacent to the breeding range.

In addition to mature pinyon-juniper-*Yucca* woodland on arid mountain slopes, Pinyon Jays occupy open montane valleys of sagebrush and grassland which are bordered by pinyons, Western Junipers, or (in the Big Bear Valley, San Bernardino Mtns.) Yellow Pines.

CLARK'S NUTCRACKER
Nucifraga columbiana

Fairly common resident in the higher mountain ranges. Very rare and irregular fall and winter visitant to the lowlands.

This corvid breeds in the White and Panamint Mtns., on Mt. Pinos and adjacent peaks (possibly to vic. of Pine Mtn. VEN, where one was noted 30 Jul 1980), and in the higher portions of the San Gabriel, San Bernardino, San Jacinto, and (at least formerly) Santa Rosa Mtns. There is some downslope movement in winter within the coniferous forest zone.

The Clark's Nutcracker is a rare and erratic visitant to the mountains of San Diego Co.; the pattern does not always conform to invasions of the lowlands. Large flocks have been noted (e.g. up to 60 on Vulcan Mtn. SD 28 Sep 1935, an invasion year), and the species has even been noted in mid-summer on Mt. Palomar.

Elsewhere outside of the breeding range, it is a very rare and irregular fall and winter visitant, the appearances of which are tied to major corvid flights. Major invasions have carried birds widely over the desert lowlands south to Imperial Dam IMP (9 Oct 1955 for the only Imperial Co. record; there are a few other records for the Arizona side of the river) and the Borrego Valley SD. In District S it was recorded in the Coachella Valley 17-18 Oct 1919 near Indio RIV and 24 Sep 1935 near Coachella RIV. It has been recorded on the coastal slope from Santa Barbara SBA to Pt. Loma SD. It has also been recorded twice, in small flocks, on Santa Cruz I. during major flights (1919-1920 and 1972-1973), and once at sea off Los Angeles ("Sep" 1919). Major flights have occurred in winter 1919-1920, fall 1955, winter 1961-1962, and fall and winter 1972-1973. There are scattered lowland records in other years. Early lowland records include: 24 Aug 1955 near Encinitas SD (dead on beach) and 25 Aug 1950 Joshua Tree National Monument (Lower Covington Flat).

Clark's Nutcrackers occupy higher montane forests, generally above the Yellow Pine belt. Favored areas are arid slopes and rocky timberline areas with firs and pines such as Limber, Lodgepole, Bristlecone, and Jeffrey. Some concentrate around higher campgrounds and picnic areas.

BLACK-BILLED MAGPIE
Pica pica Map p. 395

Fairly common to locally common resident in the Owens Valley and vicinity. Casual visitant elsewhere on the northern deserts.

This species occurs in riparian groves and shade trees bordering pastureland in the Owens Valley south to Olancha INY. It is also resident at Oasis MNO and it occurs irregularly in the adjacent Deep Springs Valley INY.

The Black-billed Magpie is very rarely noted away from the above localities. It has been recorded as a casual visitant south to China L. SBE/INY 29 DEC 1968, Tecopa INY 25 Feb 1973, and Shoshone INY 31 Jan 1973. The latter two records are from a major corvid flight year in which six magpies had been recorded the previous fall in Death Valley. Other Death Valley records are: winter 1918-1919 (invasion); winter 1933-1934; 13 Nov 1971 (n. of Furnace Creek Ranch); and 24 May 1974 (Furnace Creek Ranch).

Several additional records for District C. in Los Angeles, Orange, and San Diego Cos. are best treated as escapees, although it may be note-worthy that all three Los Angeles Co. records came from the same winter, 1956-1957. A record near Piru VEN 10 Apr 1946 may also pertain to an escapee. This species does wander widely in other parts of its range (e.g. into northwestern California).

YELLOW-BILLED MAGPIE
Pica nuttalli   Map p. 395

Fairly common to common (but very local) resident in San Luis Obispo and Santa Barbara Cos.; formerly resident east to extreme western Los Angeles Co. Some records outside the breeding range may pertain to wild birds, but many are likely of escapees.

The primary range is from the upper Salinas Valley in north-central San Luis Obispo Co. south to the Santa Ynez Valley SBA, and east through the inland limit of oak savanna in the eastern parts of the same counties. A few occur along the immediate coastal slope (e.g. w. of Gaviota SBA). There is an isolated population at ranchyards on the Carrizo Plain in e. San Luis Obispo Co. It was resident in the vic. of Goleta SBA to 1973.

Willet (1933) recorded this species as "common" in the latter part of the 1800s, south to the Conejo Valley on the Ventura/Los Angeles Co. line, but it was apparently absent from there by the 1930s. It has been recorded casually south of Santa Barbara Co. during the present century, but at least some of these records probably pertain to escapees. Records likely pertaining to wild birds include: 20 Nov 1910 Santa Paula VEN; and 26 Oct 1925 Chatsworth LA. Other records include: late Mar 1926 near Riverside RIV; 27 Dec 1955 Inglewood LA; 7 Aug 1956 San Fernando LA; 14 Feb 1960 Redlands SBE; Dec 1962 San Gabriel Valley LA; 3 Mar 1973 (and for two weeks thereafter) in the Conejo Valley VEN, near the Los Angeles Co. line; and 29 Feb 1980 Culver City LA. It is our feeling that records after about 1930 most likely pertain to escapees, and that the farther south the older records are, the more likely it is that they pertain to escapees.

Yellow-billed Magpies frequent oak savanna and areas of open oak and oak-riparian woodland which border on ranches, pastureland, etc. The contraction in range may be related to shooting and to local eradication attempts.

COMMON CROW
Corvus brachyrhynchos   Map p. 395

Common resident in District C, except on the southernmost coastal strip; also resident in the northernmost valleys of District D, and in District M (San Diego Co. only). Sporadic transient and winter visitor elsewhere in the region, including Districts S and R.

In District C the crow is abundant in interior valleys and on the northern coast. It is resident south to the vic. of Oceanside SD and was formerly resident south to the Sweetwater and San Diego Rivers. This species is common in the interior portion of District C south through San Diego Co. (e.g. El Cajon SD). In District M it is primarily limited to the mountains of San Diego Co., where it is rather common in open woodland of montane valleys. It is otherwise a scarce transient through District M.

The Common Crow nests fairly commonly, but quite locally, in the northern part of District D (Owens Valley, Fish Lake Valley). In winter it is confined mainly to the towns of the Owens Valley (e.g. Big Pine and Bishop INY). A pair nested for several consecutive years in the early 1970s at Scotty's Castle INY. Elsewhere in District D it is mainly a rare transient and casual winter visitor. This species has been noted casually in migration at Furnace Creek Ranch INY (October, November, April, and, exceptionally, 27-29 May 1979) and was also recorded 21-27 May 1980 Stovepipe Wells INY. Twenty near Baker SBE 14 Apr 1971 was a large concentration for that part of the region. Winter records for District D outside of the Owens Valley are: 4 Dec 1975-29 Jan 1976 Kelso SBE; 19 Dec 1976 Furnace Creek Ranch INY (4); and 25 Feb 1978 Daggett SBE. A bird in the New York Mtns. 30 Jul 1976 was unseasonal.

This species is a sporadic winter visitant in District S; flocks of up to 30 have occurred, but it is absent most winters and there is only a single record (one bird) since Dec 1975. Its status is similar along the Colorado R., except that major flights have occurred: 500 near Cibola RIV in mid-winter 1977-1978 and 1978-1979, with small flocks and single birds scattered elsewhere along the river those winters; and 300 north of Blythe RIV 28 Nov 1964.

Common Crows reach their peak abundance in areas where large trees and orchards exist in the agricultural areas of inland valleys in District C. They are also common in valley woodlands, residential areas with large trees, and in coastal woodlands from Ventura Co. north.

COMMON RAVEN
Corvus corax

Common resident in District D; fairly common resident in Districts R and M, locally in Districts C and S, and on the larger Channel Is.

This species is commonest in the northern deserts from the Mohave Desert and Antelope Valley north through the Carrizo Plain, Cuyama Valley, Owens Valley, and Death Valley regions. It is generally absent from the irrigated portions of Districts R and S, although it is fairly common in arid habitats adjacent to these areas. It occurs primarily from Blythe RIV north in District R.

In District C the Common (or Holarctic) Raven is rather common and widespread in the drier interior valleys and foothills. It is virtually absent along the coast north of westernmost Ventura Co.

Ravens range over a variety of arid and semi-arid habitats, and are abundant and characteristic birds of our northern deserts. They routinely occupy agricultural areas on the northern deserts, but they avoid such areas around the Salton Sea and Colorado R. Away from the deserts they occur in open montane woodlands, chaparral (especially near cliffs), and locally even in urban areas (e.g. West Los Angeles).

PARIDAE: TITMICE
MOUNTAIN CHICKADEE
Parus gambeli   Map p. 395

Common resident in coniferous forests throughout District M; rare but regular visitant to the coastal lowlands, and irregular fall visitant and

casual winter visitant to the deserts (primarily from the Mohave Desert north).

The Mountain Chickadee breeds in all the major ranges west of the deserts, including the forested mountains of Santa Barbara Co. and San Diego Co., and the Santa Ana Mtns. ORA. It also breeds on the desert ranges from the White Mtns. south to the Clark and New York Mtns. and possibly the Granite Mtns., where it has been recorded in summer.

This species is a somewhat regular winter visitant in varying numbers to the coastal lowlands; it is recorded annually in foothill regions adjacent to the breeding ranges, but it is quite irregular along the immediate coast. This chickadee is quite rare from Santa Barbara Co. north and along the southern coast, although it is regular in the vic. of Oceanside SD. This species is unrecorded on the Channel Is. Coastal birds may appear as early as August, and have remained to late May on the Palos Verdes Peninsula LA (where other montane species such as Stellers's Jay have summered).

In the desert lowlands it is a rare and irregular fall visitant and casual winter visitant which occurs primarily from the Mohave Desert north. It has been recorded with some regularity in desert mountain ranges outside of the breeding range (e.g. Providence Mtns., Little San Bernardino Mtns.) in fall and winter. This species is strictly casual on the southern deserts and is unrecorded in District R, although there are records from the Arizona side of the river. In District S it has been recorded at least three times in the vicinity of Mecca RIV (including a flock of 12, 8-15 Dec 1935) and once at SESS (5 Oct 1955 near Niland IMP). It was also recorded at Regina on the northeast side of the Algodones Dunes IMP 26 Feb-5 Mar 1978.

Mountain Chickadees occupy a wide variety of montane forests from the pine-oak and pinyon-juniper belts on up to treeline. Birds wintering in the lowlands favor planted pines.

CHESTNUT-BACKED CHICKADEE
Parus rufescens Map p. 395

Common resident in woodlands along the immediate coast of San Luis Obispo Co. and extreme western Santa Barbara Co. One extralimital record for Santa Barbara SBA.

The southernmost breeding localities are the Santa Maria R. mouth SLO/SBA, San Antonio Ck. on the Vandenberg AFB SBA, and the Santa Ynez R. mouth SBA. South of the breeding range, one was present in Santa Barbara 24 Oct 1975-10 Mar 1976.

Chestnut-backed Chickadees are local even within their limited breeding range in the region. Most occur in willow thickets along creeks; they also inhabit native coastal pine forests (vic. Cambria SLO) and plantings of conifers and shrubs (e.g. around Morro Bay SLO). Their range, as outlined here, is somewhat expanded over that described by Grinnell and Miller (1944).

PLAIN TITMOUSE
Parus inornatus Map p. 395

Common resident in oak and oak-conifer woodlands in District C and the lower portions of District M. Also resident in pinyon-juniper associations on the desert ranges.

In District C it is largely absent from the vicinity of the coast south of Oceanside SD. This species occurs at over 2000m in District M, and in arid woodlands of the desert slopes of the coastal mountains.

Interior subspecies are resident in pinyon-juniper associations in the desert mountains of Inyo and San Bernardino Cos., from the White Mtns. south to the Providence and Granite Mtns., and in the Little San Bernardino Mtns. SBE/RIV.

The Plain Titmouse occurs irregularly in fall and winter on the western edge of the deserts at localities such as Yaqui Well SD and Coyote Ck. SD on the Anza-Borrego desert. The only occurrence in the lowlands of the true interior is 26 Nov 1964 near Mecca RIV (in District S).

It is unrecorded from the Channel Is.

REMIZIDAE: VERDIN

VERDIN
Auriparus flaviceps Map p. 395

Common resident on the southern deserts; occurs less commonly through the Mohave Desert. Formerly occurred in extreme sw San Diego Co.

The Verdin is common on the Colorado Desert, including District R and, where suitable habitat remains, District S. It is much less numerous in desert scrub from the s. Mohave Desert north and west locally to the Antelope Valley (vic. Pearblossom LA and Rosamond KRN) and the Amargosa R. INY. It formerly occurred north to Furnace Creek Ranch INY, but it has only been a straggler there in recent years (since 1971, recorded only on 29 Mar 1979). It is a casual stray to the China Lake SBE area (1970-1971).

A few formerly occurred in the western part of the Tijuana River Valley SD (no breeding evidence), but there are no records from there since about 1975. It has occurred as a vagrant along the coast north to Chula Vista SD 22 Jan 1956 and San Elijo Lagoon SD 9 Jan-17 Feb 1975.

Typical Verdin habitat consists of taller desert vegetation (palo verde, mesquite, salt cedar, etc.)along washes, although the species does occur on desert flats dominated by creosote. On the Mohave Desert a mixture of creosote and Joshua Trees is occupied, especially near washes. The population in the Tijuana River Valley inhabited brush such as *Baccharis* and tree tobacco.

AEGITHALIDAE: BUSHTIT

BUSHTIT
Psaltriparus minimus *Map p. 395*

Common resident in brush and woodlands throughout District C and in the lower portions of District M; also resident in arid woodlands of the desert mountains, and on Santa Cruz I. Casual winter visitant to the desert lowlands.

The breeding range includes the desert slopes of the coastal mountains (even sporadically to Mountain Springs in extreme sw Imperial Co.), and locally onto the westernmost portions of District D (Morongo Valley SBE, Coyote Ck. SD). It is a fairly common resident in pinyons, junipers, and brush in the desert ranges from the White Mtns. south through the New York, Providence, Granite, and Little San Bernardino Mtns.

It is resident on Santa Cruz I. and, formerly, on Santa Catalina I. It has occurred as a vagrant to Anacapa I. 11 Aug 1976 (2).

This species is a fall and winter vagrant to the desert lowlands. It has been recorded at least four times in the northern part of District R (winter flocks have been found recently on the Arizona side of the river), and at Scotty's Castle, Stovepipe Wells, Furnace Creek Ranch, and Tecopa INY. There are two records for District S: several near Mecca RIV 29 Dec 1970 and five at NESS 16 Aug 1980. These lowland desert records likely pertain to interior subspecies.

SITTIDAE: NUTHATCHES

RED-BREASTED NUTHATCH
Sitta canadensis

Fairly common resident in the higher mountain ranges; irregular fall transient and winter visitant through the rest of the region. A few breed at Pt. Loma SD; has bred on Santa Cruz I. and Palos Verdes Peninsula LA.

This species breeds in the Mt. Pinos region (uncommon), the San Gabriel Mtns., the San Bernardino Mtns., and the San Jacinto Mtns. It has bred on Mt. Palomar SD, and one was on Hot Springs Mtn. SD 24 Jun 1980. It also breeds in the higher forests of the White Mtns. and has summered recently on Clark Mtn. and the Kingston Mtns. A bird in the New York Mtns. 26 May 1977 was possibly a migrant.

In District C it has bred since 1964 in planted conifers on Pt. Loma SD. It also breeds erratically on Santa Cruz I., and bred in 1970 on the Palos Verdes Peninsula LA. The Red-breasted Nuthatch is an irregular fall and winter visitant to the rest of District C and the Channel Is.; it is fairly common some years, present in small numbers most years, and virtually absent in a few years. It occurs in the lowlands of District C primarily from mid-September through March.

On the deserts it is a highly irregular fall transient which occurs primarily on the northern deserts. This nuthatch is occasionally quite common (e.g. in fall 1972 from late August through October), but it is virtually absent some years. It has been recorded as early as 12 Aug 1979 near Lancaster LA, and as late as 29 May 1976 and 27 May-1 Jun 1980 Oasis MNO. The species is much less common on the southern deserts; during flight years small numbers may occur in Distirct R (mainly in fall) and, very rarely, in District S (fall only). Birds in winter invasions undoubtedly originate from outside the region.

Breeding occurs primarily in forests of firs, Lodgepole Pines, etc. While smaller numbers nest in the Yellow Pine belt, the species is primarily a winter visitant there. Most birds in the lowlands occur in planted conifers.

PYGMY NUTHATCH
Sitta pygmaea

Common resident in forests of District M west of the deserts, and in the White Mtns. Also nests in coastal closed-cone pine forests around Cambria SLO. Very rare and erratic visitant to the coastal lowlands; casual in District D.

This species breeds from the Piute Mtns., Mt. Pinos, and the higher mountains of Santa Barbara Co. south through the Transverse and Peninsular Ranges to the mountains of San Diego Co. In the northeastern part of the region it breeds only in the White Mtns. It has occurred in late spring on Clark Mtn. (e.g. two on 18 May 1975), but there is no evidence of breeding there. In District C it nests only in the vicinity of Cambria SLO.

The Pygmy Nuthatch is a very rare and erratic visitant to the coastal lowlands; it is unrecorded most years, but during occasional flights (e.g. fall 1960, fall 1966, and fall 1972) it has been recorded from Santa Barbara SBA south to Pt. Loma SD. There are a few scattered records from non-flight years. It was recorded at Pt. Loma as late as 30 May 1966. This nuthatch is unrecorded on the Channel Is.

A casual visitant to District D, there are eight records for Joshua Tree National Monument, 23 Aug-3 Sep; and the following records from elsewhere: 22 Aug 1972 Morongo Valley SBE; 1 Sep 1972 Big Pine INY (15); 2-5 Sep 1977 Yucca Valley SBE (2); and 22 Apr 1978 Whitewater Canyon RIV.

Pygmy Nuthatches are most numerous in open Yellow Pine forests, but breeding also takes place in other associations of mixed conifers. Birds in the lowlands have occurred primarily in planted conifers.

WHITE-BREASTED NUTHATCH
Sitta carolinensis Map p. 396

Common resident in woodlands of District M and locally in foothill and canyon portions of District C. Rare winter visitant outside of breeding range in District C; casual in the desert lowlands.

It breeds in all the ranges west of the deserts and in arid conifer woodlands from the White Mtns. south to the Argus Mtns. INY. A singing bird was on Clark Mtn. 15 May 1976, but the species is not known to breed there. It also breeds locally in woodlands of District C from Orange and Los Angeles Cos. north.

Outside of the breeding range in District C, it is a rather rare winter visitant which begins arriving in August. This species is much less likely to make irregular invasions than the Red-breasted Nuthatch. There are two records from the Channel Is.: 1 Apr 1920 Santa Cruz I. and winter 1972-1973 Santa Cruz I. (up to 3). In the desert mountains outside of the known breeding range, it has been recorded in pinyon-juniper woodland in the Mid Hills SBE 30 Mar 1973, 21 Oct 1975, and 4 Dec 1975; there are also three records for Joshua Tree National Monument: 4 Sep-18 Nov (all of the coastal race, *S. c. aculeata*).

This species is casual in the desert lowlands; the records are: in District R from s. of Needles SBE (21 and 26 Dec; year?); in District D at Furnace Creek Ranch INY 12 Oct 1935 and at Kelso 30 Sep 1972; and in District S at Coachella 10 Sep 1935; from nw of Mecca RIV 15 Dec 1935; and at SESS 7 Nov 1970 and 6 Aug 1976.

While the White-breasted Nuthatch breeds in a variety of montane woodlands, over much of its range the presence of some oaks seems to be a requirement. Birds resident in District C occur mainly in mature live oak woodland. Birds breeding in the northeastern part of the region are primarily in pinyons and occur upward into Limber and Bristlecone Pines.

CERTHIIDAE: CREEPERS
BROWN CREEPER
Certhia familiaris

Fairly common resident in District M, primarily west of the deserts. Rare fall transient and winter visitant in the coastal lowlands; rare transient and visitant on the deserts, primarily in fall.

The Brown Creeper breeds from Mt. Pinos and Figueroa Mtn. south through the major forested ranges to the mountains of San Diego Co. Small numbers also breed in the White Mtns.; it has been recorded on Clark Mtn. in mid-May, but there is no evidence of breeding. It is also resident locally on the northern coast south to Morro Bay SLO. Breeding birds occur locally in densely wooded canyons in the coastal foothills of the major ranges.

There is a regular winter movement into woodlands and canyons in the higher parts of District C. Very small numbers winter through the rest of the coastal lowlands. It appears in the lowlands after mid-September; it has been recorded three times in mid-August: 11-20 Aug 1980 Los Angeles LA, 13 Aug 1970 Pt. Loma SD, and 14 Aug 1968 Santa Barbara SBA. The creeper is a rare fall transient and winter visitor on the Channel Is.

This species is a rare but regular fall transient in District D; most occur on the northern deserts. A few winter in District R; it is casual in fall and winter in District S.

Brown Creepers occupy a variety of mature coniferous forests; they are partial to the larger pines and to Incense-Cedar, but accept mixtures of other conifers and of oaks and riparian trees. Birds on the northern coast breed in forests of Monterey Pine and around planted conifers. Birds wintering below District M occur both in planted conifers and in native oak and riparian associations.

CINCLIDAE: DIPPERS

AMERICAN DIPPER
Cinclus mexicanus

Uncommon and very local resident along swift-flowing, permanent streams in montane foothills. Limited fall and winter dispersal in the northeastern part of the region and to coastal foothills. One record for the Channel Is.

Known nesting localities include Santa Paula Canyon, Agua Blanca Ck., and Sespe Ck. VEN; Santa Anita Canyon LA and locally elsewhere in the San Gabriel Mtns.; Upper Santa Ana R., Bear Ck., and Mill Ck., San Bernardino Mtns.; and Tahquitz Ck. and the north fork of the San Jacinto R., San Jacinto Mtns. It also nests locally in the White Mtns. In San Diego Co. this species is probably most regular in winter, but it has nested along the San Luis Rey R. (not recently). Recent San Diego Co. records are: 16 Jun 1971 Mt. Palomar and 27 Nov 1977 on the desert slope in the northeastern part of the county (two birds, on different streams). In the Santa Barbara area it winters sporadically along canyon streams and possibly remains to breed after wet winters. There is an old nesting record for the vic. of Carpinteria SBA at only 160m.

In the northeastern part of the region it is largely a casual fall and winter visitant away from the breeding habitat in the White Mtns. It was recorded at Deep Springs INY 18 Oct 1975 and in Surprise Canyon in the Panamint Mtns. 26 Oct-8 Nov 1978. It has been recorded regularly in winter on streams on the floor of the Owens Valley; it nests on the eastern flank of the Sierra Nevada, just outside the region. There is one record farther south on the deserts: 29 Oct 1978 Volcan Mine, Providence Mtns. SBE.

The one record for the Channel Is. is: 13-25 Jul 1975 Santa Cruz I.

Dippers occupy fast-flowing, clear streams in mountain canyons; they depart the highest streams during the colder months. Vagrants have been noted along the banks of irrigation canals, intermittent streams, and ponds.

TROGLODYTIDAE: WRENS

CACTUS WREN
Campylorhynchus brunneicapillus   Map p. 396

Common resident in Districts S and R, and uncommon to fairly common resident through most of the remainder of the desert regions. Very local resident in District C north to southern Ventura Co.

This wren is common along the length of the Colorado R., particularly in the southern part. It is also common in desert scrub in the Imperial and Coachella Valleys. It is a sparser but still fairly common resident in taller desert scrub through the remainder of the southern deserts. The Cactus Wren is an uncommon to fairly common resident north through the Mohave Desert to the w. Antelope Valley, Tecopa INY, the Kingston and Argus Mtns., and the Walker Pass area in Kern Co. (just outside the region). Its range does not extend north to the Owens Valley or Death Valley.

This species is a casual vagrant to the northernmost deserts, where it has been recorded as follows: 11 May 1972 Teakettle Jct. in the northern part of Death Valley INY; 21 Nov 1977 Mesquite Springs INY; 24 Sep 1975 Lee Flat s. of the Saline Valley INY; and 3 Oct 1978 near Deep Springs INY.

The Cactus Wren is a very local resident in District C north to s. Ventura Co. Northernmost current localities are in the vic. of Pt. Mugu, Camarillo, and Simi Valley VEN. It bred, at least formerly, north to Santa Paula and Sespe VEN. It occurs locally eastward in the larger washes of the Transverse Ranges (Tujunga Wash LA, vic. Claremont LA, etc.), and locally along the coast south to San Diego Co. (e.g. Palos Verdes Peninsula LA, Irvine/Newport Bay ORA, San Elijo Lagoon SD, Sweetwater Res. SD, etc.). It is sedentary within the limited coastal habitat. However, vagrants have been noted away from known breeding areas at Pt. Loma SD and Mission Bay SD.

On the deserts Cactus Wrens occur in riparian thickets, and in desert scrub where taller vegetation (Joshua Trees, cholla, etc.) provides nesting and foraging sites, singing posts, etc. They have adapted well to groves of salt cedar (*Tamarix*). Along the coast they occur in dry washes with yuccas and cacti, and on lower coastal slopes and bluffs with extensive patches of prickly-pear cactus.

ROCK WREN
Salpinctes obsoletus

Common resident in arid, rocky areas throughout District D and in the desert mountain ranges. Also resident in suitable rocky habitat in the mountains west of the deserts, and locally in District C. Some winter influx into Districts C, S, and R.

This species is widespread in District D and in suitable habitat in District M (where it is primarily a summer resident). In District C it is primarily an uncommon to fairly common winter visitant in suitable habitat, including bluffs on the immediate coast. This wren is a very local breeder along the immediate coast (e.g. Morro Rock SLO, Pt. Mugu VEN); it is more widespread as a breeder in arid, rocky areas of the extreme interior of District C, especially from Ventura Co. north.

The Rock Wren is a rather common resident on all the Channel Is.

This species is primarily a winter visitant in District R, although it is resident in arid areas right up to the border of that district. It is resident on cliffs around Parker Dam SBE, and locally elsewhere. An uncommon winter visitant in District S, it has summered at Rock Hill SESS.

Rock Wrens occupy a variety of rocky habitats such as cliff faces, rock outcroppings within brushy or wooded areas, gravelly washes, arid desert hills and mountains, and talus slopes and scree up to the summits of the highest mountains.

CANYON WREN
Catherpes mexicanus

Fairly common but local resident in rocky canyons nearly throughout, though absent from the flatter lowlands and higher mountains. Limited movement away from breeding areas.

The greatest numbers occur in coastal canyons and on the desert slopes of the major coastal ranges. It is also found locally in canyons and on bluffs along the immediate coast (e.g. Pt. Dume LA, Torrey Pines State Park SD). On the deserts it occurs primarily in the mountainous portions of northern and central District D. It is also found very locally along the Colorado R., as on the bluffs around Parker Dam SBE.

One or more birds have been in residence on Santa Cruz I. since 1973 and there are two older records for that island; it is otherwise unrecorded on the Channel Is.

Although this species is basically sedentary, there is limited movement away from known breeding areas (e.g. recorded on 3 Nov 1973 at Desert Center RIV).

Canyon Wrens occur around rocky stream banks and canyon sides; they are most common in well-shaded coastal canyons. Smaller numbers breed in more arid areas as long as rocky cliffs and boulders provide suitable foraging and nesting areas.

BEWICK'S WREN
Thryomanes bewickii Map p. 396

Common resident in brushy habitats throughout District C and in the lower portions of District M; also resident locally on the northern and western borders of District M, and in District R and the Channel Is. Uncommon transient and winter visitant through the remainder of the interior.

The breeding range includes pinyon-juniper associations of the desert mountains of Mono, Inyo, and San Bernardino Cos. It is resident on the desert slopes of the major coastal mountains (east to Eagle Mtn. RIV and to extreme sw Imperial Co.), and it extends locally onto the western edge of District D (Morongo Valley SBE, Mohave R. SBE, etc.). It is also resident in riparian groves in the Owens Valley INY.

Elsewhere in the desert lowlands it is primarily an uncommon transient and winter visitant. This species is a local resident in District R n. of Needles SBE; it is fairly common in the northern portion of District R in winter, but it is uncommon farther south.

The Bewick's Wren is resident on Santa Rosa, Santa Cruz, Anacapa, and Santa Catalina Is. Mainland races are very rare transients on the remaining Channel Is. The endemic subspecies of San Clemente I., *T. b. leucophrys*, has recently become extinct.

HOUSE WREN
Troglodytes aedon Map p. 396

Common summer resident in woodlands and brushy areas in Districts C and M and very locally in District D; transient and rare to locally fairly common winter visitant in lowlands throughout.

In District C it is a common breeder throughout. This species remains fairly commonly through the winter from Santa Barbara Co. south; lesser numbers stay on the northernmost coast. In District M it breeds primarily around riparian thickets and meadows throughout the ranges west of the deserts and in the White and Panamint Mtns. It departs District M in the winter.

This wren breeds very locally on the northern and western margins of District D, e.g. Oasis MNO, near Lancaster LA, and Morongo Valley SBE (not graphed). Elsewhere it is primarily a transient, uncommon in spring and fairly common in fall. In winter this species departs the colder, northern deserts and remains rarely in thick brush on the southern deserts. It is a fairly common transient and winter visitant in brushy areas in Districts R and S.

The House Wren is an uncommon transient on the Channel Is.; a few winter on the larger islands.

House Wrens reach their greatest abundance where a brushy understory occurs under oaks and riparian trees. They are also numerous in montane brush and meadows. Transients and wintering birds occur in a variety of dense, brushy situations.

WINTER WREN
Troglodytes troglodytes

Rare to uncommon transient and winter visitant on the coastal slope, but only casual s. of Los Angeles Co. May breed on the extreme northern coast. Rare transient and casual winter visitant in the interior, primarily on the northern deserts.

South of Los Angeles Co. its status borders on casual. There are a few records for Orange Co., and some dozen records (mostly of fall transients) for San Diego Co. It probably breeds regularly in coastal woodlands around Cambria SLO (e.g. three pairs present there in summer 1967 and nesting pairs summer 1978 and 1980 — not on graph).

In District D this species is primarily a rare fall transient and casual winter visitant; it is probably regular as a spring transient, but few records exist and coverage is poor on the deserts in early spring. Most records of transients have come from the northern deserts, but records extend south to Coyote Ck. SD. The northernmost winter record on the deserts is at Shoshone INY 6 Feb 1965. The latest spring record is at Whitewater RIV 24 Apr 1967. It has been recorded once in District S: 20 Dec 1976 SESS (2). It was unrecorded on the California side of the Colorado R. until the winter of 1978-1979, when small numbers were present in several areas and many were on the Arizona side.

It is a rare fall transient on Santa Cruz I.; there is one fall record for Santa Barbara I.

Winter Wrens frequent dense, tangled thickets, usually in canyon bottoms. Breeding birds in the Cambria area occur in the dense understory of coastal coniferous forests. The secretive nature of this species makes its status imperfectly known.

MARSH WREN
Cistothorus palustris

Common resident in Districts R and S; primarily a winter visitant in District C, nesting locally. Breeds very locally in District D, where primarily a transient.

While it is a common resident in the marshes of Districts S and R, there is also an influx of wintering birds. This species is a common winter visitant throughout District C in suitable marshy habitat, but it has greatly declined as a nesting species. The current status of nesting on the coast is uncertain; it is known to breed in several lagoons in coastal San Diego Co. (vic. Oceanside) and in marshy areas in w. Santa Barbara Co. (Santa Ynez R. mouth north to Santa Maria R. mouth). Breeding is suspected in a few inland areas in the southern portion of the district. It was formerly much more widespread as a nester along the coast; the decline is probably largely the result of the destruction of habitat.

The Marsh Wren breeds very locally in District D; it is resident in marshes n. of Lancaster LA, and it has summered at Furnace Creek Ranch INY. It is otherwise an uncommon spring and fairly common fall transient through District D and, rarely, District M. This species occurs in winter in suitable marsh habitat, but it is absent from the colder northern deserts at this season. It has wintered in District M (Baldwin L., San Bernardino Mtns.).

This species is a scarce transient and winter visitant on the Channel Is.

Marsh Wrens breed in extensive beds of cattails and rushes. In winter they may also occupy coastal salt marshes and low, wet, brushy areas. Transients may occur almost anywhere, but seek dense cover.

MIMIDAE: MOCKINGBIRDS AND THRASHERS

GRAY CATBIRD
Dumetella carolinensis

Casual vagrant; a total of 19 records for the region, most from spring in the northern interior and from fall along the coast.

In the northern part of District D (Oasis MNO south to Ft. Piute SBE) this species has been recorded eight times between the dates of 26 May 1977 (Scotty's Castle INY) and 10 Jun 1964 (Deep Springs INY and Oasis MNO). It has also been recorded twice in fall in the interior: 26 Oct-2 Nov 1974 Scotty's Castle and 6 Oct 1975 Deep Springs INY.

There are eight fall records for the coast: Santa Barbara SBA (twice), Santa Cruz I., San Nicolas I., Pt. Loma SD (twice), San Diego SD, and Tijuana River Valley SD. The extreme dates are 24-25 Sep 1976 Pt. Loma; and 1-3 Dec 1971 Santa Barbara and 3 Dec 1972 San Diego.

There is one record that apparently represents a wintering bird: 27 Mar-17 Apr 1980 Northridge LA (killed by a cat on the last date).

NORTHERN MOCKINGBIRD
Mimus polyglottos

Common resident in District C and in the southern interior; less common on the northern deserts. Breeds on some of the Channel Is.

This species is a common to locally abundant resident everywhere in District C except in the densest brush and woodlands. It is also a common resident in the southern deserts, including Districts S and R. It occurs more sparsely across the northern deserts to the Owens, Deep Springs, and Fish Lake Valleys and the Argus and Panamint Mtns.; there is undoubtedly withdrawal from these areas in winter. The breeding range generally lies below District M, although there is occasional late summer and fall upslope movement into that district.

This species breeds on the larger Channel Is.; it has also bred on San Nicolas I. It is a rare visitant on the other islands.

This species is most abundant in suburban areas with exotic plantings and much shrubbery. It is also quite numerous in brushlands and orchards in the southern deserts. It is less common in native chaparral, desert scrub, and woodlands. This species has clearly increased as a result of human modification of the landscape.

SAGE THRASHER
Oreoscoptes montanus

Fairly common summer resident in sagebrush habitats in the higher montane valleys of the northeastern part of the region and, at least formerly, locally farther south. Fairly common spring transient and uncommon fall transient in the interior, remaining rarely in winter. Rare transient and very rare winter visitant in District C.

This species breeds fairly commonly in the sagebrush habitats of higher montane valleys in the White Mtns. (primarily) and in the Inyo and Panamint Mtns. It has been recorded breeding near Victorville SBE, and it perhaps still breeds locally in the higher parts of District D south of Inyo Co. It formerly bred in the Lockwood Valley VEN (around 1900), but it probably does so no longer.

Spring transients through the interior may arrive as early as mid-February (exceptionally late January); spring migration peaks in early March. A very late spring record in the interior is 4 Jun 1970 Agua Caliente SD. Fall transients arrive in the middle of August. It is a very scarce transient through Districts S and R (generally away from agricultural areas) and in the interior of District C (e.g. w. Riverside Co.). In the interior it is rare in winter; most birds found there are on the southern deserts and in the extreme southwestern San Joaquin Valley.

In District C it is primarily a rare transient (mostly fall) and very rare winter visitant. Records are concentrated along the immediate coast; on the Channel Is., where it is an uncommon fall transient; and in the arid interior of the district (e.g. L. Elsinore RIV). Most records in District C are from Los Angeles Co. south. It has wintered on the coast, primarily in San Diego Co., and in the arid interior of the district. There are a few records of spring transients on the immediate coast.

Sage Thrashers breed almost exclusively in stands of sagebrush in the higher valleys; transients may occur in a variety of scrub habitats. It has declined locally as a wintering bird on the coast and as a breeder.

279

BROWN THRASHER
Toxostoma rufum

Rare but regular spring and fall vagrant, and casual winter visitant; a total of some 65 records for the region.

Almost all of the 26 coastal records are from September through very early May; many of the records pertain to spring vagrants not known to have wintered (e.g. 20 Apr 1975 San Nicolas I.). The earliest fall record is 28 Aug 1969 Griffith Park, Los Angeles LA; the latest spring record for the coast is 15 May 1979 Pt. Loma SD. There are three records for the Channel Is.

In the interior most birds have been recorded in fall from late September to early November (most in mid-October). Spring records have been in April and early May (the normal migration period of this species) and also in late May and early June (the traditional period for "eastern vagrants"). Winter records come primarily from the southern deserts. There are two records for District S (15 Jan-18 Mar 1972 Westmorland SESS, and 26 Feb 1978 SESS) and no records for District R.

BENDIRE'S THRASHER
Toxostoma bendirei   Map p. 396

Fairly common but very local summer resident on the Mohave Desert, primarily in e. San Bernardino Co. Otherwise a casual transient in the interior and rare vagrant along the coast.

This species breeds primarily in Joshua Tree woodlands from the Lanfair Valley and vic. Cima SBE north to the north slope of Clark Mtn. Smaller numbers breed on the s. Mohave Desert south to the vic. of Victorville SBE and Joshua Tree National Monument SBE/RIV. A singing bird was present in Joshua Tree woodlands near Palmdale LA 7-8 Apr 1979. There are unsubstantiated reports of nesting on the creosote desert to the west of the Colorado R. between Needles and Blythe. Breeding birds arrive in late March and early April and depart quite early — generally by late July, but they have been recorded to 22 Aug on the breeding grounds, and, exceptionally, to 8 Oct 1978 Lanfair Valley SBE.

Away from the breeding range it is a casual transient in the interior and rare vagrant to the coast. There are four spring records of vagrants north of the known breeding range: 23 May 1970 Oasis MNO; 1 Jun 1974 Stovepipe Wells INY; 23 May 1977 Mesquite Springs INY; and 28 May 1977 Furnace Creek Ranch INY. It has been recorded in the southern part of District D as follows: 8 Apr 1885 Palm Springs RIV and 22 May 1897 Whitewater RIV. Records in or near District R are: 8 Apr 1961 Imperial Dam IMP; 9 Apr 1971 Parker Dam SBE; 10 May 1979 30km nw. Blythe RIV; and 30 Apr 1972 Brock Ranch IMP. Records in District S are: 1 Nov

1964-27 Jan 1965 SESS and 12 Nov 1967 near Niland SESS. Unseasonal records from near the breeding range are: 13 Nov 1973 near Lancaster LA; 1 Jan 1966 Randsburg KRN; and 18 Nov-1 Dec 1968 Morongo Valley SBE.

In District C and on the Channel Is. it is a rare but regular fall vagrant (about 25 records to date). Most records are for September and October, but it has been recorded as early as 30 Jul-2 Aug 1976 San Pedro LA. Most records are from San Diego Co., but it has also occurred north to Los Angeles Co. (5 records), Ventura Co. (3), Santa Barbara Co. (2), and the Channel Is. (5). Unseasonal coastal records are: 8 Nov 1973-31 Jan 1974 Tijuana River Valley SD; 17 Dec 1978-10 Mar 1979 Tijuana River Valley; 21 Dec 1968 Tijuana River Valley; 14 Jan 1959 near Shandon SLO; 24 Dec 1979-4 Jan 1980 San Pedro LA; and 4 Apr 1970 Imperial Beach SD (the only coastal spring vagrant).

The breeding habitat of the Bendire's Thrasher consists of Joshua Tree woodland with scattered shrubs (creosote, etc.) and patches of grassland; on the e. Mohave Desert it also breeds away from Joshua Trees in areas where *Opuntia* cactus is plentiful (up to over 1500m).

CURVE-BILLED THRASHER
Toxostoma curvirostre

Casual winter visitant in the southeastern part of the region; 15 records.

Most of the records fall between 29 Oct 1924 Bard IMP and 22 Mar 1976 SESS (two wintering birds); they are primarily from the vicinity of Bard (7 records) and SESS (5 records). There are two unseasonal records from Brock Ranch IMP: 14 Apr 1974 and 24 Jun 1973. The only record outside of Imperial Co. is for Black Meadow Wash near L. Havasu SBE 26 Dec 1952.

All winter Bendire's/Curve-billed type thrashers in the southeastern part of the region should be carefully scrutinized; the two species are frequently confused, and both are quite rare. Several published records, including ones from coastal San Diego and Ventura Cos., either lack sufficient details or clearly pertain to Bendire's.

CALIFORNIA THRASHER
Toxostoma redivivum   Map p. 396

Common resident in chaparral and other brushy areas west of the deserts.

This species occurs in montane chaparral up to about 1500-2000m and down to the desert bases of the coastal mountains. Localities at the western edge of District D include: L. Palmdale LA; Morongo Valley SBE; the Little San Bernardino Mtns. SBE/RIV; Yaqui Well and Agua Caliente (but not the Borrego Valley) on the Anza-Borrego Desert SD; and Mountain Springs, extreme sw Imperial Co.

This species is quite sedentary; it is unrecorded on the Channel Is. and on the deserts away from the limited breeding localities. There is one record of a vagrant on the Palos Verdes Peninsula LA 25 Jan-11 Feb 1974.

California Thrashers are characteristic birds of chaparral associations; they also occur in lowland riparian thickets and other brushy habitats.

CRISSAL THRASHER
Toxostoma dorsale Map p. 396

Common resident in District R, extending uncommonly westward across the southern deserts. Also resident in the higher northern deserts of eastern San Bernardino Co. and southeastern Inyo Co.

This thrasher is a common resident along the length of the Colorado R.; it is less common to the west in the remaining riparian and mesquite associations from the Imperial and Coachella Valleys north to the vic. of Palm Springs RIV. There is also an isolated population in the Borrego Valley SD. It is absent from the remaining southern deserts.

It is an uncommon resident in the higher portions of the northern deserts from the Granite and Providence Mtns. north to Clark Mtn., and locally in mesquite north to Tecopa and Shoshone INY. The northernmost record for the region is at Death Valley Jct. INY 4 Sep 1978. It has frequently been reported at Morongo Valley SBE, but the only definite record is 25 Jan 1976 (the California Thrasher is resident here).

This species occupies both dense brush within and adjacent to desert riparian woodland (willows, cottonwoods, mesquite, etc.), and well-vegetated desert washes. On the e. Mohave it occurs up to about 1800m in washes within the pinyon-juniper woodland.

LE CONTE'S THRASHER
Toxostoma lecontei Map p. 397

Uncommon and local resident in low desert scrub through much of District D and in the southwestern corner of the San Joaquin Valley.

In District D it breeds north to the Antelope Valley (west to the vicinity of Palmdale and Lancaster LA), the Owens Valley (north to Benton MNO), and the Death Valley region. There is also an isolated population in the saltbush scrub of the southwestern corner of the San Joaquin Valley (vic. of Taft and Maricopa KRN) and extending very locally into extreme e. San Luis Obispo Co., where it has been recorded on the Carrizo Plain. This species breeds south through the southern Mohave and Colorado Deserts to the vicinity of Banning RIV and the Anza-Borrego Desert SD. It is absent from the irrigated portions of Districts S and R, but it breeds in the drier areas just outside these districts. It has been recorded near Niland and Bard IMP, which suggests at least a slight movement away from breeding localities.

There is one record that is clearly extralimital: near Moreno RIV 18 Feb 1968.

Le Conte's Thrashers require less vegetation than our other thrashers; they inhabit very sparse desert scrub (creosote, etc.), especially around small washes. They occupy Joshua Tree woodland on the Mohave Desert, although the Joshua Trees themselves seem an unimportant element. In the southwestern San Joaquin Valley stands of saltbush (*Atriplex*) are occupied; nesting usually takes place around the edges of washes.

MUSCICAPIDAE: THRUSHES AND ALLIES
TURDINAE: THRUSHES
WESTERN BLUEBIRD
Sialia mexicana   Map p. 397

Common resident in oak and conifer woodlands in Districts C and M, extending very locally in riparian woodlands to the western edge of District D. Erratic movement into the lowlands of District C and the western deserts in winter; generally quite rare in winter on the eastern deserts and District S, but erratically uncommon to fairly common in District R.

This species is resident in oak woodlands of the foothill and northern portions of District C. It also breeds throughout District M west of the deserts; in winter considerable withdrawal from the higher portions occurs. It breeds very locally onto the western edge of District D (e.g. Mohave Narrows SBE). Small numbers breed in the Panamint Mtns. INY; it formerly bred on Clark Mtn.

There is an erratic downslope movement in winter, when the species is more widespread in the lowlands of District C; it is quite local on the immediate coast. It has been recorded twice on the Channel Is., both times in winter on Santa Cruz I. This species is a fairly common but local winter visitant in the western portion of District D, primarily around trees and shrubs bearing fruiting mistletoe. In general it is a very rare winter visitant on the eastern deserts. This bluebird is present rarely and irregularly at SESS; it can be locally fairly common in mistletoe-infested mesquite along the Colorado R.

Birds breeding on the desert ranges, and the majority of specimens from the southeastern part of the region, belong to an interior subspecies, *S. m. bairdii*. This race has been recorded in winter north to Shoshone (where apparently regular) and Tecopa INY.

Western Bluebirds breed in open oak woodlands and open coniferous forests. They expand in winter into more open areas, including the northern coastal plains and the agricultural areas of interior valleys. This is more of a woodland bird than the Mountain Bluebird and, unlike that species, is not likely to be found in extensive agricultural areas of the deserts. There are also very few records from well-worked coastal migrant traps such as Pt. Loma SD.

MOUNTAIN BLUEBIRD
Sialia currucoides

Fairly common but local breeder in open, high montane woodlands and high sagebrush plains. Common to abundant winter visitant in agricultural areas of the northern deserts; more erratic and less numerous through the remainder of the interior and along the coast.

The Mountain Bluebird breeds on Mt. Pinos and in neighboring high sagebrush valleys, in the e. San Bernardino Mtns. (vic. Baldwin L., Mt. San Gorgonio), and in the White, Inyo, Panamint, and Grapevine Mtns. Suggestive of breeding in the New York Mtns. were eight adults and two juveniles present 21-30 Jul 1976. Spring records into June at Cima Dome near the New York Mtns., and a record of a juvenile in the Lanfair Valley SBE 29 Jun 1978 indicate possible breeding elsewhere on the eastern Mohave Desert.

This species is a common to abundant winter visitant in the northern agricultural areas of District D (Antelope Valley LA/KRN, Owens Valley INY, etc.), and in the Cuyama Valley and Carrizo Plain of the northern interior of District C. Numbers vary somewhat from year to year; in some years it may only be fairly common. It is less numerous and more erratic in agricultural areas of the Imperial Valley and Colorado River Valley, where it is rather common some years and quite rare others. This bluebird also winters locally across the Mohave Desert. Flocks may also winter in District M (e.g. at Baldwin L. in the San Bernardino Mtns.). On the deserts it is principally a transient away from agricultural areas; transients have been noted as late as 27 May 1980 Cartago INY and 1 Jun 1969 Saratoga Springs SBE.

It is an irregular fall transient and winter visitant on the coastal plains (scarcest on the northern coast), and on the Channel Is. Very few concentrations have been recorded recently along the coast, where this species appears to have declined somewhat as a result of the loss of suitable open habitat.

TOWNSEND'S SOLITAIRE
Myadestes townsendi

Fairly common resident within District M, with some seasonal altitudinal shifts. There is a regular winter movement into coastal foothill canyons, the western edge of District D, and the northernmost desert lowlands; quite rare in winter in the remaining interior lowlands and the coastal lowlands.

This species breeds in all of the major ranges from Mt. Pinos and vicinity (uncommon, possibly extending to Pine Mtn. VEN where found

30 Jul 1980) south to the Santa Rosa Mtns. One was on Mt. Palomar SD 19 Jul 1980, suggesting breeding there. It also breeds in the White and Panamint Mtns. Most depart the higher portions of District M in winter.

In winter there is some movement into the remaining desert mountain ranges and down the desert slope of the coastal mountains. It also occurs in winter in the mountains of San Diego Co., on the western edge of District D, and in the northernmost desert lowlands. This species is a rare and somewhat irregular transient and winter visitant to the rest of the interior lowlands, including Districts S and R. Concentrations of spring transients have been noted in the Deep Springs/Oasis area in late spring: 30 birds present as late as 19-20 May 1971. On this basis, birds observed in suitable breeding habitat on Clark Mtn. in late May are best considered late spring transients.

In District C small numbers regularly winter in coastal foothill canyons. It is primarily a rare fall transient (has wintered) along the immediate coast and on the Channel Is. A very late coastal spring transient was recorded 24 May 1963 in the Tijuana River Valley SD. An exceptionally early fall record in District C was 25 Jul 1978 Glendale LA (a juvenile below the adjacent breeding range).

Solitaires breed in higher montane forests, extending lower in well-wooded canyons. In winter they may be locally numerous around fruiting junipers in the drier parts of District M, and around clumps of fruiting mistletoe on the western edges of the deserts.

VARIED THRUSH
Zoothera naevia

Irregular winter visitant to the lowlands and mountains west of the deserts (less common to the south); regular in fall and winter on the northern deserts, but casual in the southeastern portion of the region.

Along the coast there is a decided north-south gradient in abundance; most birds occur on the northern coast, on the northern Channel Is., and on the coastal flank of the Transverse Ranges. It is fairly common (exceptionally even common) some years, but nearly absent others.

This species is fairly regular in occurrence in the northern portions of District D; it is uncommon in late fall and rare through winter. It is casual on the Colorado Desert and in Districts S and R, where it has been recorded as follows: 29 Nov 1957 Mecca RIV; 23 Nov 1973 NESS; 3 Oct 1975 NESS; 28 Dec 1972 near Niland SESS; 11 Mar 1978 Finney L. SESS; 16 Feb 1975 Brock Ranch IMP; 12 Apr 1973 n. of Blythe RIV; and winter 1977-1978 Imperial NWR IMP. There are additional records for the Arizona side of the Colorado R.

The Varied Thrush is present primarily from October through early March. Exceptionally late spring records are: 20 May 1979 Yucca Valley SBE; 24-26 May 1973 Furnace Creek Ranch INY; 26 May 1979 Buckhorn

Flat, San Gabriel Mtns.; and 1-3 Jun 1979 Deep Springs INY. It has been recorded once in mid-summer: a singing male at Mt. Pinos 20 Jul 1979.

Winter concentrations occur in shaded oak and mixed woodlands. Varied Thrushes occur most regularly and in the largest numbers in coastal San Luis Obispo and Santa Barbara Cos.

VEERY
Catharus fuscescens

Two certain records: 12-16 Oct 1974 Big Sycamore Canyon, Pt. Mugu VEN and 5 Nov 1978 Kelso SBE.

Veeries should be identified with extreme caution; they may closely resemble the Pacific coast forms of the Swainson's Thrush. We have dismissed several published reports (*AFN*) which lack sufficient documentation. Both of our accepted records were documented with photographs.

SWAINSON'S THRUSH
Catharus ustulatus   *Map p. 397*

Summer resident in District C, primarily in the northern portions. Common spring transient through most of the interior; fairly common at this season along the coast. Fall migrants are generally on the immediate coast, mainly s. of Los Angeles Co., and over the Channel Is. One early winter record of a crippled bird.

This thrush is a summer resident in District C, where it is fairly common from Santa Barbara Co. north. It is becoming increasingly scarce to the south; it is now quite rare in San Diego Co. Small numbers probably still breed locally in canyons on the coastal slope of the Transverse Ranges. It has recently nested on Santa Catalina I.

The Swainson's Thrush is a fairly common and widespread transient in District C in spring; in fall migration it is fairly common along the immediate coast and the outer Channel Is., but it is quite rare north of Orange Co. Exceptionally early spring records are 2 Apr 1966 Tijuana River Valley SD and 6 Apr 1978 San Diego SD. Other early records are 11 Apr 1964 Tijuana River Valley and 11 Apr 1896 Pasadena LA; the major spring passage takes place in May. In fall, stragglers may occur into late October; later records are: 4 Nov 1978 Santa Maria R. mouth SLO/SBA and 1 Dec 1964 San Diego. A crippled bird was in Coronado SD 15-16 Dec 1979.

This species is a common to abundant spring transient through the interior; it is less numerous in District R. It has been recorded as early as 16 Apr 1978 Yaqui Well SD, although migration does not peak until mid-May and transients may still pass through as late as mid-June. Spring transients occur uncommonly up into riparian associations of District M. It is a very rare fall transient through the interior; most records are from the northern deserts.

Swainson's Thrushes breed in shaded riparian woodlands of canyons and lowlands; this species has declined greatly as a breeder on the southern coast, undoubtedly due both to loss of lowland riparian habitat and to heavy nest parasitism by Brown-headed Cowbirds. In spring migration large numbers may concentrate at desert oases. Along the coast the largest numbers are often noted by call overhead at night along the immediate coast (e.g. Pt. Loma SD) and over the outer Channel Is. Numerous mid-winter reports of this species (especially from Christmas Bird Counts) are erroneous; the only two acceptable December records are noted above.

HERMIT THRUSH
Catharus guttatus

Common winter visitant to District C; generally uncommon in winter in the interior. Uncommon and local summer resident in montane forests.

The Hermit Thrush winters throughout District C, and locally upward into the lower portions of District M. Numbers vary somewhat from year to year; in some years it is only fairly common. This species is normally present from late September through early April, but stragglers in the lowlands may occur into late May and early June (e.g. 29 May 1975 and 31 May 1974 Santa Barbara I. and 2 Jun 1976 San Nicolas I.).

In the interior it is generally an uncommon winter visitant in lowland areas; it is irregularly fairly common in District R. Straggling migrants may occur into late May on the northern deserts.

This species is an uncommon and local summer resident in montane forests. It is most numerous in the higher portions of the San Bernardino Mtns., where it is almost fairly common; it also breeds in the San Gabriel Mtns., on Mt. Pinos (rare), and possibly in the San Jacinto Mtns. (needs verification). A singing bird on Hot Springs Mtn. SD 24 Jun 1980 suggests breeding there. A report of birds summering in the Santa Ana Mtns. ORA also requires verification (low altitude, atypical habitat). A paler, grayer Great Basin subspecies breeds on the desert mountains from the White Mtns. and Inyo Mtns. south through the Panamint Mtns. and Clark Mtn.

Hermit Thrushes breed primarily in forests dominated by firs and other high-elevation conifers; it is usually found on steep, north-facing slopes. Winter birds occupy a variety of brush and woodland habitats, especially where plentiful supplies of berries occur.

WOOD THRUSH
Hylocichla mustelina

Vagrant from the east; three records: 18 Nov 1967 Tijuana River Valley SD; 1-10 Aug 1968 Glendale LA (killed by cat); and 25-26 Oct 1978 Tijuana River Valley (also killed by cat!).

RUFOUS-BACKED ROBIN
Turdus rufopalliatus

Vagrant from the subtropics; two records: 17 Dec 1973-6 Apr 1974 Imperial Dam IMP and 19 Nov 1974 Saratoga Springs SBE.

This species is a somewhat regular visitant, primarily in winter, to southeastern Arizona.

AMERICAN ROBIN
Turdus migratorius

Fairly common resident in woodlands through much of the region west of the deserts; irregularly common to abundant winter visitant through the lowlands.

It breeds fairly commonly to commonly in District M west of the deserts, except in San Diego Co., where very small numbers breed in the mountains. This species also nests in the White Mtns., in the Owens Valley INY, and at scattered northern desert oases (e.g. Deep Springs INY). It nests fairly commonly to commonly in District C in woodlands, gardens, parks, etc., but it is scarce in coastal Ventura and Santa Barbara Cos. On the Channel Is. there is one suspected nesting: on Santa Cruz I. in 1935. Exceptionally it nests in the lower deserts (e.g. in irrigated orchards around Blythe RIV, summer 1977 and 1979).

This thrush is an erratic winter visitant to the lowlands throughout, including the Channel Is.; it is abundant in some winters and almost uncommon in others. Over most of the deserts it is usually present only in small numbers, but in some years it is quite common. Most nesting birds tend to depart District M in winter, although winter invasions may bring large numbers to the mountains.

Robins breed in humid, montane forests and woodlands. They have adapted very well to parks and suburban plantings in the lowlands. In winter flocks exploit crops of berries and other fruit. On the deserts they often occur in groves of date palms.

SYLVIINAE: OLD WORLD WARBLERS
GOLDEN-CROWNED KINGLET
Regulus satrapa

Irregular winter visitant, rarest in the southeastern portion of the region. Uncommon and very local breeder in fir forests in the higher portions of District M.

This species is primarily an irregular winter visitant to the region; in general the greatest numbers appear in the northern coastal areas, and the lowest numbers occur in the southeastern part of the region. It is a rare transient through the northern parts of District D; it has wintered in the Owens Valley INY, and there are winter records for the New York

Mtns. This species is a rare visitant in fall and early winter in the northern part of District R; it is strictly casual in the southern part of District R. It is casual in District S: there are six records extending from 22 Oct 1977 SESS to 30 Dec 1970 SESS (2), and there are two additional records for nearby Brock Ranch IMP.

On the coast this species usually first arrives in October and it remains through early winter. Exceptionally it has been recorded as early as 7 Sep 1972 Santa Cruz I. The Golden-crowned Kinglet is fairly common in some winters, but almost absent in others. There has been a series of good flights since the fall 1972, which suggests at least a temporary increase in the region. It is most regular in San Luis Obispo and Santa Barbara Cos. This species is an uncommon transient and winter visitant on the Channel Is. The winter pattern in the mountains west of the deserts is much like that in District C. In general, it is casual throughout the lowlands in spring; there are a few April records of spring transients, the latest coastal record being 21 Apr 1975 Santa Barbara I.

This kinglet is an uncommon and very local breeder in fir forests in the higher parts of District M (Mt. Pinos, San Bernardino Mtns., San Jacinto Mtns.). It has also bred in the higher portions of the White Mtns. However, the greatest numbers in District M occur in fall and winter during flight years. Golden-crowned Kinglets occur in winter in a variety of woodlands, including oak and riparian, but are partial to conifers, whether native or planted. Breeding birds occupy dense fir forests on cool northern slopes.

RUBY-CROWNED KINGLET
Regulus calendula

Common transient and winter visitant throughout, including the Channel Is., although most depart the higher portions of District M and the colder northern deserts in winter. Very local breeder in high montane forests.

Along the coast this species generally arrives in late September and departs by mid-April; spring migration extends somewhat later on the northern deserts and individuals are recorded into late May. Notable early fall records on the coast include: 30 Aug 1975 Big Sycamore Canyon VEN; 30 Aug 1978 Santa Barbara SBA; 6 Sep 1973 Pt. Loma SD; and 6 Sep 1973 Otay Mesa SD. Along the coast an exceptionally late spring bird was recorded 2 Jun 1976 San Nicolas I. (a number of late May records exist for the Channel Is.).

The Ruby-crowned Kinglet breeds fairly commonly in the White Mtns. and summers (and probably breeds) on Clark Mtn. Otherwise it is a very rare breeder in montane forests; very small numbers summer in the San Bernardino Mtns., in the San Jacinto Mtns., and on Mt. Pinos, but it is possibly extirpated in the latter two ranges. A singing male was in the Laguna Mtns. SD (south of the known breeding range) 30 May 1974; another was near Big Pines in the San Gabriel Mtns. 26 May 1979. The breeding status in the region is imperfectly known; it was possibly more widespread formerly (Grinnell and Miller 1944). There is an old nesting record at only 480m elevation in Redlands SBE, well below the normal altitudinal range.

In winter Ruby-crowned Kinglets are widespread in woodlands and dense brush in the lowlands and in forests in the lowest parts of District M. Breeding occurs in high montane forests (firs, etc.).

BLUE-GRAY GNATCATCHER
Polioptila caerulea

Uncommon to fairly common summer resident in woodlands of Districts C, D, and M. Fairly common winter visitant in the southern portions of Districts C and D, and in Districts R and S; rare in winter n. of Santa Barbara.

This gnatcatcher breeds uncommonly in wooded canyons and bordering chaparral in District C, where it occurs on the coastal slope south to Los Angeles Co. and through montane foothills in the interior portion south to the Mexican border. It also breeds uncommonly on Santa Cruz I. and possibly Santa Catalina I.; it is an uncommon transient and winter visitant on the other islands. This species breeds up to about 1500m in the coastal mountains, along most of the desert slopes of those mountains, and locally to the western edge of District D, e.g. Yaqui Well SD. It also breeds in pinyon-juniper associations in the desert ranges and locally in riparian scrub and woodlands in the northern part of District D (e.g. Scotty's Castle INY and Ft. Piute SBE). Breeding birds arrive in the southern part of their range by late March, and in the remainder by early April.

The Blue-gray Gnatcatcher winters fairly commonly throughout the southern portion of District D, from the s. Mohave Desert south. There are no winter records farther north (e.g. unrecorded on e. Mohave Desert, 4 Sep-24 Mar). It borders on common in winter in riparian scrub and brush at SESS and in District R. It is a fairly common winter visitant in District C, but it is rare north of Santa Barbara SBA. This species departs higher elevations in winter. Late records of spring transients, outside of the breeding range, are: 27 May 1979 Furnace Creek Ranch INY; 29-30 May 1975 Santa Barbara I.; and 7-8 Jun 1975 Santa Barbara I. (2).

Blue-gray Gnatcatchers breed in oak and oak-riparian woodland in canyon bottoms and on slopes bordered by chaparral. In the interior they are partial to arid woodlands, particularly of pinyon and juniper. In winter, they occupy riparian thickets and brush in the lowlands. They are partial to screwbean mesquite in winter in District R. On the southern deserts they may even range into open creosote scrub in winter. Lowland breeding populations have been greatly reduced by cowbird brood parasitism (for example, the species no longer breeds in the coastal lowlands of San Diego Co.).

BLACK-TAILED GNATCATCHER
Polioptila melanura   *Map p. 397*

Fairly common resident on the Colorado Desert (common in District R), extending locally and uncommonly north through the e. Mohave Desert. Also resident locally in arid coastal sage scrub in District C from Los Angeles Co. south.

The desert subspecies, *P. m. lucida*, is a common resident along the Colorado R., and fairly common resident in the southern part of District D west to the Anza-Borrego Desert SD and Palm Springs RIV. It occurs north through the e. Mohave Desert to the Lanfair Valley SBE and the Amargosa R. INY (where scarce). It extends west on the Mohave Desert to the vicinity of Yermo SBE. A report of nesting at Mesquite Springs in the northern part of Death Valley INY (Grinnell and Miller 1944) most likely pertains to the Blue-gray Gnatcatcher. It avoids the agricultural portions of District S, but it occurs on the arid fringes of that district.

Lucida gnatcatchers reach peak abundances in desert washes with a dense growth of mesquite, palo verde, ironwood, and acacia. They also occur sparingly in other desert scrub habitats such as creosote flats (mostly in winter). They avoid agricultural areas and scrub composed of the introduced salt cedar.

The coastal subspecies, *P. m. californica*, is an uncommon and local resident in arid, coastal sage scrub from the lower, coastal slopes of the San Gabriel Mtns. LA (very rare; perhaps extirpated) and w. Riverside Co. south locally through San Diego Co. Along the immediate coast it occurs on the Palos Verdes Peninsula LA, vic. Laguna ORA, at Camp Pendleton SD, and in the Tijuana River Valley SD. The center of abundance may be on the arid interior slopes in e. Orange Co. and sw Riverside Co. south through the foothills of San Diego Co. (e.g. El Cajon, Sweetwater Res.). It is unrecorded on the Channel Is.

A vagrant *californica* was collected with *lucida* at Palm Springs RIV 1 Jan 1904 for the only record of this race outside of District C.

Californica formerly bred northwest to the vicinity of the Santa Clara R. VEN and the northern San Fernando Valley LA. Local declines have resulted from the destruction of habitat for housing tracts, etc., and perhaps from pressures of cowbird brood parasitism. This race breeds in low, dense scrub in arid washes, on mesas, and on the slopes of coastal hills. California sagebrush and patches of prickly-pear cactus are particularly favored. This subspecies is quite distinct from the desert races in plumage, voice, and habitat preference.

TIMALIINAE: BABBLERS

WRENTIT

Chamaea fasciata   Map p. 397

Common resident in brushy areas throughout District C and in the lower portions of District M. Quite sedentary.

The breeding range coincides fairly well with the distribution of coastal sage scrub and chaparral habitats, and includes the desert slopes of the coastal mountains. A pair frequented a patch of honey mesquite near Palm Springs RIV in April 1980. It has nested in District M at over 2000m (near Big Bear L., San Bernardino Mtns.), and has been found in late summer to 2500m in the San Jacinto Mtns. It was recorded 26 Sep 1964 at Arraste Ck., San Bernardino Mtns., which is several km from the nearest breeding localities. Thus, while the species is generally extremely sedentary, limited upslope movement may occur after nesting.

It is unrecorded from the Channel Is., from portions of the outer coast (e.g. Palos Verdes Peninsula LA), and (exception noted above) from the deserts.

MOTACILLIDAE: WAGTAILS AND PIPITS

WHITE WAGTAIL
Motacilla alba

Two records along the immediate coast: 18-20 Oct 1972 Santa Clara R. estuary VEN and 9-11 Oct 1978 Devereux Slough, Goleta SBA. Both birds were at the edges of coastal estuaries.

There are three additional records for northern California and one for Baja California.

RED-THROATED PIPIT
Anthus cervinus

Casual fall transient along the immediate coast; small flocks have been noted.

Years of occurrence are: 1964, 1966, 1967, 1970, 1974, 1977, 1978, and 1979. Extreme dates are: 28 Sep 1978 San Nicolas I. to 10 Nov 1974 Santa Cruz I. Most occur between 10 and 25 October. Most records, including all prior to 1974, are from the Tijuana River Valley SD. It has also been recorded from San Nicolas I., Santa Cruz I., San Miguel I.; vic. Guadalupe SBA; Goleta SBA; Oxnard Plain VEN; and Carson LA. Maxima include up to 15 in fall 1964, 12 in fall 1978, and 10 in fall 1966 and fall 1967.

Red-throated Pipits have mostly occurred with flocks of Water Pipits in short grass or dirt agricultural fields. Their occurrence in the region appears to be irregular. Most birds have been immatures.

WATER PIPIT
Anthus spinoletta

Common transient and winter visitant to lowlands nearly throughout. One probable nesting record for the San Bernardino Mtns.

In winter the Water Pipit is found nearly throughout the lowlands, including the Channel Is. It is, however, principally a migrant through much of the northern desert regions, although it remains commonly there in winter in areas of extensive agriculture. The first fall birds arrive in mid-September, and the species is common by mid-October and remains so through to mid-March. It is regular into mid-May on the northern deserts. Extreme dates are: 29 Aug 1895 near Pasadena LA and 7 Sep 1979 Mt. Pinos summit VEN to 25-26 May 1976 San Nicolas I. and 27 May 1980 Baker SBE (2).

In District M it is primarily a fairly common fall transient which remains uncommonly and locally through the winter (conditions permitting). The only summer record is of a pair that probably nested on the summit of Mt. San Gorgonio SBE. The pair was present 15 Jun-6 Jul 1978 and was observed carrying food from 20-24 Jun. This area has not been checked in other recent years. Just outside of our region it nests very sparingly in the Sierra Nevada.

Water Pipits can be quite abundant in open agricultural fields (alfalfa, etc.) in the desert and coastal lowlands; they also occur on lakeshores, beaches, bare dirt fields, and other open areas. Breeding takes place above timberline.

SPRAGUE'S PIPIT
Anthus spragueii

Casual fall transient along the coast; the nine records are: 19-27 Oct 1974 Tijuana River Valley SD (2-3); 23 Oct 1975 Carson LA; 22 Nov 1975 Tijuana River Valley; 19 Dec 1975 Fiesta Island, Mission Bay SD (2); 21-24 Oct 1976 Carson; 22 Nov 1977 Tijuana River Valley; and 27 Oct 1978 Santa Clara R. Estuary VEN; and two records from the interior — 2 Oct 1979 Furnace Creek Ranch INY and 23 Oct 1979 Furnace Creek Ranch.

This species has also been recorded several times in winter on the Arizona side of the Colorado R., and it may be regular there in very small numbers in fields of dry alfalfa mixed with bermuda grass. It is to be looked for in District R, especially just south of Blythe RIV. Sprague's Pipits recorded in the region have generally not associated with Water Pipits.

BOMBYCILLIDAE: WAXWINGS

BOHEMIAN WAXWING
Bombycilla garrulus

Rare and irregular fall transient and winter visitant, primarily in the northern portions of Districts C and D. Occurrences are usually, but not always, tied to major flights throughout the west; absent many years, but can occur in large flocks during flight years.

Major flights of recent years include the fall and winter of 1968-1969 when the species was recorded through the region south to San Juan Capistrano ORA (the only Orange Co. record). Flocks included 40 at Scotty's Castle INY 30 Nov 1968; up to 120 in the Holcomb Valley, San Bernardino Mtns., in Dec 1968; and, coastally, 20 in Santa Barbara SBA. Scattered small flocks and individuals occurred elsewhere in the region, and several thousand were present just east of the region at Las Vegas, Nevada. Another flight occurred in fall 1972, primarily in the northeastern part of the region. A flock of 65 was in the Saline Valley INY 23-25 Nov 1972; 20 were at Furnace Creek Ranch INY 19 Nov 1972; and 4-6 were as far south as Yaqui Well SD 3-5 Dec 1972 (one of only three records for San Diego Co.). Historically, other large flights have occurred, for instance, in winter 1919-1920 when the largest flock on record (150 birds) was found in Claremont LA 22 Feb 1920. Another notable concentration was of 120 birds at Valyermo LA 6 Feb-late Mar 1977 (very few others were present in the region that winter).

Most birds in the northern deserts are late fall transients that depart by mid-January; in flight years records are generally concentrated in the northern part of District D. There are scattered early March records (spring transients) on the northern deserts. Late spring records for the deserts include 13 Apr 1969 Antelope Valley, and, just outside the region, 19 May 1974 Weldon KRN. On the coast its occurrence is generally slightly later in fall, and records are scattered through the winter. Notable late records include three from Los Angeles and Santa Barbara Cos. in mid-late April, and 21 May 1969 Santa Barbara SBA (the latest record for the region).

In the interior Bohemian Waxwings usually form pure flocks and often feed on mistletoe berries. Coastal birds are generally mixed in with flocks of Cedar Waxwings. It is unrecorded on the Channel Is.

CEDAR WAXWING
Bombycilla cedrorum

Irregularly common to abundant transient and winter visitant in District C; generally less common in the interior. Casual in summer; has bred once in District C.

Along the coast this species may be abundant some years, but it is distinctly uncommon others; the timing of invasions is variable. It is an irregular transient and winter visitant on the Channel Is. Elsewhere the Cedar Waxwing is primarily an uncommon fall transient and winter visitant; there is often an influx of spring transients. It is unrecorded in midwinter and early spring on the e. Mohave Desert. In District R it may be irregularly common; numbers often do not appear until midwinter. It may also be irregularly common in winter in District M. During fall invasions it is generally not common until late November. The first fall transients may arrive much earlier, e.g. 19 Aug 1932 Big Pines, San Gabriel Mtns. LA (3-4); and 22 Aug 1970 Encino LA. This species may be quite common well into May; exceptionally it remains into mid-June on the coast.

This species occurs casually through the summer. It was recorded in summer 1974 (one pair) and summer 1965 (adults with three fledglings on 7 Jul) at Dana Pt. ORA. Other summer records are: 16 Jun 1897 South Pasadena LA (undoubtedly a late spring transient), 9 Aug 1908 L. Hemet RIV (specimen of full grown juvenile suggesting local breeding), and mid-Jul 1980 Ojai VEN (up to eight birds, with 3-4 observed through the remainder of the summer — no evidence of nesting).

Winter flocks of Cedar Waxwings exploit a variety of berry sources, particularly toyon *(Heteromeles)*, mistletoe, and ornamental shrubs such as pyracantha. The species occurs in any wooded habitat or suburban area that provides such food, and it frequently flocks with other berry-eating species such as the American Robin.

PTILOGONATIDAE: SILKY-FLYCATCHERS

PHAINOPEPLA
Phainopepla nitens

Status complex, involving a seasonal shift in numbers from the deserts (primarily winter and early spring) to the coastal areas (primarily late spring and summer). May be locally quite common.

In general, this species is a common fall, winter, and spring visitant and nester on the deserts from the Colorado R. west to the Anza-Borrego Desert and north through the Mohave Desert to Tecopa and vicinity INY. On the Colorado Desert breeding primarily takes place from February through April, and the species largely departs the lower deserts by early May; it disperses primarily westward. It is scarce in the far northern parts of District D, where it occurs mainly in spring, summer, and fall.

In District S the Phainopepla occurs primarily in fall, winter, and spring; most depart in summer. Locally it is rather common, although suitable habitat is limited.

In District C birds arrive primarily in late April and they breed fairly commonly along the length of District C in oak and oak-riparian woodlands bordered by chaparral-covered slopes. They may also breed up into the lowest portions of District M. Varying numbers remain in oak woodlands through the winter. At this season they are rare to uncommon and they generally occur away from the immediate coast. This species is a scarce transient (mostly fall) on the southern coastal plain. It is a scarce spring, summer, and fall visitant on the Channel Is.; it has bred (1977) and wintered on Santa Catalina I.

On the deserts Phainopeplas occupy desert washes, oases, and riparian groves where the larger shrubs (such as mesquite, acacia, ironwood, and palo verde) bear mistletoe, upon whose fruits this species is heavily dependent. The habitat of coastal birds is described above. There is some evidence that individual Phainopeplas may nest on both the lower deserts (late winter) and coastal slope (late spring) in a given year.

LANIIDAE: SHRIKES

LOGGERHEAD SHRIKE
Lanius ludovicianus

Fairly common resident in open areas throughout the region. In Districts C, R, and S, more widespread in winter and fall. Absent from most parts of District M and from the more heavily wooded and heavily urbanized portions of District C.

This species is resident on Santa Rosa, San Miguel, Santa Cruz, Anacapa (sporadically), and Santa Catalina Is. The endemic subspecies on San Clemente I., *L. l. mearnsi*, is rare. This species is a rare transient on the remaining islands.

Loggerhead Shrikes are very widespread in open and semi-open habitats throughout the lowlands of the region. Often only very limited taller vegetation is required. There is some expansion into open agricultural areas in winter.

NORTHERN SHRIKE
Lanius excubitor

Rare but somewhat regular winter visitant in the vicinity of the Owens Valley in the northern portion of District D. Quite rare farther south and west, with only two records for the coastal lowlands and one for District S.

An average of three or four are recorded annually in the region, primarily between late October and early February. Extreme dates are 19 Oct 1975 Oasis MNO and 26 Mar and 9 Apr 1978 near Big Pine INY. It has been recorded about six times in the Death Valley area. Records for farther south in the interior are; 11 Feb 1972 Elizabeth L. LA; 24 Nov 1973 Lockwood Valley VEN; and 11 Nov 1977 upper Cuyama Valley VEN (these three records come from the high, northeastern border of District C and are not graphed); 26 Dec 1978 Harper Dry L. SBE; 24

Nov 1979 and 15 Dec 1979 Antelope Valley; also, during the winter of 1977-1978, up to six were recorded in or near the Antelope Valley, and individuals were in the Lucerne Valley SBE and at Afton Canyon SBE.

There is one record for District S: 23-26 Jan 1971 SESS. It is unrecorded in District R, but two were near Parker, Arizona, during the winter of 1977-1978.

In the coastal lowlands it has been recorded 7 Jan-18 Feb 1973 Eaton Canyon, near Pasadena LA; and 27 Jan-3 Feb 1978 Santa Clara R. estuary VEN.

Northern Shrikes inhabit semi-open woodlands and groves, and appear to require more trees and shrubs for perches and vantage posts than do wintering Loggerhead Shrikes. All records for the region are since 1969; it was undoubtedly overlooked before then. Although the majority of birds in the region have been immatures, there are records of adults.

VIREONIDAE: VIREOS

WHITE-EYED VIREO
Vireo griseus

One record: 31 May-2 Jun 1979 Oasis MNO. There are three additional late spring records of this eastern North American species from northern California.

BELL'S VIREO
Vireo bellii

Now a rare and local summer resident in lowland riparian woodlands; formerly more common and widespread. Very few recent records of transients away from breeding areas; casual in winter.

The race *V. b. pusillus* (endemic to California and Baja California) breeds in riparian woodlands and thickets in the lowlands of District C and on the western edge of District D; it arrives by the end of March (exceptionally to 11 Mar 1900 near Los Angeles LA) and remains through August. Sites are concentrated in the upper Santa Ynez River Valley SBA (especially Mono Ck.), and in the river valleys of San Diego Co. Other sites are in Ventura Co. (12 pairs east of Piru in 1979, one pair at La Jolla Canyon in 1978); Los Angeles Co. (two sites); San Bernardino Co. (east to Morongo Valley SBE on the western edge of District D); and Riverside Co. (several sites). Sites on the desert slopes of the major mountains extend south to Coyote Ck. and San Felipe Ck. SD.

The race *V. b. arizonae* is now a rare summer resident in District R from the vicinity of Needles SBE south to Blythe RIV; summering birds were present at Laguna Dam IMP to at least 1974. It was formerly common along the length of the Colorado R.

This vireo also breeds at at least two sites along the Amargosa R. near Tecopa INY (subspecies undetermined).

The Bell's Vireo is very rarely noted in migration (*pusillus* and *arizonae* are not separable in the field). There are seven recent records of spring transients or vagrants on the northern deserts; these records extend from Kelso SBE north to Big Pine and Furnace Creek Ranch INY and are from 24 Apr 1976 Kelso to 30 May 1977 Furnace Creek Ranch. The only fall record for the northern deserts is 12 Sep 1974 Scotty's Castle INY. It has been recorded three times in fall on the southern deserts: 19 Oct 1977 Morongo Valley (well after breeding birds had departed); 18 Nov 1968 Thousand Palms RIV; and 28 Nov 1964 Parker Dam SBE.

There have been four records of fall transients on the coast in the last 15 years, all from Pt. Loma and the Tijuana River Valley SD (7 Sep-1978 to 28 Oct 1975). There have also been six records of wintering birds or very late fall stragglers in coastal San Diego Co. between mid-December and late January. The only interior winter record is also the only recent record for District S: Ramer L. SESS 28 Dec 1963-8 Feb 1964. It is unrecorded on the Channel Is.

Two of the records of fall transients along the coast (28 Oct 1975 and 7 Sep 1978 Tijuana River Valley) involved birds showing the bright plumage that is characteristic of the eastern nominate race, *V. b. bellii*; because they are sight records these must be regarded as very tentative.

Bell's Vireos were formerly widespread in lowland riparian habitats in the region. Willett (1933) described them as "common in summer in willow thickets from coast to foothills"; however, Grinnell and Miller

(1944) had noted a decline starting in the late 1930s, coincident with the increase of Brown-headed Cowbirds in the region. While destruction of lowland riparian habitat has played a large role in driving this species to its present precarious situation, brood parasitsm by cowbirds must be cited as the single most important factor in its decline.

Bell's Vireos breed in willow thickets and other dense, low riparian growth in the lowlands and the lower portions of canyons. They are generally found along permanent or near-permanent streams. Along the Colorado R., riverbottom thickets of willow and honey mesquite are occupied.

GRAY VIREO
Vireo vicinior

Local and quite uncommon summer resident in arid montane woodland and brush; very few acceptable records of transients away from breeding grounds.

This species breeds on slopes of the desert ranges (Grapevine, Kingston, Clark, and New York Mtns.), on the drier northeastern slopes of the San Bernardino Mtns. (Rose Mine, Round Valley), in the San Jacinto Mtns. (vic. Pinyon Flat), and on the southern slopes of the Laguna Mtns. (Kitchen Ck., Campo). Birds breeding in San Diego Co. arrive by the end of March; other populations may not arrive until early May.

This vireo is virtually unknown as a migrant. The only certain records of migrants or vagrants are: 26 Mar 1911 Mecca RIV; 1 May 1962 Bonita SD (2); 2 May 1964 Whitewater RIV; 7 Sep 1973 Santa Catalina I.; 9 Sep 1967 Pt. Fermin LA (specimen); 14 Sep 1976 Anacapa I.; 23 Sep 1976 San Clemente I.; and 24 Sep 1977 Santa Cruz I. There are at least seven additional reports of transients in the Morongo Valley/Whitewater Canyon area which have been published in *AFN* and *AB*. We feel that most or all of these (plus two late fall reports from Furnace Creek Ranch INY) pertain to the *plumbeus* race of the Solitary Vireo, or to Bell's Vireos.

The Gray Vireo was formerly somewhat more widespread as a breeder; it nested on the northern and western foothills of the San Gabriel Mtns. and more widely in the other ranges. It bred, at least formerly, in western Joshua Tree National Monument. Much field work is needed to document the extent and causes of the decline of this species; its breeding habitat presently receives inadequate coverage.

Gray Vireos breed on brushy slopes covered by pinyon and juniper, but they are local within this habitat. Birds in southern San Diego Co. breed in a mixture of *Ceanothus* and chamise chaparral and scattered oaks.

300

SOLITARY VIREO
Vireo solitarius   Map p. 397

The species as a whole is an uncommon to fairly common transient and an uncommon summer resident in woodlands (primarily in District M); rare but regular winter visitant, primarily in District C. There are three distinct subspecies that occur in the region, each with different status described below.

V. s. cassinii ("Cassin's Vireo") is an uncommon transient and local summer resident in Districts C and M. It breeds in oak and mixed woodlands and is found primarily in the northern part of District C and on the coastal slopes of the major mountains south through San Diego Co. Its range extends into the lower portions of District M. This vireo does not breed on the immediate coastal plain. Breeding birds arrive in late March or early April; away from breeding areas (including the Channel Is.) it is rather uncommon in spring in District C and quite rare in fall.

This subspecies is a fairly common spring transient through the interior; numbers peak in late April and early May. It is uncommon in fall, when the passage is primarily through the mountains. A pair present in the Kingston Mtns. 22 Jun 1977 provides the only summer record on the desert ranges (see below under *V. s. plumbeus*).

V. s. cassinii is a rare but regular winter visitant in District C; the great majority of records are from San Diego Co. There are two winter records north of Los Angeles Co.: 29 Dec 1979 Santa Barbara SBA and 24 Jan-14 Feb 1980 Goleta SBA. It is casual in winter in the interior: 31 Dec 1971 Westmorland SESS, and 22 Dec 1977-19 Feb 1978 Laguna Dam IMP. There are additional winter records for the Arizona side of the Colorado R.

V. s. cassinii breeds in canyons in dense, shaded woodlands dominated by oaks. Its present breeding range is imperfectly known, and the subspecies appears to be absent from large tracts of suitable habitat.

V. s. plumbeus ("Plumbeus Vireo") is an uncommon summer resident in arid woodlands in some of the ranges in the northeastern part of the region from the White Mtns. south to Clark Mtn.; it is, however, not known to breed in the Grapevine, Inyo, Coso, Argus, or Panamint Mtns. It breeds locally away from the desert ranges in the San Bernardino Mtns. in the vicinity of upper Arrastre Ck., and, possibly, in Big Rock Creek Canyon on the north slope of the San Gabriel Mtns. (two pairs present 15 Jul 1978). This subspecies appears to be a relatively recent colonist. It was not recorded in California until 26 Nov 1960 when a specimen was taken north of Needles SBE; it was located in suitable breeding habitat in the White and San Bernardino Mtns. soon afterward.

V. s. plumbeus is a rare to uncommon spring transient and rare but regular fall transient through the interior. Along the coast it is a casual spring and fall vagrant (April-May, September-October), but it has been recorded annually in recent years. Most coastal records are for San Diego Co. and the Channel Is. The seven spring records from District C are all from the immediate coast and the Channel Is. and extend from 9 Apr 1978 Encinitas SD to 3 Jun 1976 San Nicolas I.

This subspecies has been recorded casually in winter along the length of the Colorado R. (about six records) and at SESS (three records). It is more likely in mid-winter in the interior than *cassinii*. A small number of additional interior winter records were not assigned to subspecies. There are also about six recent winter records for coastal San Diego Co.; farther north it has been recorded in winter only on 17 Dec 1978-30 Jan 1979 Riverside RIV, 26 Dec 1978 Rancho Park, Los Angeles LA, 16 Dec 1979 Malibu LA, 25 Jan 1980 Ventura VEN, and 28 Feb 1980 Hansen Dam LA.

V. s. plumbeus breeds in arid woodlands of mature pinyons, firs, Jeffrey Pines, etc., and often ranges into adjacent riparian growth (e.g. Black Cottonwoods). While its habitat preferences are somewhat different than those of *cassinii*, the two races come close to overlapping in the Transverse Ranges and have even been found together in mid-July at Big Rock Creek Canyon on the north slope of the San Gabriel Mtns. There are no other known areas of sympatry involving these two races. The *plumbeus* race is readily separated from *cassinii* in the field; with increased observer awareness, the relationships and habitat requirements of these subspecies may be clarified.

V. s. solitarius ("Blue-headed Vireo") has been recorded with certainty once in the region: a specimen taken on San Nicolas I. 30 Sep 1973. Other sight records believed to pertain to this bright eastern subspecies are: 26-27 Sep 1971 Tijuana River Valley SD, 29 Sep 1972 Tijuana River Valley, 20 May 1976 Westmorland SESS, and 10 Nov 1979 Tijuana River Valley.

YELLOW-THROATED VIREO
Vireo flavifrons

Casual vagrant, primarily in spring. One wintering bird. Twelve records as follows: 7 May 1963 Wildrose INY; 24 May 1966 Cambria SLO; 5 Dec 1969-19 Mar 1970 Riverside RIV; 27 Oct 1974 Santa Catalina I.; 5-9 May 1976 Morongo Valley SBE; 23-26 May 1976 Deep Springs INY; 30 Apr-1 May 1977 Morongo Valley; 13 Jun 1977 Morongo Valley; 28-30 May 1978 Oasis MNO; 28 May 1978 Ft. Piute SBE; 30 May 1979 Ft. Piute; and 29 Apr 1980 near Banning RIV.

HUTTON'S VIREO
Vireo huttoni
Map p. 398

Fairly common resident in oak and oak-riparian woodlands in District C and the lowermost portions of District M. Casual in District D.

This species is a fairly common to common resident in coastal oak and oak-riparian woodlands south to Santa Barbara and Ventura Cos. It is fairly common along the coastal slope of the Transverse Ranges and Peninsular Ranges south to the mountains of San Diego Co.; it is very local on the desert slopes of these mountains (e.g. Banner Grade SD). This vireo occurs up to almost 2000m in District M, but it is most numerous in foothill woodlands.

On the coastal plain south of Los Angeles Co. it breeds along the upper San Luis Rey River Valley in northern San Diego Co. and irregularly at Mission Gorge and other riparian areas on the coast of southern San Diego Co. It is strictly a casual transient and winter visitant on the immediate coast away from breeding areas.

The Hutton's Vireo is resident on Santa Rosa, Santa Cruz, and Santa Catalina Is.; it has bred on Anacapa I.

This species is casual in the interior. Specimen records for District D are: 28 Dec 1904 Victorville SBE; 25 Jan 1913 Palm Springs RIV; and 22 Oct 1945 Eagle Mtn. RIV. Sight records for District D are best treated as probable; they are: 26 Sep 1971 Deep Springs INY; 13 May 1972 Deep Springs; 24 Apr 1977 Butterbread Springs KRN; 4 May 1977 Big Pine INY; and 19 Apr 1980 Scotty's Castle INY. It is unrecorded in Districts S and R, although there are winter records from the Arizona side of the Colorado R. in the vicinity of Parker and Yuma. This species should be identified with great care in the interior.

While Hutton's Vireos are primarily birds of live oak woodlands, they also breed in oak-conifer and riparian associations, and locally in arborescent chaparral.

WARBLING VIREO
Vireo gilvus   Map p. 398

Fairly common but declining summer resident in Districts C and M. Fairly common to common transient in lowlands throughout; recorded regularly into early winter, but only two certain records of overwintering birds.

A summer resident in District C, it is fairly common in riparian and mixed woodlands from Los Angeles Co. north, but it is now quite rare in San Diego Co. (only one pair found in 1978) and it is probably declining elsewhere. This vireo is a fairly common spring and common fall transient through District C; the majority of fall transients pass through the southern coast and the Channel Is. Spring transients arrive very early and are present by early March and, exceptionally, late February (e.g. 26 Feb 1972 SESS and 24 Feb 1977 Riverside RIV). The spring migration is protracted; numbers are still passing through the northern interior in late May, and a few occur into early June. While it is a common spring transient through the interior, it is much less numerous there in fall.

The Warbling Vireo is a fairly common summer resident in District M where suitable deciduous woodland habitat exists. The breeding range includes the White Mtns. and possibly some of the other desert ranges—it has summered on Clark Mtn. and in the Kingston Mtns. It breeds in the Transverse Ranges, but its status in the Peninsular Ranges is uncertain (it may not breed in ranges such as the San Jacinto Mtns. or the Laguna Mtns.).

This species formerly bred commonly in many parts of the southern coast; the decline there can probably be attributed in large part to brood parasitism by Brown-headed Cowbirds.

The first fall transients may appear quite early, e.g. 10 Jul 1977 Ft. Piute SBE. Late fall transients are recorded regularly on the coast into early December; a few even occur into early January: about 12 records exist between mid-December and early January. The only definite records through the winter are: 13 Dec 1969-12 Mar 1970 Santa Barbara SBA, and Jan-Feb 1977 Pasadena LA (not on graph). The only late straggler in the interior was 20 Dec 1976 Niland SESS.

PHILADELPHIA VIREO
Vireo philadelphicus

Casual vagrant: 26 records for the region, mostly in fall. Four spring records (all in the interior); one winter record (coastal).

On the coast it has been recorded 11 times in coastal San Diego Co., twice on the Channel Is., once on Pt. Fermin LA, and once at Big Sycamore Canyon VEN. All coastal records fall between 14 Sep 1975 Anacapa I. and 9 Nov 1969 Pt. Loma SD, except for one bird present at Harbor L., San Pedro LA 30 Dec 1978-12 Jan 1979 (the only winter record for California).

In the interior it has been recorded six times in fall with dates from 3 Oct 1970 Kelso SBE to 25 Oct 1975 Furnace Creek Ranch INY. Four of these records are from Kelso; the others are from Furnace Creek Ranch and Shoshone INY. There are also four spring records from the interior: 24-25 May 1976 Oasis MNO; 26-27 May 1976 Scotty's Castle INY; 27-30 May 1976 Furnace Creek Ranch; and 14 May 1978 Scotty's Castle.

This species should be identified with caution in the region; bright fall immature Warbling Vireos are frequently mistaken for Philadelphias.

RED-EYED VIREO
Vireo olivaceus

Rare but regular spring and, mainly, fall transient in the extreme north-eastern part of the region, with a few additional records for the southern deserts. Casual vagrant along the coast, primarily in fall. The "Yellow-green Vireo" is a casual fall vagrant to District C.

Recent coverage on the northern deserts from early to mid-September has shown this species to be regular in very small numbers (some 20 records for this period). In the interior the latest fall record is 2 Nov 1974 Scotty's Castle INY. The only fall records for the southern deserts are: 7-10 Sep 1977 Blythe RIV and 4 Sep 1972 Finney L. SESS. Spring occurrences on the northern deserts are primarily in late May and early June (about 15 records for this period). There are five spring records for the southern deserts: 5 Jun 1964 Laguna Dam IMP; 2 Jun 1974 Morongo Valley SBE; 30 May 1976 Desert Center RIV; 23 May 1978 Morongo Valley; and Jun-Jul 1976 Blythe (singing male). The earliest record for the region is 20 May 1979 Oasis MNO; the latest spring record is 23 Jun 1977 Ft. Piute SBE.

This species is a casual vagrant along the coast. There are about 14 records between 4 Sep 1972 Goleta SBA and 3 Nov 1974 Tijuana River Valley SD; half of these are for October. Coastal records from late spring and summer are: 17 May 1980 near Escondido SD; 29 May 1975 Santa Barbara I.; 5 Jun 1979 Tijuana River Valley; 26-27 Jun 1976 San Nicolas I.; and 12-13 Jul 1971 San Pedro LA.

In the interior most fall records of Red-eyed Vireos are from early September; this suggests that we receive a regular migration of birds out of their westerly breeding areas.

The "Yellow-green Vireo", *V. o. flavoviridis*, is a casual vagrant to District C from the south. There are ten records (mostly immatures) as follows: 1 Oct 1887 Santa Ana R. near Riverside RIV; 22-27 Sep 1964 Dana Pt. ORA; 3 Oct 1967 Costa Mesa ORA; 23 Sep 1967 Tijuana River Valley; 7 Oct 1967 San Diego SD; 19-20 Sep 1974 Tijuana River Valley; 25 Oct 1976 Imperial Beach SD; 15-19 Oct 1977 Pt. Loma SD (appeared to be an adult); 13 Sep 1978 Pt. Loma; and 8 Sep 1979 Gaviota SBA.

Yellow-green Vireos breed north to Sonora, Mexico, and are highly migratory.

EMBERIZIDAE:
WOOD WARBLERS, TANAGERS, CARDINALS, BUNTINGS, AND SPARROWS

PARULINAE: WOOD WARBLERS

BLUE-WINGED WARBLER
Vermivora pinus

Five records; 16 Jun 1954 Wyman Ck., White Mtns. INY, 19 Sep 1964 Pt. Loma SD; 26 Sep 1964 Imperial Beach SD; 27 May 1975 Deep Springs INY; and 28 May 1977 Ft. Piute SBE.

GOLDEN-WINGED WARBLER
Vermivora chrysoptera

Casual vagrant; 13 records for the region.

In spring there are six records for the northern desert oases, with extreme dates 20-21 May 1973 and 5 Jun 1972 (both at Deep Springs INY). The only other spring record is 4 Jun 1977 San Nicolas I.

Fall records are: one from the coast (23-24 Oct 1960 Santa Barbara SBA), two from the northern deserts (29 Sep 1974 Deep Springs INY and 15-17 Oct 1976 Scotty's Castle INY), and three in late fall from the interior of District C (8 Dec 1962 San Bernardino SBE, 20 Dec 1972 Claremont LA [found dead], and 30 Nov 1974 Big Tujunga Canyon LA).

TENNESSEE WARBLER
Vermivora peregrina

Rare but regular transient or vagrant; most fall records are coastal, and most spring records are for the northern deserts. Casual through winter on the coast.

About three-fourths of the fall records are for the coast and the species approaches uncommon status in fall on the immediate coast and Channel Is. Along the coast it has been recorded as early as 29 Aug 1973 Imperial Beach SD; there are many records extending into December. Very late fall stragglers may be recorded into late December and even early January, especially in the San Diego and Santa Barbara areas. A few have successfully wintered in the Santa Barbara and Ventura areas, remaining to mid-March. Two early spring records from the coast may pertain to birds that wintered locally: 16 Mar 1968 Tijuana River Valley SD and 21 Mar-1 Apr 1967 Pt. Loma SD. There are several fall records and one winter record (30 Dec 1978-24 Feb 1979 Riverside RIV) for the interior of District C.

Fall records for the interior extend from early September to late November, and come primarily from the northern deserts. There is one winter record for the true interior: 8 Jan 1974 Brock Ranch IMP.

This species is scarcer in spring than in fall, but it is recorded regularly in small numbers at the northern desert oases from mid-May through early June. It has been recorded as early as 13 Apr 1970 Morongo Valley SBE. A few spring records also exist for the immediate coast. The only records for District S are 4 May 1969 Finney L. SESS and 11 May 1974 Westmorland SESS. Notable late spring records are: 21 Jun 1980 Coronado SD; 23 Jun 1977 Ft. Piute SBE; 24 Jun 1977 Goleta SBA; and 2 Jul 1970 Pt. Loma SD (2).

ORANGE-CROWNED WARBLER
Vermivora celata　　　　　　　Map p. 398

Fairly common summer resident through most of Districts C and M.

Fairly common to common winter visitant in the lowlands of Districts C, S, and R. Common transient throughout.

The bright *V. c. lutescens* breeds fairly commonly in brushlands, willow thickets, oak woodlands, and taller chaparral. Along the coast it breeds from San Luis Obispo Co. south to the Santa Monica Mtns. LA; in the foothills and mountains it is found breeding along the length of the district (including the Santa Ana Mtns. ORA). *V. c. sordida*, the dusky island race, nests on all the Channel Is., and very locally on the coast of the immediate mainland (Palos Verdes Peninsula LA, Pt. Loma SD, and possibly coastal Orange Co.). There is some decrease of *sordida* on the Channel Is. in fall and early winter, at which time it is more widespread on the coast of the mainland. An interior gray-headed race, *V. c. orestera*, breeds in the White and Panamint Mtns. INY, and has been recorded in summer on Clark Mtn.

This species is a common transient throughout. Spring migration is quite early, beginning in the first half of March. On the northern deserts spring birds may linger into early June and fall birds have been recorded into early November.

This warbler is a common winter visitant in Districts S and R; it also occurs locally in winter in the southern part of District D (e.g. Palm Springs RIV and Brock Ranch IMP). Birds wintering in the interior include *lutescens* and the gray-headed forms *orestera* and nominate *celata* (winter distribution of subspecies based on specimen evidence cited in Grinnell and Miller 1944). Along the coast in winter, it is fairly common from Santa Barbara Co. south (uncommon in San Luis Obispo Co.). *Lutescens* and *sordida* are the main races represented. Wintering birds are most numerous around extensive plantings of exotic trees and shrubs, and in riparian growth.

NASHVILLE WARBLER
Vermivora ruficapilla

Common spring transient and uncommon to (in District M) fairly common fall transient; a few annually linger in District C through early winter. Small numbers regularly summer (and probably breed) in montane forests.

In spring it is rather common, particularly in District C; numbers also pass through the interior and the lower parts of District M. Spring migration begins 20-25 Mar, and is largely over by the first week of May. Spring stragglers occur into mid-May, and even to late May on the northern deserts.

In fall this warbler is generally uncommon, though widespread, in the lowlands; fall passage is more marked in the interior than in District C, and the species may be fairly common in District M and locally common in District D. Fall migration may begin by the first week of August; the majority pass through by late September. Birds linger regularly into early winter, primarily in the coastal lowlands. This warbler has occasionally successfully overwintered along the coast, primarily around extensive plantings of exotic shrubs from Los Angeles Co. south. In the interior it has been recorded on 15 Jan 1966 and 11 Feb 1967 SESS; it is otherwise unrecorded in mid-winter, although there are three late December records for District S, and a record 22 Dec 1975 at Ft. Tejon KRN.

It is an uncommon spring and fall transient on the Channel Is.

In recent years this species has been recorded regularly in summer in very small numbers in the San Gabriel and San Bernardino Mtns. and in the Mt. Pinos area (to vic. Pine Mtn. VEN), but with no definite evidence of nesting. Summer habitat consists of shaded slopes of mixed coniferous forest (especially California Black Oaks and Yellow Pines) and brush. North of our region this species breeds commonly in the Sierra Nevada.

VIRGINIA'S WARBLER
Vermivora virginiae

Uncommon and very local summer resident in arid montane woodland. Rare but regular vagrant or transient in the lowlands, primarily in fall; a few winter records.

This species is an uncommon and local summer resident in brushy areas within arid coniferous woodlands in the White Mtns. (Wyman Ck. and Cottonwood Ck.), Clark Mtn. (a few pairs), New York Mtns. (a few pairs), and in the ne San Bernardino Mtns. (a few pairs along the upper Arrastre Ck. and upper Santa Ana R. drainages). It arrives on its breeding grounds by early May.

This warbler is a rare fall vagrant along the coast; it has approached uncommon status in some years, particularly in the 1960s and early 1970s. Most fall records are for the immediate coast and the Channel Is., and are mainly from Los Angeles Co. south. In fall most Virginia's Warblers occur from the end of August through late September; it is casual after early October. There are eight very late fall and winter records from as far north as San Luis Obispo SLO (5-6 Jan 1980). Most winter records are from December through February; one that remained later was 8 Nov 1974-11 Apr 1975 Riverside RIV.

About nine spring records exist for the coast (extreme dates 19 Apr 1980 Newport ORA to 20 May 1970 Los Angeles LA), all from Los Angeles and Orange Cos. and the Channel Is.

The Virginia's Warbler is a very rare but regular vagrant or transient in the interior lowlands; records are about evenly divided between spring and fall. Most records are for the northern deserts, but the species is also probably regular in Districts S and R and in the remainder of District D.

In the breeding season Virginia's Warblers occupy brushy areas (manzanita, mountain mahogany, serviceberry) within arid coniferous forest. In the San Bernardino Mtns., locations of summer occurrence are very near those of the Nashville Warbler; some authorities consider these two forms to be conspecific. Birds along the coast in fall usually occur in low brush such as fennel (*Foeniculum*) and tree-tobacco.

LUCY'S WARBLER
Vermivora luciae

Summer resident in District R (common) and locally farther west and north in Districts S (rare) and D. Rare transient through the interior and fall vagrant to the coast; five winter records, all for the coast.

This warbler is a common summer resident along the length of the Colorado R.; there are somewhat fewer birds in the southern portions. It is partial to stands of honey mesquite, but will also range into other riparian scrub including salt cedar. Its range includes the desert washes just west of the Colorado R. This species is a very local summer resident elsewhere on the deserts; localities include: NESS (rare), Thousand Palms Oasis RIV, Morongo Valley SBE, vic. Barstow SBE, Baker SBE, Amargosa R. SBE, Klinefelter SBE, and Furnace Creek Ranch INY.

The Lucy's Warbler is very rarely noted as a transient through the interior; migrants have been noted in spring north to Scotty's Castle INY. An unusually high record was of a bird at 2200m on Clark Mtn. SBE 29 May 1979. One at Finney L. SESS 17 May 1969 is one of only two recent records for District S (apart from the breeding locality at NESS). Fall transients in the interior have been noted as follows: 26 Aug 1967 Jacumba SD (2); 28 Sep 1974 SESS; 12 Oct 1969 Borrego Springs SD; and 4 Nov 1978 Scotty's Castle.

This species is more regular as a fall vagrant to the coast; some 45 records extend from 18 Aug 1966 Imperial Beach SD to 24-25 Nov 1972 Morro Bay SLO. It has been recorded from all coastal counties, but the great majority of the records are from San Diego Co. While this species is graphed as rare in fall along the coast, it is decidedly less frequent than the Virginia's Warbler.

There are two records for the Channel Is.: 15 Nov 1975 San Nicolas I. and 14 Nov 1977 Santa Cruz I.

The winter records are: 11-31 Jan 1968 Costa Mesa ORA; 11 Nov 1979-29 Feb 1980 Harbor L. LA; 15-20 Dec 1979 Coronado SD; 15-25 Dec 1979 Otay SD; and 22 Dec 1979-22 Jan 1980 Ventura VEN. The four records for winter 1979-1980 follow an exceptional fall (14 records) in District C.

NORTHERN PARULA
Parula americana

Rare spring and fall vagrant, with over 100 records for the region. Over half of all records are for the desert oases in spring, primarily from mid-

May through early June. Casual in late fall and winter, with most records from Districts S and R.

A few records exist for April and early May in the interior, but most are from mid-May through early June; exceptionally it has been recorded as early as 24 Mar 1978 Borrego Springs SD (possibly wintering?). Spring interior records extend as late as 20 Jun 1977 Tollhouse Spring INY. In District C there are about ten spring records from 7 Apr 1966 Pt. Loma (possibly wintering?) to 14 Jun 1960 Fallsvale SBE.

In fall, there are about 25 records for the coast and the Channel Is., and about 17 records for the interior. Fall records extend from 29 Aug 1976 Furnace Creek Ranch INY through November. Late fall and winter records include about six from Districts S and R (with one at SESS 22 Mar 1969 possibly representing an early spring transient), two from Imperial Beach SD (16-24 Dec 1978 and 2 Nov-2 Jan 1970), and one from Saratoga Springs SBE 1 Jan 1966. Some of these records involve birds remaining through the entire winter.

YELLOW WARBLER
Dendroica petechia   *Map p. 398*

Common transient throughout (including the Channel Is.), and uncommon to locally common summer resident in lowland and foothill riparian woodlands. Remains rarely but regularly in lowlands in winter.

This warbler breeds fairly commonly to commonly in riparian woodlands of the lowlands and foothill canyons south to Ventura Co. and across the foothills of the Transverse Ranges. It is quite uncommon along the coastal lowlands from Los Angeles Co. south. This species breeds locally up mountain canyons into the lower portions of District M, including a few desert ranges (White, Panamint, and possibly Grapevine Mtns.). It also breeds locally in District D: along the Mohave R. SBE (possibly), Tecopa INY, the Owens Valley, and the northernmost desert oases (e.g. Oasis MNO). Birds breeding in the coastal lowlands arrive as early as the end of March.

The majority of the Yellow Warblers in the region in spring are pure transients, the first birds arriving in mid-to-late April and the bulk passing through in May. On the northern deserts the species peaks in mid-to-late May, and birds are still passing through in early June.

The first fall transients arrive in late July; migration peaks from late August to late September and stragglers may occur into early December. Small numbers winter regularly in Districts S and R. It has also wintered annually, but rarely, along the coast in recent years, primarily in the vicinity of Goleta SBA and San Diego. Birds in District S and R that are present prior to mid-April are more likely to be wintering birds than early migrants.

As a breeding species the Yellow Warbler has declined considerably in the southern coastal lowlands, and is believed to have been completely extirpated from the Colorado R. (where the subspecies *D. p. sonorana* formerly bred along the length of the river). A few singing males have been recorded recently in summer in District R, but there is no evidence of breeding. The decline and local disappearance of this species can be convincingly linked to the effects of cowbird brood parasitism, a factor which was considered serious as early as the early 1930s (Willett 1933). Destruction of lowland riparian habitats has undoubtedly also been a factor. Yellow Warblers breed in tall riparian growth of cottonwoods, alders, willows, etc.

CHESTNUT-SIDED WARBLER
Dendroica pensylvanica

Rare but regular spring and fall vagrant; about 110 records for the region.

The majority of fall records are for District C; most are from the immediate coast and the Channel Is. Fall records extend from 9 Sep 1974 Santa Barbara SBA to 17 Nov-2 Dec 1979 Marina del Rey LA. There are only three fall records from the southeastern portion of the region: 5 Oct 1952 SESS; 8 Oct 1978 Glamis IMP; and 11 Oct 1978 Blythe RIV.

There are four early winter records and one of a wintering bird, all from District S: 28-29 Dec 1964 Thousand Palms Oasis RIV; 24-29 Dec 1970 NESS; 27 Dec 1974 NESS; 23 Dec 1976 NESS; and 18 Dec 1979-28 Feb 1980 SESS.

About twenty spring records exist, with dates from 21 May 1976 Kelso SBE to 8 Jun 1973 Deep Springs INY. All of these are for the northern interior south to Morongo Valley SBE.

MAGNOLIA WARBLER
Dendroica magnolia

Rare but regular spring and fall vagrant; about 110 records for the region, the majority in fall. Two winter records.

Fall records extend from 11 Sep 1977 Tijuana River Valley SD to 10-22 Nov 1964 Rancho Santa Fe SD and, exceptionally, earlier (19 Aug 1972 and 27 Aug- 2 Sep 1972 Deep Springs INY). The majority of fall records are from the coast (including the Channel Is.). Fall records from the interior are for the northern deserts, except for one at West Pond IMP 12 Oct 1968. There is one record for District M: 2 Oct 1979 Mt. Palomar SD.

About one-fourth of all records are for the spring, and the majority (two-thirds) of these are from the oases on the northern deserts; six of the spring records are from the Channel Is. Spring records extend from 23 May 1908 Santa Cruz I. to 20 Jun 1974 Palos Verdes Peninsula LA, with an earlier date of 15 May 1897 Santa Barbara I.

The species has been recorded twice in winter: 26-27 Mar 1975 Earp SBE (probably wintered) and 17 Nov 1978- 26 Feb 1979 Riverside RIV.

CAPE MAY WARBLER
Dendroica tigrina

Very rare fall vagrant and casual spring vagrant, with five late fall and winter records. About 45 records for the region.

In fall there are about 20 records for the coast (13 Sep 1974 Pt. Conception SBA to 23 Nov 1962 Buena Vista Lagoon SD) and 12 records for the interior (29 Aug- 5 Sep 1976 Scotty's Castle INY to 10 Nov 1973 Desert Center RIV and 10 Nov 1974 Scotty's Castle). There is an additional record just outside of the region at Spicer City KRN 10 Nov 1978. Later records are: 7 Dec 1975 Morongo Valley SBE (probably a late fall vagrant); 18 Dec 1976 Mill Creek Canyon SBE (in the interior of District C, also probably a late fall vagrant); 4 Jan 1976 Brock Ranch IMP; 5-20 Mar 1978 Finney L. SESS; 29 Dec 1979-13 Apr 1980 Goleta SBA; and 10 Nov 1979-6 Jan 1980 Pt. Loma SD.

This species is casual in spring. There are three coastal records: 16 May 1976 Santa Barbara I., and 1-3 Jun and 9 Jun 1977 Pt. Loma. The six records for the northern deserts extend from 26 May 1980 Deep Springs INY to 30 May 1977 Furnace Creek Ranch INY.

Two of the spring records and one fall record are from the Channel Is. While the majority of all interior spring and fall records are for the northern desert oases, records also exist for Desert Center (2), 1 Nov 1979 Finney L. SESS, and 23 Sep 1924 Laguna Dam IMP. In District C all records are for the immediate coast except the Mill Creek Canyon record near the lower border of District M (cited above).

BLACK-THROATED BLUE WARBLER
Dendroica caerulescens

Rare but regular fall vagrant; two spring records. A total of about 130 records for the region.

The majority of records are from the coast, especially the immediate coast and Channel Is. It has been recorded in all coastal counties. Interior records come primarily from Morongo Valley SBE north; the only records for District S are: 13 Oct 1968 SESS; 7 Nov 1970 SESS; and 10 Oct 1975 NESS. Very few records exist for the interior of District C. Most birds have been recorded in October; the earliest records are in late September, exceptionally 13-16 Sep 1969 Pt. Fermin LA. This warbler is regularly recorded into early November, and exceptionally to 16-20 Dec 1974 Morro Bay SLO; 23 Dec 1979 near Pt. Sal SBA; and 25 Dec. 1974- 5 Jan 1975 San Diego SD. Over 30 birds were recorded in the region in the fall of 1974.

There are two spring records. A male was present on San Nicolas I. 15-17 Jun 1976 (photographs revealed that it had been banded elsewhere!) and a male was at Scotty's Castle INY on 26 May 1979.

YELLOW-RUMPED WARBLER
Dendroica coronata

Common to abundant winter visitor in the coastal lowlands, Channel Is., southern deserts, and in Districts S and R; fairly common summer resident in montane coniferous forests. "Audubon's" Warbler is the breeding form in the region, and it greatly predominates over the "Myrtle" Warbler in winter.

The "Audubon's" Warbler, *D.c. auduboni*, is a fairly common summer resident in montane coniferous forests from the Piute Mtns. and the Mt. Pinos region east and south through the Transverse Ranges to the San Jacinto and Santa Rosa Mtns. It also nests in the White and Inyo Mtns.; it probably nests on Clark Mtn., where it has summered in recent years, and on the Kingston and New York Mtns. There is one recent summer record for the mountains of San Diego Co. (29 Jul 1978 Cuyamaca Peak). There is also an old summer record (3 Jul 1909) well below typical breeding habitat on the upper Santa Ynez R. SBA.

Transient and wintering "Audubon's" begin arriving in the lowlands in mid-September and have largely departed by early May. Exceptionally late individuals have been recorded on Pt. Loma SD 1 Jun 1979 and 5-6 Jun 1979. In the interior birds tend to arrive slightly earlier (exceptionally in late August) and depart later. This race is quite widespread and abundant as a winter visitor, although it is considerably less numerous in the colder northern deserts and in District M, where it is restricted in winter to the lower portions.

The "Myrtle" Warbler (largely or entirely *D. c. hooveri* in this region) is a winter visitant in the lowlands. It is locally fairly common along the coast south to Santa Barbara Co.; it is uncommon elsewhere in District C, including the interior portions and on the Channel Is. It is generally uncommon in the interior; it is most numerous in the northern deserts, where it is a fall (primarily) and spring transient and scarce winter visitant. This form is an uncommon winter visitant on the southern deserts, including Districts S and R. There are a few late May records for the immediate coast, Channel Is., and northern deserts. Exceptionally, it was recorded as late as 15-17 Jun 1976 San Nicolas I.

Winter habitats of the Audubon's and Myrtle races differ on the average. Myrtles are somewhat localized in riparian thickets and other wet, brushy woodlands with small numbers scattered through other habitats. Audubon's are quite widespread; they occupy brush and woodland habitats, residential areas, brushy fields, and even grasslands and agricultural areas which are bordered by trees or brush. Breeding Audubon's Warblers occur in montane coniferous forests, primarily at the higher elevations where firs dominate.

313

BLACK-THROATED GRAY WARBLER
Dendroica nigrescens

Fairly common transient and rare winter visitant; breeds uncommonly to fairly commonly in oak woodlands and arid coniferous woodlands, primarily in District M.

This species breeds fairly commonly in arid coniferous woodlands (pinyon-juniper associations, open pine and fir forests) on the desert ranges. West of the deserts it also breeds in wooded mountain ranges in live oak woodlands and pine-oak associations (generally uncommon). It nests in some of the immediate coastal ranges such as the Santa Ynez Mtns. SBA. The breeding range of this species needs more accurate determination.

In spring the Black-throated Gray Warbler is a fairly common transient in all districts. It is one of our earlier spring arrivals; the first birds arrive in late March (an early concentration was eight in Mecca RIV 21 Mar 1911). Spring migration peaks from mid-to-late April and is largely over by 10 May; later stragglers may occur at oases on the northern deserts.

The fall migration is protracted; the first birds appear in early August and numbers still pass through well into October. It is widespread in the interior (including District M) during fall migration, although the majority pass through the coastal areas. Late fall stragglers continue into December. It is a rare but regular winter visitant throughout the warmer lowland portions, especially in woodlands and planted pines in District C. It has been recorded only twice in winter in District S (17 Dec 1977 NESS and four at Finney L. SESS 8-9 Feb 1964), although it is regular at this season in riparian woodland along the Colorado R. It has been recorded at Brock Ranch IMP, between Districts S and R, three times in winter: 21 Jan 1972, 16 Feb 1974 and 17 Feb 1979. On the Channel Is., where it is a regular transient, there is one winter record: 1 Feb 1975 Santa Cruz I.

TOWNSEND'S WARBLER
Dendroica townsendi

Fairly common to common transient, primarily west of the deserts. Uncommon winter visitant in District C; casual at this season in the interior.

This species is a common spring transient through District C, including the Channel Is. It arrives in mid-April and peaks from late April to mid-May. Stragglers are noted into early June. It is also a common spring transient through the southern mountain ranges. It is generally uncommon in the interior, although greater numbers may pass through the woodlands of the desert ranges. Stragglers may pass through the northern deserts into early June.

The fall migration is protracted — it begins in late August and lasts well into October. The fall passage peaks in late September. The majority of fall birds pass through the coastal lowlands and District M.

In winter this warbler is fairly common on the northern coast from San Luis Obispo Co. south through Santa Barbara Co.; it favors moist live oak woodlands and planted conifers. It is increasingly scarce to the south, although it occurs throughout District C and exceptionally into District M (Mt. Wilson, San Gabriel Mtns. LA). Small numbers winter on the larger Channel Is. This warbler is casual in winter in the interior: 17 Dec 1977 NESS (possibly a late fall straggler); Dec 1977-Jan 1978 near Vidal SBE (not on graph); 25 Mar 1978 near Brawley SESS; and 15 Jan 1966 Finney L. SESS (3). Note that the records from late March almost certainly pertain to locally wintering birds rather than to spring migrants.

Hybrid Townsend's X Hermit Warblers are noted almost annually during migration. A hybrid Townsend's X Black-throated Gray Warbler was noted in Imperial Beach SD 4 May 1975.

HERMIT WARBLER
Dendroica occidentalis

Generally a fairly common transient (primarily through Districts C and M in spring and District M in fall), and rare winter visitant. Scarce summer resident in District M.

In spring this warbler is fairly common in District C, including the Channel Is.; it is sometimes common in coastal San Diego Co. It is also a fairly common to common spring transient in District M, especially in the mountains of San Diego Co. This species is a rather uncommon spring transient on the desert lowlands, where it is primarily restricted to the southern portions. It is casual in the lowlands of the northern deserts.

In fall the great majority pass through the mountains, where the species is common. The Hermit Warbler is rare but regular in fall on the northern deserts and casual on the southern deserts, even though numbers pass through the adjacent mountains. In fall it is rare along the coast except in San Diego Co., where it is uncommon. This species is an early fall migrant. The first birds sometimes appear by late July; fall stragglers may remain into November.

This species is a rare but regular winter visitant in the coastal lowlands, primarily in coastal Santa Barbara Co. Winter records extend through the coastal lowlands and east to Mill Creek Canyon SBE. During the winter it inhabits tall shaded woodlands of live oaks and, especially, planted conifers.

In summer Hermit Warblers have been recorded annually in recent years in the San Gabriel and San Bernardino Mtns.; nesting has been documented for the latter range. At this season it occurs in mature mixed forests of Yellow Pines, Sugar Pines, and White Firs.

BLACK-THROATED GREEN WARBLER
Dendroica virens

Rare but regular fall vagrant and casual spring vagrant; two winter records. A total of about 95 records for the region.

Fall records are about evenly divided between the coast and the interior and fall mainly between 7 Sep 1979 Goleta SBA and 8 Dec 1963 San Diego SD; most are from late September through early November. A record at NESS 23 Dec 1976 (the only record from District S) likely pertains to a late fall straggler. Most interior records are for the northern deserts. It has been recorded once in District R: 14 Oct 1979 Blythe RIV. Records for the southern part of District D are: 22 Oct 1976 Desert Center RIV; 20 Oct 1979 Corn Spring RIV; and 24 Oct 1963 Yaqui Well SD. Records west of the deserts come primarily from the immediate coast; there is one record from well into the interior of District C: 2 Oct 1979 Colton SBE. There are three records for the Channel Is.

The four spring records are: 5 Jun 1953 Whittier LA; 26 May 1975 Santa Barbara I.; 22 May 1976 Oasis MNO; and 29 May 1977 Deep Springs INY.

It has been recorded twice in winter: 22 Dec 1978-24 Feb 1979 Goleta SBA, and 16 Dec 1978-6 Jan 1979 and again 26 Jan 1980 Otay R. near Imperial Beach SD.

BLACKBURNIAN WARBLER
Dendroica fusca

Rare but regular fall vagrant and casual spring vagrant. About 80 records.

In fall it has been recorded from 30 Aug 1976 near Malibu LA to 12 Nov 1978 Kelso SBE; most records are in October. About three-fourths of the fall records are from the coast (unrecorded in fall on the Channel Is.), and the majority of these are from San Diego Co. The interior records (about 15) range from the northern desert oases south to Morongo Valley SBE and Agua Caliente SD. It has also been recorded once in the interior of District C: 21 Oct 1977 Sunnymead RIV.

There are three spring records: 26-29 May 1975 Santa Barbara I.; 31 May 1976 Deep Springs INY; and 17 Jun 1976 San Nicolas I.

YELLOW-THROATED WARBLER
Dendroica dominica

Casual vagrant; 22 records for the region, with the majority for spring.

Of the 15 spring records, six are from the northern desert oases and extend from 24 May 1975 Deep Springs INY and 24 May 1980 Furnace Creek Ranch INY to 1 Jun 1980 Oasis MNO. The nine coastal spring records are from 18 Apr 1979 Pt. Loma SD to 14 Jun 1979 Santa Barbara SBA.

All but one of the seven fall records come from the coast from 16 Sep 1976 Goleta SBA to 5 Nov 1969 Pt. Loma SD. The only fall record from the interior is: 28 Oct- 4 Nov 1978 Deep Springs.

All records appear to pertain to the white-lored subspecies, *D. d. albilora*, except for one certain record of nominate *dominica* 15 Oct-5 Nov 1969 Pt. Loma (photographed and measured), and two other records from San Diego Co. in which the subspecies was undetermined. This species is unrecorded on the Channel Is.

GRACE'S WARBLER
Dendroica graciae

Casual vagrant, although three of the ten records are from montane coniferous forest in late spring and summer. Two winter records, and five records of fall vagrants on the coast.

Records for District M in late spring and summer are: 30 May 1974 Clark Mtn. SBE; 15 Jun-3 Jul 1975 upper Arrastre Ck. San Bernardino Mtns.; and 21 May 1977 Clark Mtn. Eventual nesting is to be watched for in arid stands of Yellow Pines, as in the San Bernardino Mtns. between Big Bear L. and Onyx Summit.

The five fall records are for the coast: 29 Oct 1966 Tijuana River Valley SD; 8 Sep 1968 Pt. Loma SD; 20-22 Sep 1977 Tijuana River Valley; 24-25 Sep 1977 Tijuana River Valley; and 30 Sep 1979 near Malibu LA.

There are two recent winter records from coastal Santa Barbara Co.: 6 Jan-2 Apr 1980 Montecito; and 24 Feb-11 Apr 1980 Carpinteria.

PINE WARBLER
Dendroica pinus

Six records: 22 Oct 1966 Tijuana River Valley SD; 28 Oct 1967 Pt. Loma SD; 18 Sep 1971 Tijuana River Valley; 13-16 Oct 1976 Pt. Loma; 4-26 Feb 1978 Regina, northeast corner of the Algodones Dunes IMP (the only winter record for California); and 15 Oct 1979 Gaviota SBA.

Fall Blackpoll Warblers, incorrectly portrayed in many field guides, are frequently mistaken for this species. All Pine Warblers should be identified with extreme caution and must be extensively documented.

PRAIRIE WARBLER
Dendroica discolor

Very rare but annual fall vagrant. One winter record and two spring records. A total of 46 records for the region.

Almost all fall records are for the coast; it has been recorded in all coastal counties. Records extend from 16-17 Aug 1977 Tijuana River Valley SD to 8 Nov 1971 Goleta SBA, and, exceptionally, to 2-6 Dec 1979

L. Cachuma SBA. There are 11 records prior to 15 Sep. It has been recorded twice in the interior of District C: 5 Oct 1978 Rialto SBE and the L. Cachuma record above. There are three interior fall records: 11-28 Nov 1976 Scotty's Castle INY; 15-16 Oct 1977 Oasis MNO; and 24 Oct-2 Nov 1977 SESS.

There are two winter records: 19 Dec 1969-24 Jan 1970 Otay R. SD and 15 Dec 1979-6 Jan 1980 Coronado SD.

The two spring records are: 29 May 1976 Furnace Creek Ranch INY and 2 Jun-1 Jul 1978 Tollhouse Spring, White Mtns. INY.

It is unrecorded on the Channel Is.

PALM WARBLER
Dendroica palmarum

Rare to uncommon fall vagrant or transient; very rare winter visitant, and casual spring vagrant. The great majority of records are coastal. About 450 records for the region.

In fall, numbers vary somewhat from year to year; the species can go almost unrecorded on the southern coast in an off-year. In any year, the majority of records come from the northern coast and the Channel Is. Most occur from mid-October through early November. One of our latest vagrant warblers, it is casual before the very end of September; it has been recorded as early as 26 Sep 1971 Imperial Beach SD. Vagrants regularly linger into early winter (January), but very few remain through the entire winter. Birds that do winter may remain into late April.

This species is of casual, almost annual, occurrence in fall in the interior. There are 20 records for District D, most of which come from the northern portions. In the southeastern part of the region it has been recorded twice in fall: 22 Sep 1942 Imperial Dam IMP (the only record for District R) and 8 Oct 1978 Glamis IMP. There are also several fall and winter records for the interior of District C. In District S it has been recorded six times (7 Nov 1979 Finney L. SESS to 10 Apr 1963 SESS, all but the one above prior to 1969). There are also three late fall or winter records for District D: 25-28 Nov 1965 Furnace Creek Ranch INY; 28 Dec 1966-27 Jan 1967 Saratoga Springs SBE; and 30 Mar 1975 Morongo Valley SBE (possibly a very early spring vagrant).

This species is a casual spring vagrant. It has been recorded 30 Apr-1 May 1975 Big Pine INY; four times at the northern desert oases (24 May 1975 Deep Springs INY to 28 May 1977 Furnace Creek Ranch); 4 May 1975 Santa Barbara SBA; and 12 May 1973 Santa Barbara I. Several other late March and April coastal records may either pertain to spring vagrants or to birds that had wintered locally.

The "Yellow" Palm Warbler, *D. p. hypochrysea*, has been recorded eight times in District C in late fall and winter.

BAY-BREASTED WARBLER
Dendroica castanea

Rare but regular fall vagrant and casual spring vagrant; the majority of fall records are coastal. About 53 records for the region.

Of the 35 fall records, 24 are coastal (16 Sep 1973 Pt. Loma SD to 16 Nov 1977 Pt. Loma). The 11 fall records from the interior extend from 2 Oct 1979 Stovepipe Wells INY to 27 Nov 1966 Furnace Creek Ranch INY and are scattered across the northern desert oases south to Kelso SBE and the Antelope Valley LA/KRN.

There are 11 spring records for the interior: 20 May 1973 Morongo Valley SBE to 4 Jun 1978 Oasis MNO (from the northern desert oases south to Morongo Valley, and San Andreas Canyon near Palm Springs RIV). Of the seven spring coastal records, six are for the Channel Is. and one is 5-6 Jun 1979 Pt. Loma. Five occurred between 26 May 1976 San Nicolas I. and 12 Jun 1974 Santa Rosa I.; the two later records are: 26-28 Jun 1976 San Nicolas I.; and 9 Jul 1975 San Clemente I.

BLACKPOLL WARBLER
Dendroica striata

Rare to uncommon fall vagrant or transient (almost all records coastal); casual spring vagrant. There are now over 500 records for the region.

Fall numbers are somewhat variable; as many as 78 (1979) and 69 (1974) have been recorded in a season, but numbers are usually far lower than this. Fall records extend from 3 Sep 1973 Otay Mesa SD to 5 Nov 1966 San Diego SD and, exceptionally, 22 Nov 1979 Pt. Loma SD. Most are along the coast and on the Channel Is.; a few records exist for the interior of District C. It is quite rare, but regular, in fall on the northern deserts (south to Morongo Valley SBE). Fall records farther south in the interior are: 4 Sep 1976 Indian Wash near Glamis IMP; 16 Sep 1976 NESS; and 4 Oct 1977 Agua Caliente SD.

In spring there are 15 records for the deserts (10 May 1979 Blythe RIV to 23 Jun 1977 Imperial NWR IMP). Most records are from the northern deserts; the other records are the two above and 15 May 1955 West Pond IMP. There are also 11 coastal spring records (19 May 1975 10km off Huntington Beach ORA to 28 Jun 1971 Palos Verdes Peninsula LA). Six of these records are from mid-to-late June. Most spring coastal records are from the Channel Is.

It is interesting that this species was unrecorded in California prior to 1955, even though there are now over 500 records from southern California alone. This recent proliferation in records points to increased observer awareness and changed patterns of coverage (observers now devote much field time to finding vagrants).

CERULEAN WARBLER
Dendroica cerulea

Five records: 1 Oct 1947 SESS; 26 Oct 1967 Pt. Loma SD; 27 May 1974 Oasis MNO; 22 Oct 1978 Pt. Loma; and 26-27 May 1979 Pt. Loma.
There are four additional records for northern California.

BLACK-AND-WHITE WARBLER
Mniotilta varia

Rare but regular transient or vagrant; most spring records are for the interior, and most fall records are for the coast. Casual in winter.
In spring, some two-thirds of the records are for the interior. The earliest interior spring record is 6 Apr 1922 Thermal RIV (may have wintered locally; otherwise, records extend from 4 May to early June. Exceptionally late interior spring records are: 20 Jun 1975 Tecopa INY and 9 Jul 1977 Kelso SBE.

Along the coast in spring, it has been recorded as early as 27 Mar 1927 Santa Barbara I. Otherwise it is generally found from mid-to-late April through early June. Late spring and summer records are: 26 Jun 1971 Santa Barbara SBA; 27 Jun 1976 San Nicolas I.; 7 Jul 1974 e. of Santa Maria SBA; 13 Jul-21 Aug 1975 Otay L. SD; and 17-19 Jul 1980 Garey SBA.

In fall about two-thirds of the records are coastal. It has been recorded as early as 20 Aug 1972 Kelso in fall in the interior. There is one record from District M: 6 Oct 1964 Laguna Mtns. SD. Some late fall records in

District D (e.g. 13 Dec 1969 Morongo Valley SBE) may represent birds attempting to winter.

All winter records from the interior are for Districts S and R: 31 Jan 1965 SESS; 27 Jan-24 Feb 1973 SESS; 21 Dec 1974 SESS (possibly a late fall vagrant); 25 Jan 1976 SESS; and 18 Dec 1973-28 Jan 1974 Laguna Dam IMP.

The Black-and-white Warbler is casual, but perhaps regular, in winter along the coast; about 30 records cover the length of the coast and include a few for the interior of District C. Most winter records are from riparian woodlands, but some come from exotic residential plantings or other types of woodland. This species' winter range includes western Mexico, possibly accounting for the many records in our region in winter and its occasional appearance as a transient in early spring.

AMERICAN REDSTART
Setophaga ruticilla

Primarily a rare to uncommon transient; small numbers winter, primarily in Districts S and R.

This species is an uncommon transient through the interior. Spring transients have been recorded there 3-4 May 1969 Morongo Valley SBE to 25 Jun 1977 near Blythe RIV and, exceptionally, as early as 24 Apr 1967 Whitwater Canyon RIV and as late as 3 Jul 1975 Arrastre Ck., San Bernardino Mtns. The peak passage is in late May and early June. In fall in the interior, most occur in late August and early September. Stragglers may occur into early November, and, exceptionally, later: 28 Nov 1970 Saratoga Springs SBE and 7 Jan 1973 Brock Ranch IMP (2, perhaps wintering).

The American Redstart is a rare but regular spring vagrant along the coast (including the Channel Is.); most occur in late May and early June. Stragglers have been noted into July as follows: 9 Jul 1967 Pt. Loma SD; 10-13 Jul 1959 UCLA Campus, Los Angeles LA; 11-13 Jul 1971 Pt. Fermin LA; 17 Jul 1975 San Diego SD; and 17-23 Jul 1980 Garey SBA. It is rare to uncommon in fall along the coast (including the Channel Is.); the major passage is in September and early October.

Small numbers winter regularly at the Salton Sea and, to a lesser extent, along the Colorado R. The species is partial at this season to thickets of tamarisks, cottonwoods, and to plantings around ranchyards. It is of casual, but nearly annual, occurrence in District C in winter, primarily along the immediate coast.

PROTHONOTARY WARBLER
Protonotaria citrea

Casual vagrant; 28 records for the region, with the majority in fall; one winter record.

The 10 spring records (19 May 1978 Tijuana River Valley SD-11 Jun 1977 Oasis MNO) include seven for the coast (one from the Channel Is.) and three from the deserts. The 17 fall records (17 Aug 1977 Oasis-5 Nov 1977 Stovepipe Wells INY) include 11 from the coast (one from the Channel Is.) and six from the interior. Four of the fall records are from the interior before mid-September. All interior records are from Kelso SBE north, except for one record for District R: 8-16 Oct 1979 n. of Blythe RIV.

There is one winter record: 30 Dec 1978-10 Mar 1979 Santa Barbara SBA.

WORM-EATING WARBLER
Helmitheros vermivorus

Casual vagrant; 14 records, most in fall.

Of the 11 fall records, seven are for coastal San Diego Co., and only one is for the interior (11-13 Oct 1975 Saline Valley INY). There is one record for the interior of District C: 30 Oct-6 Nov 1975 Riverside RIV. Fall records extend from 10 Sep 1974 Tijuana River Valley SD to 27 Nov 1975 near Malibu LA, except for one in San Diego SD 17-21 Aug 1973.

The three spring records are: 16 May 1976 San Nicolas I.; 14-16 May 1977 Yucca Valley SBE; and 23 Jun-10 Jul 1977 Ft. Piute SBE.

OVENBIRD
Seiurus aurocapillus

Rare but regular spring and fall vagrant; three winter records. About 100 records for the region.

Fall records extend from 30 Aug 1978 Kelso SBE to 18 Nov 1978 Santa Monica LA. Most records are from mid-September through mid-October. There are two fall records for District S.

In spring most records are from late May to early June (latest 12 Jun 1968 Pt. Loma SD). Spring records before mid-May are: 3 May 1975 Finney L. SESS and 17 Apr 1973 Imperial Dam IMP (only record for District R). Most spring records are from the northern interior, although this may be largely a function of coverage.

There are 15 spring and fall records from the Channel Is., all from Santa Barbara and San Nicolas Is.

The three winter records are: 1-27 Mar 1964 Bellflower LA; 12 Feb-9 Apr 1977 Riverside RIV; and 28 Dec 1977-4 Jan 1978 San Francisquito Canyon LA.

NORTHERN WATERTHRUSH
Seiurus noveboracensis

Primarily a rare spring and fall transient through the interior. Rare but

regular in fall and winter along the coast; casual there in spring. Has also wintered in Districts S and R.

In the interior this warbler is more numerous in fall than in spring; it may be uncommon on the northern deserts. Fall passage is early; most birds occur from late August to mid-September. It has been recorded as early as mid-August and, exceptionally, as late as 12 Nov 1978 Kelso SBE. Spring dates in the interior are 19 Apr 1975 Furnace Creek Ranch INY to 10 Jun 1967 Wyman Ck. INY.

It is rare but regular in fall along the coast including the Channel Is. The earliest record is 13 Aug 1966 San Diego SD. It also winters quite rarely but regularly along the coast; wintering birds may linger into April. Most winter records are from coastal San Diego Co., but records also extend through the interior of District C and up the coast to Pt. Mugu VEN. A few spring records exist for District C (including two from the Channel Is.); the latest is 3 Jun 1979 Santa Barbara SBA.

The Northern Waterthrush has wintered casually in District S at SESS, where it is also a casual fall migrant. It has been recorded in winter in District R 1 Apr 1978 near Blythe RIV (likely a wintering bird) and 20 Dec 1977 Lost L. RIV.

A record 30 Jun 1968 e. of Big Bear L., San Bernardino Mtns. SBE, may pertain to an extremely late spring vagrant.

Northern Waterthrushes are to be looked for in the vicinity of shaded streams, ponds, and ditches. Winter records come primarily from willow bottomlands with some standing water.

LOUISIANA WATERTHRUSH
Seiurus motacilla

One record: 17 Aug 1908 Mecca RIV (specimen).

This is the only record for California. There is an additional record for the Bill Williams R. delta on the Arizona side of the Colorado R. Jul-Aug 1977.

KENTUCKY WARBLER
Oporornis formosus

Five records: 4 Jun 1968 Pt. Loma SD; 1 Jun 1973 Santa Barbara I.; 27 May 1977 Ft. Piute SBE; 8 Jun 1977 Oasis MNO; and 24 Oct 1979 Imperial Beach SD.

Additionally, there are about a dozen records for Arizona, and seven for northern California, most of which are from late spring.

The four warblers of the genus *Oporornis* are placed in *Geothlypis* by many recent authors.

CONNECTICUT WARBLER
Oporornis agilis

Casual vagrant, primarily in fall. Seven records as follows: 27 Sep 1963 Tijuana River Valley SD; 19 Sep 1974 Tijuana River Valley; 22 Sep 1974 Stovepipe Wells INY (the only interior record for California); 29-30 Sep 1974 San Nicolas I.; 14 Sep 1978 San Diego SD; and, in spring, 4 Jun 1968 Pt. Loma SD and 31 May 1974 Santa Barbara I.

There are over 20 records for northern California. This species should be identified with caution.

MOURNING WARBLER
Oporornis philadelphia

Six records: 3 Oct 1968 Pt. Loma SD (specimen); 12 Jun 1968 Deep Springs INY (specimen); 29 May 1976 Furnace Creek Ranch INY (male); 4 Jun 1977 Mesquite Springs INY (male); 2 Sep 1979 Pt. Mugu VEN (female); and 10 Nov 1979 Baker SBE (specimen).

Many authorities consider the Mourning Warbler conspecific with the MacGillivray's Warbler. Caution should be used in identification as both species vary considerably in plumage.

MacGILLIVRAY'S WARBLER
Oporornis tolmiei

Uncommon to common spring and fall transient; most numerous in the interior. Uncommon and local summer resident in District M, and casual winter visitant in District C.

This species is a common spring and fall transient through the interior; it is far less numerous on the coast and Channel Is., where it is an uncommon spring and fairly common fall transient. The spring migration is protracted; the first birds may appear in late March, and birds may still be passing through the northern interior into early June. In fall, the latest interior records are 27 Nov 1971 and 22 Dec 1977 Laguna Dam IMP. Along the coast migrants regularly linger into early November and the species is recorded casually in winter (about 15 records, mostly from San Diego Co., but north to Duarte LA, Riverside RIV, and Santa Barbara SBA).

This species is an uncommon summer resident in the White Mtns., San Gabriel Mtns. (undoubtedly nests), and San Bernardino Mtns. (nesting documented); it appears to be a recent colonist in the latter two ranges. A singing male with a female was in upper Quatal Canyon, w. of Mt. Pinos, 16 June 1980. A pair was at Thorn Meadows near Pine Mtn. VEN 22 May 1980. A singing male was at Upper Agua Blanca Ck. VEN 1977 suggests the possibility of breeding on the ranges in the e. Mohave Pinos region. A singing bird in a brushy area in the Kingston Mtns. 22 Jun

324

1977 suggests the possibility of breeding on the ranges in the e. Mohave Desert. Breeding birds usually occur in willow thickets and other moist brushy areas within coniferous forest from about 2000m to 2800m.

COMMON YELLOWTHROAT
Geothlypis trichas

Fairly common resident in the region, with local seasonal movement. Primarily a transient through District D and on the Channel Is.

In Districts S and R this warbler is a fairly common transient and summer resident and an uncommon winter visitant. It is common in suitable habitat in District C, especially in the northern counties; some depart in spring and summer, when it is generally fairly common. Transients occur in District C well away from breeding areas; they have been recorded on Pt. Loma SD into early June. This species is a transient (mostly in fall) on the Channel Is.; a few winter on the larger islands.

The Common Yellowthroat is primarily a fairly common transient through the deserts. A few also move through District M. It remains to breed in suitable marsh habitat in District D (Owens Valley, Furnace Creek Ranch INY, vic. Lancaster LA, etc.). In winter this species generally departs the deserts.

For breeding, Common Yellowthroats occupy freshwater and brackish marshes of cattails, bulrushes, and other emergent aquatic vegetation and also occupy dense brush in damp areas. They also breed in more terrestrial habitats (stands of Giant Coreopsis, mustard fields, etc.) where annual growth proliferates after the rainy season. In migration they may occur in almost any brushy habitat. This species has declined somewhat as a breeder in northern California; breeding populations in the region should be carefully monitored.

HOODED WARBLER
Wilsonia citrina

Casual vagrant; 38 records for the region, a slight majority for spring. One winter record.

Of the 23 spring records, 17 are for the interior and extend from 2 May 1977 Iron Mtn. Pump Station SBE (2) to 10 Jun 1972 Deep Springs INY. Two earlier interior records are: 8 Apr 1978 Saline Valley INY and 15 Apr 1977 Kelso SBE. Additionally, there are six spring records from the coast that extend from 12 May 1973 Santa Ana ORA to 16 Jun 1962 Topanga Canyon LA. The eight records from the spring of 1977 was an exceptional total.

In fall there are six records for the northern deserts (10 Oct 1972 Kelso to 31 Oct-1Nov 1975 Mesquite Springs INY). Two records falling outside these dates are: 25 Aug 1967 Deep Springs and 24-28 Nov 1967 Borrego Springs SD. There are also six fall records from the coast; five are from 24-

26 Sep 1977 Tijuana River Valley SD to 26 Oct 1968 Pt. Loma SD and an earlier one is 22 Aug-4 Sep 1979 Santa Barbara SBA. All of these records are from the immediate coast except for one at Placerita Canyon, near Newhall LA 24 Oct 1971.

There is one winter record: 17 Dec-27 Jan 1978 near San Diego SD. It is unrecorded on the Channel Is.

WILSON'S WARBLER
Wilsonia pusilla

Common to abundant transient throughout; remains rarely in District C in winter. Uncommon summer resident in riparian thickets in District M and local breeder on the northern coast.

In spring it is a common to abundant transient in the lowlands throughout; it is one of our most numerous passerine migrants. The first birds arrive in mid-March, and migration peaks from mid-April to mid-May. Some birds still pass through the northern interior in early June.

In fall it is slightly less numerous as a transient, but it is still common. Passage through the region occurs primarily from mid-August through September. This species is generally gone from the interior by mid-October, although stragglers occur into early November (exceptionally to 24 Nov 1973 near Tecopa INY). There are five late records for District S: four in late December and one 15 Jan 1966 SESS. There are no interior records extending through the winter.

Along the coast it remains rarely but regularly through the winter in lowland willow thickets and other wet, brushy areas (e.g. Otay R. SD). Most winter records are from Ventura Co. south; some come from the interior of District C.

This species currently breeds uncommonly around montane meadows and in low, dense thickets of willows and other shrubs on steep mountain slopes. It nests in the White Mtns., on Mt. Pinos, in the San Gabriel and San Bernardino Mtns., and south, at least formerly, to the mountains of San Diego Co. In District C it still breeds in riparian growth in the lowlands of w. Santa Barbara Co. (e.g. Santa Maria R. mouth SBA/SLO) and, presumably, in similar habitat throughout coastal San Luis Obispo Co. While it is still common in these areas it has been extirpated as a breeding bird in most of the lowlands. Willett (1933) termed it "common" over much of the coastal slope; its subsequent decline is undoubtedly due in large part to the effects of cowbird parasitism. Breeding populations persist in the region today only in the higher mountains and on the north coast where there is less pressure from cowbirds.

CANADA WARBLER
Wilsonia canadensis

Casual vagrant along the coast in fall, now of almost annual occurrence; four spring records, all for the interior. About 40 records for the region.

There are about 33 records for the coast in fall (7 Sep 1976 Pt. Mugu VEN to 3 Nov 1976 San Clemente I.). Later records are: 15 Nov 1969 Tijuana River Valley SD and 21 Nov 1965 Morro Bay SLO. The only fall records from the interior are: 28 Sep 1976 Morongo Valley SBE and 5-6 Oct 1968 Barton Flats, San Bernardino Mtns. (2; District M). It has been recorded twice in fall on the Channel Is.

All four spring records are from the interior: 21 May 1969 Deep Springs INY; 30 May 1980 Oasis MNO; 3 Jun 1978 Sacramento Mtns. SBE; and 13 Jun 1967 Panamint Mtns. INY.

RED-FACED WARBLER
Cardellina rubrifrons

Casual vagrant; eight records for the region, half of which come from montane forests in late spring and summer, suggesting the possibility of breeding.

This warbler has been recorded in District M as follows: 14 Jun 1973 Buckhorn Flat, San Gabriel Mtns. LA (not present after this date); 17 May 1975 and 22 Jun 1975 Clark Mtn. SBE (possibly the same individual); and 17 Jun-3 Jul 1978 Charlton Flat, San Gabriel Mtns. (two birds). This species has expanded its breeding range in Arizona to the northwest in recent years, and nesting is to be watched for in the region. Summer birds in the San Gabriel Mtns. have been in mixed oak-conifer forests in the vicinity of canyon streams.

There are four records of vagrants in the lowlands: 30 May 1970 Brock Ranch IMP; 26 Aug 1974 San Deigo SD; 21-24 May 1977 Pt. Loma SD; and 4 Jun 1977 Morongo Valley SBE.

PAINTED REDSTART
Myioborus pictus

Casual visitant, primarily in fall and winter in District C, spring in District D, and late spring and summer in District M (has nested once). About 55 records for the region.

The ten spring records for District D are mostly from 13-16 Apr 1973 Cottonwood Canyon, Panamint Mtns. INY to 2-8 May 1965 Morongo Valley SBE; this is the normal migration period for the species in Arizona. The earliest record is 1 Apr 1979 Borrego Springs SD.The northernmost records are: 16 May 1980 Scotty's Castle INY, 27 Apr 1975 Panamint Springs INY and the Cottonwood Canyon record above. The only coastal records in spring are: 22-23 May 1969 Tuna Canyon LA and 22 Apr 1975 "base of San Gabriel Mtns." LA.

In fall there are about 17 coastal records which extend from 27 Aug 1956 Santa Barbara SBA to 1-3 Nov 1973 W. Los Angeles LA (most in September). It has been recorded once on the Channel Is.: 10 Oct 1975 Santa Cruz I. There are five fall records from the interior: 12 Sep 1950 near "Stubby Spring" RIV; 19 Sep 1956 Cottonwood Springs RIV; 9 Sep

1978 Morongo Valley SBE; 15 Sep 1978 Iron Mtn. Pump Station SBE; and 27 Sep 1979 Corn Spring RIV.

This species is casual in winter in District C; there are 11 records, three of which (Santa Barbara SBA, Mill Creek Canyon SBE, and Del Mar SD) involve individuals returning three consecutive winters. Some of these records come from the interior of the district.

There are about eight records for District M in late spring and summer. It nested near Agua Dulce Campground in the Laguna Mtns. SD, 23 May-29 Jul 1974. Otherwise it has been recorded: 25 Jun-6 Aug 1969 "lower" Mt. Palomar SD; 26 May 1973, 8-15 May 1976, and 23-29 May 1979 (2) Clark Mtn. SBE; 28 May-15 Jul 1974 and 30 May-12 Jul 1975 South Fork Campground, upper Santa Ana R., San Bernardino Mtns. (probably the same pair both years); 16 Jun 1975 Arrastre Ck., San Bernardino Mtns.; and 20 Jun 1977 New York Mtns. (pair). Just north of the region, it has been recorded 4 Jul 1969 near Springville KRN. Several of the above records come from apparently suitable breeding habitat (mixed oak-conifer forest in montane canyons), and additional nesting is to be watched for.

YELLOW-BREASTED CHAT
Icteria virens

Uncommon and local summer resident in riparian thickets of the lowlands and lower portions of foothill canyons. Rare to uncommon transient throughout. A few late fall and early spring records, but unrecorded in mid-winter.

This species breeds locally through District C and very locally in Districts D (Mohave R. and Morongo Valley SBE, Owens Valley and possibly Death Valley INY, etc.), R and (at least formerly) S. It has greatly declined as a breeder in recent years.

The Yellow-breasted Chat is an uncommon spring transient thoughout, including the Channel Is.; it is decidedly more numerous in the interior than on the coast. In fall it is a rather rare transient throughout. Fall passage is early; only stragglers occur into October. Later fall records are: 2-7 Nov 1969 Oceanside SD; 15 Nov 1974 Tijuana River Valley SD; 2 Dec 1973 Otay SD; and 5 Dec 1958 Los Angeles LA. The earliest spring birds arrive in mid-April (occasionally early April). Earlier spring records which likely pertain to wintering birds are: 22 Feb 1972 Pasadena LA and 15 Mar 1951 Loma Linda SBE.

Yellow-breasted Chats breed in dense riparian thickets and brushy tangles, especially in the vicinity of lowland watercourses. The clearing of much of this habitat has caused a noticeable decline in the number of breeding birds; cowbird parasitism may have played an additional role in their decline.

THRAUPINAE: TANAGERS

HEPATIC TANAGER
Piranga flava

Rare summer resident in arid montane woodland; casual transient and winter visitant in the remainder of the region.

In summer it occurs on Clark Mtn. (about two pairs), the Kingston Mtns. (three pairs in 1977, with nesting documented), the New York Mtns. (one pair in 1977), and the northeastern San Bernardino Mtns. In the last range, one to two pairs were recorded in the upper Arrastre Ck. drainage from the late 1960s through the mid-1970s, with nesting documented in 1972 and 1973; a pair was again present in 1980. Breeding habitat in the region consists of mature Pinyon Pine woodland with a mixture of taller conifers (White Firs or Yellow Pines). It arrives on its breeding grounds in late April or early May; the latest date for District M is 28 Aug 1976 Clark Mtn.

There are six spring records of transients through the interior: five from the northern deserts from 15 May 1976 Furnace Creek Ranch INY to 8 Jun 1977 Afton Canyon SBE and one from Morongo Valley SBE 19 Apr 1977. There are four fall records from the interior: 6 Sep 1972 Scotty's Castle INY; 13 Oct 1972 Morongo Valley; 1 Oct 1977 Morongo Valley; and 15 Sep 1978 Iron Mtn. Pump Station SBE. There are five winter/early spring records for the interior, all of which probably involve birds that wintered locally: 19 Dec 1973 Imperial Dam IMP; 9 Mar 1974 Agua Caliente SD; 28 Dec 1974 Imperial Dam; 27 Mar-12 Apr 1975 Parker Dam SBE; and 2-5 Apr 1980 Blythe RIV.

This tanager is a casual vagrant to the coastal slope (about 15 records). There are seven late fall and winter records for coastal San Diego Co. Farther north there are five fall and winter records extending from 1-14 Oct 1973 Norwalk LA to 31 Mar 1967 Los Angeles LA (wintering). These include one for San Luis Obispo Co. (near Shandon 8 Nov 1959), one for Orange Co., and three for Los Angeles Co. One of the Los Angeles Co. records involves a bird returning to Rancho Park, Los Angeles, for seven consecutive winters (1963-1970). There is one early fall record: 5-13 Sep 1973 Starr Ranch ORA. The one spring record for the coast is 9 Apr 1966 Pt. Loma SD (possibly wintered locally). Unseasonal was a bird in Santa Barbara SBA 16 Jul 1973.

SUMMER TANAGER
Piranga rubra

Uncommon summer resident along the Colorado R. and very locally westward in District D. Rare but regular fall, winter, and late spring visitant elsewhere in the region.

This tanager breeds along the length of the Colorado R. Known or suspected nesting localities outside of District R are: Brock Ranch IMP, vic. Borrego Springs SD, Thousand Palms Oasis RIV, Palm Springs (Palm Canyon) RIV, Whitewater Canyon RIV, vic. Mecca RIV (formerly), Morongo Valley SBE (two or more pairs annually), Mohave R. near Victorville SBE, Valyermo LA (1976-1977), and Tecopa INY. It may also nest just outside of the region near Weldon, on the south fork of the Kern R. KRN. It has been recorded in District R from 13 Apr 1915 Bard IMP to 24 Sep 1925 Bard. A late concentration at a nesting locality was ten at Morongo Valley 20 Sep 1969. Summer Tanagers nest in mature riparian groves dominated by cottonwoods; destruction of this habitat along the Colorado R. and elsewhere on the deserts has resulted in a decline in past decades.

Elsewhere in the region it is a rare but regular fall, winter, and late spring visitant; there are a few records through the summer period. It is unrecorded in District M. Most records of vagrants pertain to the eastern subspecies *P. r. rubra* (based on specimen evidence) rather than to our local breeding race *P. r. cooperi.*

In the interior, transients have been recorded away from breeding localities from 10 May 1978 near Independence INY to 12 Jun 1977 Oasis MNO (and exceptionally to 24 Jun 1977 Cadiz SBE), and again from 31 Aug 1972 Oasis to 22 Nov 1962 Anza-Borrego State Park SD. There are four fall records for District S. While most of these records may pertain to vagrant nominate *rubra*, a transient or vagrant in the Kingston Mtns. 28 May 1979 was felt to be *cooperi.* The only winter records from the interior are: 8 Jan 1966 and 22 Dec 1975 SESS.

Along the coast this species is rare but regular in fall, winter, and late spring (unrecorded 13 Apr-17 May). It is casual on the Channel Is., with a slight majority of records for spring. Four records for the immediate coast in early July probably pertain to late spring vagrant nominate *rubra*, but many other late spring and summer records in potentially suitable breeding habitat in the interior of District C may pertain to *cooperi* (e.g. Saugus LA, Piru VEN, Mission Gorge SD). The only documented record of *cooperi* from the coastal slope is a specimen from Hueneme VEN 23 Feb 1918. In winter along the coast this species is recorded mostly in San Diego Co., but it is also regular north to Los Angeles Co. There are only seven winter records for the coast of the region n. of Los Angeles Co. (the *cooperi* specimen cited above and six records for the Santa Barbara area).

While the *rubra* and *cooperi* subspecies of the Summer Tanager are not readily separable in the field, we have dealt with their status to illustrate the point that birds just outside the range of local breeding populations may actually be long-distance vagrants. More work is needed to confirm the rarity of migrant *cooperi* in the region and to show whether late spring and summer records away from known *cooperi* breeding areas actually pertain to that race or to wandering *rubra*.

SCARLET TANAGER
Piranga olivacea

Casual vagrant; 27 records for the region.
The majority of records are for the coast, including the Channel Is. There are 11 fall coastal records which fall between the dates of 7 Oct 1978 near Oxnard VEN and 20 Nov 1977 near Malibu LA; six of these are from the San Diego area. Outside of these dates are: 23 Aug 1964 Dana Pt. ORA; 14-19 Sep 1977 Goleta SBA; and 27 Nov-13 Dec 1976 San Luis Obispo SLO. There are five coastal spring records: 31 May 1958 Squaw Flat, Sespe Canyon VEN; 1 Jun 1973 San Nicolas I.; 20-24 Jun 1976 Palos Verdes Peninsula LA; 21 Jun 1977 Santa Catalina I.; and 26-28 May 1979 Pt. Loma SD.

In the interior there are five fall records: 26 Oct 1975 Kelso SBE; 2 Nov 1975 Panamint Springs INY; 4-8 Nov 1975 Furnace Creek Ranch INY; 11 Nov 1970 Emigrant Ranger Station INY; and one record from near Bard IMP 18 Oct 1970 (in District R, for the only record from the southeastern part of the region). The three spring records from the interior are: 23-29 May 1970 Scotty's Castle INY; 31 May 1971 Saratoga Springs SBE (2); and 5 Jun 1975 Morongo Valley SBE.

WESTERN TANAGER
Piranga ludoviciana

Fairly common summer resident in montane forests. Common transient throughout, remaining rarely through winter on the coast.
In summer it is found fairly commonly in montane forests, even those dominated by oaks in the lower portions of the mountains. This species breeds in all major mountain ranges west of the deserts (including the Santa Ynez Mtns. SBA and the Santa Ana Mtns. ORA); it also breeds in the White and Panamint Mtns. There are additional late spring and early summer records for the pinyon zone in other desert ranges, but breeding has not been documented. It is uncommon in the mountains of San Diego Co.

The Western Tanager is a common transient throughout. The first spring migrants arrive in mid-April. Most birds seen prior to mid-April probably wintered locally; however, a bird on San Clemente I. 23 Mar 1915 may have been an exceptionally early spring transient. In spring it is numerous into the third week of May; a few are still passing through into mid-June (especially on the northern deserts). There are a few mid-summer (late June, early July) records for District C.

In fall it may appear in the lowlands as early as 10 July; the major fall passage is in September, and the majority of birds pass along the southern coast and through the Channel Is. Stragglers may occur from mid-October into early November.

This species winters rarely but regularly along the coast, primarily from Santa Barbara south; it is partial at this season to extensive plantings of exotic trees, particularly flowering eucalyptus (a winter habitat preference shared with many orioles). There are a few winter records for the interior of District C, and one from the Channel Is.: 2 Jan 1976 Santa Catalina I.

CARDINALINAE:
CARDINALS, GROSBEAKS, AND BUNTINGS

NORTHERN CARDINAL
Cardinalis cardinalis

Very rare resident along the Colorado R.; most frequently recorded in the vicinity of Earp SBE, but also recorded at Laguna Dam IMP and (at least on the Arizona side of the river) nr. Winterhaven IMP.

Along the Colorado R. cardinals inhabit brushy riverbottom thickets and wooded washes. The only documented nestings in the region are for near Parker Dam SBE 7 May 1946 and 1 Jun 1963.

Northern Cardinals introduced from eastern North America nest locally along the San Gabriel R. and Rio Hondo in the vicinity of El Monte LA. Other records of cardinals in District C (e.g. many records for the San Diego area) almost certainly pertain to escapees.

PYRRHULOXIA
Cardinalis sinuatus

Casual visitant to the southeastern part of the region; eight records, one of which involves nesting.

The records are: 24 Feb-8 Mar 1971, 31 Dec 1971-27 Mar 1972, and 28 Jan-23 Mar 1973 nr. Westmorland SESS (same bird, only extreme dates graphed); 17 Dec 1972-19 Feb 1973 nr. Calipatria SESS; 28 Apr 1974 mouth of New River SESS; 23 May 1974 Brock Ranch IMP; 14 Jul 1974 nr. Palo Verde IMP; 18 Jul 1974 nr. Westmorland; 6 Jun-1 Jul 1977 30 km n. of Vidal Jct., SBE (a pair of Chemeheuvi Wash, with female on nest in late June); and 23 Dec 1977 Brock Ranch.

An individual of questionable origin was recorded at Cottonwood Springs RIV 6-7 May 1961.

ROSE-BREASTED GROSBEAK
Pheucticus ludovicianus

In general, a rare but regular spring and fall vagrant throughout, and rare winter visitant coastally. Recorded casually through summer, primarily on the coast.

This species is most numerous as a spring transient through District D, where it may actually be of uncommon status on the northern desert oases in late May and early June.

It is also regular in late spring along the coast. A few late spring records exist for District M (San Bernardino Mtns., Clark Mtn., Laguna Mtns.). The earliest recorded spring transient is 8 May 1970 Morongo Valley SBE.

In fall it has been recorded regularly both along the coast and in the interior, but the majority pass through District C (including the offshore islands). Fall records in the interior are from late August to late November.

The Rose-breasted Grosbeak is less numerous in winter than in fall, but it is still regular (about 40 records, all from the coastal slope). Winter birds may remain into mid-April; and one record is as late as 25 Apr 1979 Santa Barbara SBA. One in Glendale LA 23 Apr 1939 may have wintered locally.

This species has been recorded casually (perhaps regularly) through the summer, mostly on the coast. In the interior, spring records extend to late June. A record of an adult male with a female and begging young in El Cajon SD 29 Jul-10 Aug 1969 suggests that spring vagrants reaching the region may occasionally remain to breed. This is surely exceptional, and, based on the situation with Indigo Buntings and "Baltimore" Orioles in the region, in most instances it is likely to involve mixed Black-headed X Rose-breasted pairs.

Records for the southeastern part of the region are quite few; the only records for District S are from SESS: 25 May 1970, 12 Aug 1972, and 26 May 1978. It has also been recorded three times at nearby Brock Ranch IMP. It is casual on the California side of the Colorado R.; there are many records for the Arizona side.

BLACK-HEADED GROSBEAK
Pheucticus melanocephalus   Map p. 398

Common summer resident in woodlands throughout Districts C and M. Common spring transient and fairly common fall transient through the remainder of the region. Casual through winter along the coast.

This species is a common summer resident in oak, oak-conifer, and oak-riparian woodlands throughout District C and in all but the highest portions of District M. It breeds in all mountain ranges west of the deserts, and also in the White, Inyo, Panamint, Grapevine, Kingston, Clark, and New York Mtns. Within District C it is commonest as a breeder on the northern coast and in foothill canyons of the Transverse Ranges. This grosbeak nests on Santa Cruz I.; it is otherwise a common transient on the Channel Is.

The first spring transients generally arrive in the last week of March; numbers of spring transients may still pass through the northern interior into the end of May and early June. Very small numbers may linger through the summer on the desert lowlands, but no nesting has been recorded there. Nesting was suspected at Ft. Piute SBE in 1977. The fall passage in the region peaks from late August through mid-September.

Fall stragglers may remain on the coast regularly into early November, but this species is casual (nearly annual) through the winter season. Extensive records now reveal that the Rose-breasted Grosbeak is actually

333

somewhat more likely to be found in the region in winter than the Black-headed. We suspect that some of the older reports of female Black-headed Grosbeaks in winter may actually pertain to Rose-breasteds.

BLUE GROSBEAK
Guiraca caerulea   *Map p. 398*

Fairly common but local summer resident in brushy riparian thickets bordered by open weedy fields in lowlands throughout. Scarce migrant and casual winter visitant.

On the deserts it breeds in riparian situations and around well-irrigated areas where there is a mixture of dense brush and open weedy fields. Such areas occur through District R, locally in District S, and also in District D along the major watercourses and at oases (e.g. Morongo Valley SBE, Mohave R. SBE, Amargosa R. INY, Owens Valley INY, Oasis MNO).

This species breeds locally through the coastal lowlands; the smallest numbers are on the northern coast. It has undoubtedly declined somewhat as a result of both cowbird parasitism and habitat destruction caused by stream channelization and suburban growth. It does, however, breed successfully in young willow thickets bordering flood control basins and channels and does not appear to be particularly threatened.

Small numbers of transients are noted in spring and fall on the deserts. It is also an uncommon transient along the coast (primarily from Los Angeles Co. south), including the Channel Is. Most occur in late August and early September; late records extend to 8 Nov 1975 Santa Barbara SBA and 16 Nov 1971 Goleta SBA. Spring birds generally appear in mid-April; it has been recorded as early as 5 Apr 1964 Twentynine Palms SBE. A female at Imperial Dam IMP 30 Mar 1978 may have wintered locally. Otherwise, the only winter records (all coastal) are: 20-22 Feb 1957 near Escondido SD; 29 Jan 1964 San Ysidro SD; 22 Feb-13 Mar 1964 Solano Beach SD; and 12 Dec 1979 Otay SD.

Most recent authors merge the monotypic genus *Guiraca* into *Passerina*.

LAZULI BUNTING
Passerina amoena

Common spring transient and fairly common fall transient throughout; fairly common summer resident in brushy areas in mountains and foothills.

Spring birds arrive in early April (earliest date is 1 Apr 1977 San Diego SD); the peak spring movement is from mid-April to early May. The largest numbers pass through the desert oases and the coastal chaparral. Transients are noted rarely into early June. Fall transients appear by mid-July. This species is quite rare after September; there are no substantiated records from November through March, even though this species winters in fair numbers in southeastern Arizona.

The Lazuli Bunting breeds fairly commonly in open montane chaparral, burned-over woodland, and brushy riparian borders west of the deserts. It also breeds in willow thickets in some of the northern desert ranges (White, Inyo, Panamint, Grapevine and possibly Kingston Mtns.). Two pairs nested at Ft. Piute SBE in District D in 1978; it possibly nests at Scotty's Castle INY. Singing males have been noted in District R in June and July in citrus groves around Blythe RIV (1979-1980) suggesting nesting there. Singing birds were present through the summer of 1978 on Santa Catalina I.; it is otherwise strictly a transient on the Channel Is. The breeding distribution of this species in the region is rather spotty, and much needs to be learned.

INDIGO BUNTING
Passerina cyanea

Rare transient and rare and local summer resident in the lower portions of the region. Six late fall and winter records.

The Indigo Bunting is actually an uncommon spring transient through the northern desert oases in late May and early June. In District C vagrants (or transients) are noted in spring and, especially, fall; a high proportion of records are from the Channel Is. In spring it has been recorded as early as 11 Apr 1908 Mecca RIV, but it is not normally present until about 10 May. Stragglers in fall may occur into late November (the latest date for District D is 26 Nov 1967 Furnace Creek Ranch INY). Records after late November are: 10-23 Dec 1967 San Diego SD; 31 Dec 1977 Palos Verdes Peninsula LA; 2 Jan-29 Feb 1980 Long Beach LA; 17 Feb 1976 Goleta SBA; 9 Mar 1976 San Marcos SD; and 18 Mar 1978 Brawley IMP (apparently the only record for District S).

Singing males have been noted in summer in various parts of District C (e.g. San Luis Obispo SLO, vic. Malibu LA, Palos Verdes Peninsula, San Juan Capistrano ORA, and Mill Creek Canyon SBE). A male nested with a female Lazuli Bunting at Soledad Canyon LA during the summer of 1956 (and a male was collected there 10 Jun 1957). A male with a female Lazuli Bunting was feeding juveniles near San Diego 2-10 Jun 1973. Summering birds have also been noted on the northern deserts (Morongo Valley SBE, and several riparian groves in the White Mtns. and bordering the Owens Valley INY). Small numbers also summer in District R in the Topock Swamp near Needles SBE, vic. Blythe RIV, Imperial National Wildlife Refuge IMP, etc. (pure pairs have been noted in willows and salt cedar burns). Some summer records come from the lower border of District M; one was on Mt. Palomar SD 20 Jul 1979.

In recent years Indigo Buntings have greatly expanded their range westward, colonizing brushy, riparian second-growth habitats. Westward wandering males often pair with Lazuli Buntings (frequently the only available congeneric mates).

335

VARIED BUNTING
Passerina versicolor

Two certain records: Feb 1914 near Blythe RIV (a flock of 15+ with an ad. male and female taken 8-9 Feb), and 18-21 Nov 1977 Mesquite Springs INY (ad. male, photographed).

The Blythe record, while remarkable because of the season and the number of individuals involved, appears valid and has been accepted by the CBRC. The two specimens were taken on the edge of a cotton field. One reported 7 Aug 1966 Arcadia LA, if correct, may pertain to an escapee; similarly, a pair at a feeder at Cottonwood Springs RIV in April 1956 was thought to have been released there.

PAINTED BUNTING
Passerina ciris

Casual vagrant, primarily along the southern coast in September. Status is complicated by the frequency of escape of captive birds. Fourteen "acceptable" records.

Since captive birds are most often adult males, we have not included records of them which lie outside the established seasonal and spatial patterns of occurrence. Of the "acceptable" records, half come from coastal San Diego Co. with dates extending from 11 Sep 1975 Pt. Loma SD to 12 Oct 1974 Tijuana River Valley SD. Another was in the Tijuana River Valley 10 Nov 1962. Adult males at Imperial Beach SD 17-24 Sep 1967 and 3 Nov 1979 fit the pattern of occurrence, but are suspect because adult males are kept in captivity in nearby Tijuana, Mexico.

There are six interior records: 31 Aug 1971 Deep Springs INY (female); 21 Oct 1972 Kelso SBE (ad. male); 4 Nov 1972 Furnace Creek Ranch INY (ad. male); 27-28 Nov 1976 Scotty's Castle INY (imm. male); 4 Oct 1977 Vallecito SD (ad. male); and 13 Nov 1978 near Blythe RIV (female).

Any one record is to some extent suspect, although the distribution of records of this species elsewhere in the southwest suggests that genuine vagrants should reach California.

DICKCISSEL
Spiza americana

Rare but regular fall vagrant along the coast; casual spring and fall vagrant in the interior. Two winter records. About 75 records for the region.

Fall records for the coast extend from 23 Aug 1979 Goleta SBA to 2 Nov 1974 San Nicolas I., except for 9 Aug 1976 Santa Barbara SBA. The majority of records are for the last third of September, and are concentrated in the vicinity of Santa Barbara, San Diego SD, and the Channel

Is. An exceptional maximum was 12 in the Tijuana River Valley SD 20 Sep-1 Oct 1963 (with 7 on 27 Sep 1963).

This species has been recorded twice in winter along the coast: 2 Dec 1963-16 Mar 1964 San Diego and 26 Jan-27 Mar 1977 Los Osos SLO. There is one spring record for the coast: 9 May 1976 Santa Barbara I.

The Dickcissel is casual in the interior; there are about 20 records (most in fall). Fall records lie primarily in the period from 4 Sep 1970 Deep Springs INY to 4 Oct 1972 Yucca Valley SBE; five later records extend to 28 Nov 1964 SESS (the only record for District S). There are four interior spring records: 25 Apr 1968 Saratoga Springs SBE; 27 May 1972 Furnace Creek Ranch INY (2); 1 Jun 1973 Furnace Creek Ranch; and 10 Jun 1964 Deep Springs.

Dickcissels are generally found in weedy fields and ditches, often with other seed-eaters.

EMBERIZINAE: SPARROWS

McCOWN'S LONGSPUR
Calcarius mccownii

Very rare fall transient and winter visitant; all but one of the roughly 30 records are since 1965; some records involve small flocks.

In District C there are 14 records in the period from 19 Oct 1969 Imperial Beach SD to 7 Dec 1975 Tijuana River Valley SD, plus one winter record: 30 Nov 1979-18 Feb 1980 near Santa Maria SBA. Most coastal records come from the Tijuana River Valley, but there are also three records from Carson LA. It has been recorded once in the interior of District C: 15-20 Nov 1977 near Lakeview RIV.

Fall and early winter records from the interior are: 16 Oct 1949 Deep Springs Valley INY; 22-23 Oct 1977 Lanfair Valley SBE (2); 28 Oct 1974 Panamint Valley INY; 18-20 Nov 1979 Harper Dry L. SBE (2); 15 Dec 1979 nr. Lancaster LA; and 26 Dec 1978 Harper Dry L. (5).

This longspur is a very rare, but probably regular, winter visitant in District S. It has been recorded in eight winters since 1965, with dates ranging from 18 Nov 1973 SESS to 20 Feb 1972 SESS. Numbers are usually small, although up to 20 were near Westmorland IMP from 24 Nov 1966 to mid-Feb 1967.

McCown's Longspurs are usually found in largely barren fields (even bare dirt) and playas, and are generally in the company of Horned Larks. They are occasionally found in grasslands and in newly planted agricultural fields.

LAPLAND LONGSPUR
Calcarius lapponicus

Rare but regular fall transient in Districts C and D; winters regularly, primarily in District S.

In fall most occur in late October and November, but this species is regularly recorded as early as mid-October (exceptionally to 2 Oct 1909 near San Diego SD). While it is mainly recorded on the coastal plains, records also extend through District D (locally regular, e.g. the Antelope Valley LA/KRN), locally into District M (L. Henshaw SD), and to the Channel Is. It lingers casually into early winter on the coast (including the Channel Is.) and in the northeastern part of the region (to 10 Feb 1980 Pt. Mugu VEN, and to 19 Feb 1978 in the Lanfair Valley SBE). A spring migrant was at Furnace Creek Ranch INY 26 Mar 1980. It probably winters regularly in the Antelope Valley and on the Carrizo Plain SLO. It may also winter regularly in the Cuyama Valley SBA/SLO, where it has been recorded as late as 10 Mar 1979.

In Districts S it is a rare but regular winter visitant; numbers vary somewhat from year to year. In District R the only record is 4 Mar 1979 near Laguna Dam IMP; there are several additional records for the Arizona side of the river, and good habitat exists in the vicinity of Blythe RIV.

One at Kelso SBE 9 Jun 1977 was completely out of season.

Lapland Longspurs are usually found with large flocks of Horned Larks; while most occur in agricultural fields (including plowed dirt fields), they may also be found in other short grass habitats.

CHESTNUT-COLLARED LONGSPUR
Calcarius ornatus
Rare to uncommon fall transient throughout, including the Channel Is.; scarcest in Districts S and R and on the northern coast. Casual in winter.

Flocks may be found locally in Districts D and M, where the species borders on fairly common in fall (e.g. 35 at Baldwin L. SBE 25 Nov 1977, 60 in the Antelope Valley LA/KRN 17 Nov 1974, and 40 in the Antelope Valley 30 Oct-7 Nov 1971). Forty on San Nicolas I. 18-21 Oct 1974 was a large concentration for the coast. Numbers vary somewhat from fall to fall; several hundred birds are recorded in the region some years. It can first appear in late September (exceptionally as early as 12 Sep 1974 Furnace Creek Ranch INY), and lingers into early winter. The latest concentration in District D was 30 near Lancaster LA 15 Dec 1979. It is casual through winter; occasional concentrations are noted in the southern coastal counties (e.g. 75 near O'Neill Park ORA 26 Dec 1976 and 25 near Oceanside SD 6 Feb 1977). A late concentration in the montane grasslands was 20 at L. Henshaw SD 7 Jan 1978; four to six birds were present 5 Jan-11 Mar 1980 at Baldwin L. SBE in District M. Overwintering in District M depends on snow conditions.

This species is casual in District S: there are five records with dates ranging from 4 Dec 1971 SESS (4) to 31 Jan 1965 Westmorland IMP; some records involve flocks. It is unrecorded on the California side of the Colorado R., but there is much suitable habitat (vic. Blythe RIV, etc.) and the species is regular in numbers on the Arizona side of the river.

This longspur is casual in spring; flocks have been noted in the interior of District C as follows: 13-15 Mar 1969 Temecula RIV (30), and 17-23 Mar 1968 near Lakeview RIV (40).

Chestnut-collared Longspurs occur in a variety of grasslands and open fields (agricultural or otherwise). While often with flocks of Horned Larks, they associate less strictly with larks than do our other longspurs. They also prefer, on the average, a denser cover than our other longspurs, sometimes occurring in dense grassland.

SNOW BUNTING
Plectrophenax nivalis

Three late fall records: 14 Nov 1970 Scotty's Castle INY; 15 Nov 1971 Saratoga Springs SBE; and 23-27 Dec 1978 Kelso Valley KRN.

LARK BUNTING
Calamospiza melanocorys

In general, a rare and irregular spring and fall transient and casual winter visitor; one nesting record. Well over 100 records for the region, many of which involve small to moderate flocks.

There are about 38 records of migrants in the interior (22 fall, 16 spring). Fall records (27-28 Aug 1972 Morongo Valley SBE to 25-26 Nov 1977 Deep Springs INY) are mostly from September; the earliest fall records are for the northern interior. Most fall records involve single individuals (maximum of eight near Earp SBE 28 Oct 1951). Spring records extend from 23 Mar 1968 near Desert Center RIV to 14 May 1884 near Victorville SBE; most are from April and many involve small flocks. The largest recent spring concentration was up to 40 near Ocotillo IMP 2 Apr-1 May 1978 (after a flight winter). There are about ten winter records for the interior; most of these are for District R, but others are north to Ludlow SBE and L. Tami SBE. It has also been recorded in winter at Maricopa KRN 4 Mar 1972. There are four winter records (Jan-Feb) from SESS. The maximum winter concentration in the interior was 30 near Vidal SBE 23 Dec 1977.

Along the coast there are over 60 records (30 fall, 19 spring, 14 winter). In spring it has been recorded north through Los Angeles Co. The largest recent spring concentration was ten in the Tijuana River Valley SD 10-19 Apr 1966. It was considered "common" near National City SD in May 1884; there are also other old spring concentrations on record. One on San Clemente I. 10 Jun 1973 was quite late, and represents the only spring record for the islands. Fall records come primarily from the immediate coast from Los Angeles Co. south, and from the Channel Is. The majority of fall records are from San Diego Co. There are four records for Ventura Co. (one in winter), and six for Santa Barbara Co. Early fall records include 20 Jul 1905 Santa Barbara SBA and 28 Jul 1953 Whittier LA; this species arrives in southeastern Arizona as early as late July.

This species is at the northwestern limit of its winter range in southern California and its appearance at that season (and in migration) is quite erratic. The lone regional nesting record was obtained in spring 1978 after a large winter flight in the region. Singing adult males had been present in the Lanfair Valley SBE through May 1978, and on 27 May 1978 a nest with four young was discovered. Two females, each accompanied by young, were noted on 4 Jun 1978, and one female was still present with two juveniles on 17 Jun. This nesting record, some 1000 km outside of the species' known breeding range, came after an unusually wet winter on the deserts.

Lark Buntings are usually found in weedy fields and pasturelands, often in the company of other sparrows.

FOX SPARROW
Passerella iliaca

Common summer resident in the mountains. Fairly common winter visitant through the coastal lowlands and the montane foothills; rare in winter in the interior.

This species breeds commonly in the White Mtns. (*P. i. schistacea*), on Mt. Pinos and neighboring mountains west to Santa Barbara Co., and in the San Gabriel, San Bernardino, San Jacinto, and Santa Rosa Mtns. (all *P. i. stephensi*). It was present 25 Jun 1917 at Jackass Springs in the Panamint Mtns. and was throught to be breeding. It undoubtedly nests on Cuyamaca Peak SD where three to four pairs were noted Jun-Jul 1978-1980, but there is no definite evidence of nesting in those mountains. It breeds in brushy thickets and tracts of montane chaparral; important plants include willows, *Ceanothus*, manzanita, and chinquapin.

The Fox Sparrow is uncommon to common in winter throughout District C; it occurs mostly from mid-September to the end of April. It has been recorded as early as 30 Aug 1974 San Nicolas I. This sparrow is common in the taller, denser chaparral of the mountain foothills (south to the San Diego Co. mountains) and in the northern coastal foothills south to Los Angeles Co. It is fairly common in winter on the larger Channel Is. and it is an uncommon transient on the smaller islands. This species is uncommon on the immediate coast. Most of our wintering birds appear to come from outside of the region (the breeding race *stephensi* has largely departed the region by mid-September). Various gray-headed montane races from the Sierra Nevada and the Rockies are the most widespread in winter in the region. Darker, brown-headed northwestern races winter primarily on our northern coast; these are scarce on the southern coast and in the interior, where they occur primarily in fall. Rusty birds from the far north, mostly or all *P. i. zaboria*, are noted rarely but regularly in fall and primarily in the

340

interior; there are a few coastal winter records, and one late spring record: 8 Jun 1974 San Nicolas I.

Fox Sparrows are rare in the interior lowlands; most occur in fall, but there are a few winter records (north to the e. Mohave Desert). It borders on casual in Districts S and R.

SONG SPARROW
Passerella melodia   Map p. 399

Common permanent resident in riparian thickets and a variety of other wet, brushy situations throughout District C and locally into Districts D and M. Uncommon resident in Districts S and R; also resident on some of the Channel Is. Transient through most of District D.

The subspecies *P. m. cooperi* is resident throughout District C (replaced by *heermanni* in sw Kern Co., e.g. Ft. Tejon); it is also resident locally in District D, primarily in riparian areas on the western edge of the deserts (Morongo Valley SBE, Mohave R. SBE, and possibly near Lancaster LA). It is resident locally in the lower border of District M; small numbers breed higher in District M (to about 2500m), but most or all depart in winter. *P. m. fisherella* is resident in the Owens Valley.

The pale subspecies *P. m. saltonis* is generally an uncommon resident in wet, brushy areas in Districts S and R (salt cedar thickets, riparian borders, marshes, etc.). *Saltonis* appears to be declining in the region. Song Sparrows are rather common in summer at NESS, but these appear to be *cooperi* rather than *saltonis* (specimens are needed). A vagrant *saltonis* was collected at Furnace Creek Ranch INY 5 Apr 1920.

Song Sparrows are resident on San Miguel I. (*P. m. micronyx*), and Santa Rosa and Santa Cruz Is. (*P. m. clementae*, which was also formerly resident on San Clemente I.). The endemic race *P. m. graminea* from Santa Barbara I. has been extinct since about 1960. Mainland Song Sparrows are casual transients and winter visitants on the remaining islands.

Subspecies originating from outside the region augment our resident birds in District C in winter, and undoubtedly occur in District M also. Through the interior they are also uncommon to fairly common transients (mainly in fall), remaining locally in winter in river valleys and wet, brushy areas around ranches and oases (e.g. Furnace Creek Ranch).

LINCOLN'S SPARROW
Passerella lincolnii

Fairly common winter visitant through the lowlands of District C and the southern interior; migrant throughout the region. Uncommon and local summer resident in montane meadows.

In winter this species is fairly common to locally common in overgrown weedy fields and wet, brushy thickets and channels. It is found primarily

341

in the coastal lowlands and the lowlands of the southern interior, including Districts S and R. Small numbers winter north very locally through the remainder of District D (e.g. Furnace Creek Ranch INY). It has been recorded in the lowlands from 1 Sep 1979 Goleta SBA to mid-May (casually to 2 Jun 1979 Deep Springs INY on the northern deserts and, exceptionally, to 26 Jun 1976 San Nicolas I.). There are a few winter records for District M (e.g. Big Bear L. SBE).

It is a fairly common transient and rare winter visitant on the Channel Is.

The Lincoln's Sparrow breeds very locally in wet montane meadows of corn lily, sedges, low willows, etc. It has been recorded breeding on Mt. Pinos (two pairs on 18 Jun 1978, and present in summer 1979), the San Gabriel Mtns. (two pairs at Big Pines LA in summer 1978-1980), the San Bernardino Mtns. (vic. Big Bear L., Green Valley, and south fork of Santa Ana R.), and San Jacinto Mtns. (formerly, at least, in Tahquitz and Round Valleys).

SWAMP SPARROW
Passerella georgiana

Rare transient and winter visitant; most often recorded in the northern interior in fall.

Fall dates for the northern interior extend from 10-11 Oct 1979 Kelso SBE to 6 Dec 1977 Furnace Creek Ranch INY. Later records are: 11 Dec 1977 Antelope Valley (Holiday L.) LA and 8 Mar 1966 Saratoga Springs SBE (probably wintered). There are nine records of spring transients scattered through the interior (24 Mar 1967 Thousand Palms Oasis RIV to 27 May 1979 Scotty's Castle INY); some of the later records probably pertain to vagrants.

This species is a rare fall transient and winter visitant in Districts C, S, and R; it occurs from mid-October through early April. Later spring records are: 21 Apr 1979 Pt. Mugu VEN; 9 May 1964 NESS; and 20 May 1975 Playa del Rey LA. It has been recorded only once on the Channel Is.: 29 Mar 1976 Santa Cruz I.

Swamp Sparrows are usually found in low, wet, brushy tangles and on the borders of marshes.

WHITE-THROATED SPARROW
Zonotrichia albicollis

Rare but regular fall transient and winter visitant throughout, including the Channel Is.; most numerous (uncommon) at the northern desert oases in fall (mid-October to late November).

This species is rarely found before October; early dates include: "late Sep" 1950 San Gabriel River Wildlife Sanctuary LA and 24 Sep 1972 Tollhouse Spring INY. It regularly lingers into April and early May; some of the later birds may be spring vagrants. Late records (after mid-

May) are: 23 May 1977 Scotty's Castle INY; 26 May 1975 Oasis MNO; and 25 May-5 Jun 1977 Deep Springs INY.

White-throated Sparrows usually associate with other *Zonotrichia*; they prefer the vicinity of moist, shaded thickets, but range into other brushy habitats. They are often found at feeders.

GOLDEN-CROWNED SPARROW
Zonotrichia atricapilla

Common winter visitant through most of District C and up into the lower, brushy portions of District M. Rare to uncommon transient and winter visitant in the interior.

Winter birds normally arrive in the last third of September; an exceptionally early bird 14 Aug 1974 near San Diego SD may have summered locally. This species tends to linger slightly later in spring than the *gambelii* White-crowned Sparrow. Very late spring dates are: 3 Jun 1978 near Imperial Beach SD; 8 Jun 1974 San Nicolas I.; and 18 and 27 Jun 1968 Griffith Park, Los Angeles LA (possibly different individuals, graphed separately). Winter birds inhabit thick, shaded brush and chaparral, and the borders of oak and riparian woodland. They avoid dry, open chaparral.

This species is a rare to uncommon transient (mostly in fall) in the interior; most occur on the western edge of the deserts, but records are scattered through Districts D, R, and S. It is a rare but regular winter

visitant on the deserts (e.g. Morongo Valley SBE and Furnace Creek Ranch INY). The latest spring record from the interior is 24-26 May 1975 Deep Springs INY.

This sparrow is relatively quite abundant in winter on the larger northern Channel Is.

A few hybrid Golden-crowned X White-crowned Sparrows have been noted in the region.

WHITE-CROWNED SPARROW
Zonotrichia leucophrys

A common to abundant winter visitant in the lowlands throughout, common permanent resident on the northern coastal strip, and very local summer visitant in the highest portions of District M.

Our dominant subspecies, Z. l. gambelii, is an abundant winter visitant through most of the region, including the Channel Is.; it is uncommon in winter only in the mountains and the coldest high deserts. This form begins arriving in mid-September (exceptionally to the first week of September); numbers diminish after mid-April, and it is largely absent after early May. It has lingered to 14 May 1912 Hollywood LA and 23 May 1976 Mesquite Springs INY, and exceptionally to 18 Jun 1978 Goleta SBA (injured bird). Wintering gambelii occur in almost any brushy or weedy habitat, from sparse desert scrub to chaparral, weedy fields, and gardens.

Z. l. pugetensis (similar to the next race and, like it, very different in song from gambelii) augments gambelii along the immediate coast in winter; it is common in coastal San Luis Obispo and Santa Barbara Cos., and fairly common south to Los Angeles Co. (probably quite scarce south of there).

The brownish, yellow-billed Z. l. nuttallii is a common resident along the immediate coastal strip in San Luis Obispo and Santa Barbara Cos. south to Pt. Conception. It was recorded nesting farther south at Goleta SBA 21 May 1910. This race is quite sedentary. It occupies coastal sage scrub and gardens within a few km of the coast.

The only black-lored race recorded in the region is Z. l. oriantha (although it is possible that Z. l. leucophrys occurs on occasion). Oriantha breeds very locally in willow thickets near or above timberline in the White Mtns. and in very small numbers on Mt. San Gorgonio in the San Bernardino Mtns. (since at least 1956). This race is also a fairly common spring transient through Districts D, S, and R; it appears in mid-to-late April. Most pass through in May, and a few migrants occur into early June. It is a rare fall transient through the interior; most move through in September (in the northern interior, fall migrants arrive earlier than gambelii). It has been recorded on the northern deserts as late as 11 Nov 1978 w. Antelope Valley LA (2). This race is probably casual in winter on the southern deserts, although definite records are few. The scattered records are north to Twentynine Palms SBE and west to the Volcan Mtns. SD. On the coast *oriantha* is a very rare spring transient (based mostly on old specimen records — the paucity of recent records may be the result of the failure of most observers to deal with subspecies). Eight were banded 18 Apr-29 May between 1928 and 1932 in Pasadena LA. Early spring records are: 8 Apr 1904 Witch Ck. SD and 12-13 Apr 1980 Goleta. One was present 22 Dec 1979-15 Apr 1980 Goleta. Two black-lored birds were recorded 15 Dec 1922 Los Angeles LA. A very late bird in San Diego SD 2-11 Jun 1975 was either *oriantha* or *leucophrys* (these races are easily differentiated from other California races, but not from each other). The only fall coastal record of a black-lored bird is 20 Sep 1974 Santa Barbara I., although separation of immatures in the field is not possible, thus clouding the issue in fall.

Subspecific treatment here follows the American Ornithologists Union's 1957 Check-List. More attention should be paid to racial distribution in this sparrow.

HARRIS' SPARROW
Zonotrichia querula

Rare fall transient and winter visitant throughout.

In fall it may be irregularly uncommon in the northern part of District D; concentrations have been noted, e.g. 25 at Furnace Creek Ranch INY in late Nov 1972 (up to 18 present into the following January), and 15+ at Furnace Creek Ranch 3-4 Jan 1947. It has wintered as far north as Oasis MNO. This species has been recorded annually in winter in District C (1-3 per winter most years). There are six records for the Channel Is. There are only about five records for Districts R and S, where it may be overlooked among the very large flocks of White-crowned Sparrows. Winter 1972-1973 was exceptional for this species in the region; over 40 birds were recorded.

This sparrow generally appears in mid-October; wintering birds (and spring vagrants) may be present until about 10 May. Later records are: 20 Jan-17 May 1977 Santa Barbara I.; 28 May 1972 Westgard Pass INY; 2-5 Jun 1961 Morro Bay SLO; and 8 Jun 1973 Big Pine INY.

An apparent hybrid Harris' X White-crowned Sparrow was photographed at Furnace Creek Ranch 5-6 Nov 1977.

DARK-EYED JUNCO
Junco hyemalis   Map p. 399

In general, a common winter visitant throughout, and common resident in woodlands of District M and locally on the northern coast. "Oregon," "Slate-colored," "Pink-sided," and "Gray-headed" types are discussed separately below.

The "Oregon" Junco breeds throughout District M in conifer and mixed oak-conifer forests; in the desert ranges it breeds from the White

345

Mtns. south to the Argus and Panamint Mtns. It also summers irregularly on Clark Mtn. Along the coast it breeds in mature oak woodlands from the northern coast south locally to the Santa Monica Mtns. LA/VEN. It breeds in eucalyptus groves on the immediate coast in areas such as Morro Bay SLO, Goleta SBA, and Oxnard VEN. This bird is resident throughout its breeding range, except for some withdrawal from the highest portions of District M. There is one mid-summer record for the Channel Is., 3 Aug 1975 Santa Catalina I.

This form winters throughout the coastal lowlands (including the Channel Is.) and less commonly around trees and brushy areas on the deserts (including Districts R and S). Wintering birds arrive in late September (exceptionally to early September) and linger to late April and early May. It has been recorded to 31 May 1974 (Santa Barbara I.) on the Channel Is. Numbers in the lowlands vary somewhat from year to year.

All of the above pertains to the "Oregon" Juncos (*J. h. thurberi* and intergrades breeding in our region, with additional races occurring in winter). Birds in the northern desert ranges intergrade to an extent with "Gray-headed" Juncos, *J. h. caniceps*.

The "Slate-colored" Junco (nominate *hyemalis* and the less well-marked *cismontanus*) is an uncommon winter visitant throughout (including District M) and usually occurs with flocks of "Oregon" Juncos; it is probably most numerous on the southern deserts, including Districts S and R. It has been recorded from 17 Sep 1974 Deep Springs INY to mid-April; later dates are 6 May 1972 Morongo Valley SBE; 17 May 1976 Santa Barbara I.; and 26 May 1975 Santa Barbara I. Intergrades with "Oregon" Juncos are frequent.

The "Pink-sided" Junco, *J. h. mearnsi*, is a rare to uncommon winter visitant to Districts S and R and to the southern part of District D (e.g. Regina and Brock Ranch IMP). It is a casual late fall and winter visitant to District C (six records, mid-October to late February). It has been recorded twice in the northern part of District D: 15 Dec 1979 near Palmdale LA and (very late) 31 May 1980 Scotty's Castle INY. It is undoubtedly overlooked in the region.

The "Gray-headed" Junco, *J. h. caniceps*, is a rare to uncommon winter visitant throughout, and a scarce and local summer resident in the northeastern part of the region. The largest numbers of wintering birds are found in the southern interior, especially in District R, and in the southern mountains from the San Bernardinos south through the mountains of San Diego Co. This race also occurs regularly in District S. In District C, most occur in San Diego Co.; there are only eight records north of Los Angeles Co. It is largely a fall transient through District C, but it does regularly overwinter. The maximum for the region (away from certain breeding areas) is 12 in the New York Mtns. 14-15 Oct 1967. It is primarily present from October through March. Early dates are: 20 Sep 1964 Deep

Springs (near breeding areas); 26 Sep 1970 SESS; and 29 Sep 1974 San Nicolas I. It has lingered in the lowlands to 14 Apr 1974 and 17 Apr 1971 Brock Ranch and 26 Apr 1970 San Pedro LA. One on San Nicolas I. 26 Jun 1976 is difficult to explain.

"Gray-headeds" breed in small numbers in the White Mtns., Grapevine Mtns. (at least on the Nevada side), and on Clark Mtn. Hybrids with *J. h. thurberi* are known from the Grapevine Mtns. and Clark Mtn. There are early summer records for the New York Mtns. and it possibly nests there. Nesting habitat consists of arid coniferous woodland (Pinyon Pines, White Firs, Bristlecone Pines, etc.) with some brushy understory.

AMERICAN TREE SPARROW
Spizella arborea

Rare but regular fall transient in the northern interior and casual fall transient in District C; four late fall and early winter records for Districts S and R. Only six records after December.

Most records for the northern interior extend from 12 Oct 1975 Furnace Creek Ranch INY to 27 Dec 1964 Emigrant Ranger Station INY; maxima are of seven at Furnace Creek Ranch 5-12 Nov 1978 and six there 1 Nov 1975. Furnace Creek Ranch is the most consistent locality in the region for this species. South of there it has been recorded in District D to Saratoga Springs SBE, Baker SBE, Kelso SBE, Harper Dry L. SBE, near Lancaster LA, and Desert Center RIV. Records after December in District D are: 22 Jan 1972 Furnace Creek Ranch and 7 Apr 1974 Deep Springs INY.

This species has been recorded four times in late fall and early winter in Districts S and R: 23 Nov 1968 Bard IMP; 28 Nov 1968 SESS; 26-29 Dec 1972 SESS; and 28 Jan 1973 SESS.

Of the 15 coastal records, 11 fit the late fall pattern in the northern interior (2 Nov 1975 San Clemente I. to 21 Dec 1975 San Diego SD). Earlier and later records are: 11-12 Oct 1970 Pt. Loma SD; 30 Jan-2 Feb 1969 Arcadia LA; and 7 Feb 1888 Riverside RIV. An anomalous record is of a bird found dead at Pt. Piedras Blancas SLO 20 Jul 1979 (there are also several May and June records for the Farallon Is. in northern California). Of the coastal records, there are five from Los Angeles Co., three from San Diego Co., two from Ventura Co., and one each from San Luis Obispo, Santa Barbara, and Riverside Cos., and from Santa Cruz and San Clemente Is.

Tree Sparrows winter more or less regularly in northeastern California; they are not known to occur south of our region. They prefer weedy and brushy borders to open grassy areas (e.g. the golf course at Furnace Creek Ranch), and often associate with juncos and other sparrows.

CHIPPING SPARROW
Spizella passerina

Fairly common summer resident in montane woodlands (and locally into District C); fairly common transient through the lowlands, and uncommon to fairly common winter visitant in the southern lowlands.

This species breeds fairly commonly to commonly throughout District M, including the desert ranges south to the Panamint and Argus Mtns. (and possibly the Kingston Mtns.). It also breeds locally in District C; it occurs primarily in the foothill regions, but it even breeds on the immediate coast (e.g. Pt. Loma SD). This sparrow is a summer resident on the larger Channel Is. and Anacapa I. For nesting it utilizes open conifer and oak-conifer woodlands with a grassy understory; locally it occurs in pure oak woodland and even orchards.

This sparrow is a fairly common transient throughout the lowlands (including the Channel Is.) although it is rather uncommon on the immediate coast north of Los Angeles Co. It is most numerous in District C in fall.

The Chipping Sparrow winters locally in District C; it is generally scarce north of Ventura Co. and in that area most occur in the interior. It has wintered on the Channel Is. (San Clemente). This sparrow also winters on the southern deserts from the s. Mohave Desert south through the Colorado Desert, including Districts S and R. A concentration of 75 near Cedar Canyon SBE on the e. Mohave Desert 2 Jan 1978 was exceptional for so far north. It is partial in winter to orchards, ranchyards, other areas with brush, weedy fields, and scattered trees. It often winters in flocks and it may even be locally common. Transients and wintering birds are noted on the deserts away from breeding areas from the end of July to late May.

CLAY-COLORED SPARROW
Spizella pallida

Rare fall vagrant to Districts D and C; casual in winter and spring.

In fall most records come from the northern desert oases, the immediate coast, and the Channel Is. Fall records are mostly from about 10 Sep to late November; it has been recorded as early as 28 Aug 1968 Tijuana River Valley SD. The latest record for the interior is 29 Nov 1975 Furnace Creek Ranch INY. All records from the interior are from Kelso SBE north, except for one at Desert Center RIV 12 Oct 1975.

There are about ten records of very late fall stragglers (after November) or wintering birds; all of these are from District C from Santa Barbara SBA south. Wintering birds have remained as late as 30 Apr 1978 Arcadia LA.

Of the seven spring records, three are for the northern desert oases: 24 May 1975 Deep Springs INY (2); 1 Jun 1974 Stovepipe Wells INY; and 1

Jun 1978 Furnace Creek Ranch. The others are: 8 Apr 1970 Tijuana River Valley (may have wintered); 19 May 1980 Pt. Loma SD; 25 May 1976 San Nicolas I.; and 28 May 1977 Long Beach LA.

Clay-colored Sparrows are usually found with other *Spizella* in weedy or brushy fields and, occasionally, on lawns with some available cover.

BREWER'S SPARROW
Spizella breweri   Map p. 399

Common resident on the deserts as a whole, but breeds primarily in higher sagebrush valleys and on montane slopes, and winters mainly on the southern deserts. Rare to uncommon transient and casual winter visitant in District C.

The Brewer's Sparrow breeds commonly in sagebrush and other brushy tracts on all of the desert mountains south to the Kingston and Providence Mtns., and in the higher desert valleys (e.g. Deep Springs Valley INY, Fish Lake Valley MNO, the arid borders of the Owens Valley INY, and the Lanfair Valley SBE). It also breeds westward locally to the sagebrush valleys around Mt. Pinos, the e. San Bernardino Mtns. (vic. Baldwin L.), and, at least formerly, in the San Jacinto Mtns. and on the Carrizo Plain SLO. There is no conclusive evidence of breeding in the mountains of San Diego Co. It formerly bred in the drier interior valleys of District C (San Fernando Valley LA, Simi Valley VEN, San Bernardino Valley SBE, etc.), but it has been largely or completely extirpated from those areas.

This species winters on the southern deserts in brushy areas, weedy fields, cotton fields, and open desert scrub with herbaceous growth. It is common at this season in Districts S and R and in suitable habitat through the Colorado Desert; it winters less commonly north to the s. Mohave Desert and the Antelope Valley.

It is an uncommon fall transient (September-October) and rare spring transient (April-early May) in District C, including the interior of the district and the Channel Is. North of los Angeles Co. it is quite rare; in this area it has been unrecorded recently in spring. It remains casually through winter on the coastal slope; of some ten records, most come from the interior of District C and very few of them are recent. In spring it has been recorded as late as 24-26 May 1975 Santa Barbara I. (1-2).

BLACK-CHINNED SPARROW
Spizella atrogularis   Map p. 399

Fairly common to common summer resident in open chaparral on arid rocky slopes in District M and locally in Districts C and D. Noted only casually in migration and winter, primarily along the coast.

This species breeds on all of the desert ranges from the White Mtns. south through the Providence and Granite Mtns. and on the Eagle Mtns.

RIV, on arid brushy slopes on the western edge of the deserts (e.g. vic. Morongo Valley SBE), and on the more arid slopes of the major coastal ranges south through San Diego Co. It breeds very locally closer to the coast (e.g. Cuesta Summit SLO, coastal ridges of Santa Barbara Co., Mission Gorge SD, El Cajon SD, and the slopes bordering the Tijuana River Valley SD). Most arrive in late March and early April (as early as 17 Mar 1965 Santa Ana Mtns. ORA); it is generally absent from its breeding grounds after mid-August.

In fall it has been recorded about ten times in District C (including the Channel Is.) from late August to early November, and as follows in the interior: 13 Aug 1974 SESS (the only other record for District S is of a spring transient 13 May 1972 Finney L. SESS); 24 Aug 1974 Brock Ranch IMP; 30 Aug 1955 Imperial Dam IMP; and 10-11 Nov 1968 Cottonwood Springs RIV. It is occasionally noted in spring away from breeding localities (as late as 31 May 1974 Santa Barbara I.).

In winter there are about 15 records scattered through District C between November and early March (including four birds on Santa Cruz I. 11 Mar 1950). The only interior winter records are: 7 Feb 1965 Blythe RIV and 3 Mar 1910 opposite "the Needles" on the Colorado R. SBE.

SAVANNAH SPARROW
Ammodramus sandwichensis

Common transient and winter visitant in open fields and grasslands throughout; various subspecies breed locally in coastal salt marshes and interior grasslands.

Subspecies breeding in the interior (*A. s. nevadensis, etc.*) are common to abundant winter visitants throughout the lowlands (including the Channel Is.); they are limited only by the availability of open grassland habitat. This species is sparse in the northern interior and is restricted in District M. to grasslands of the lower portions (e.g. L. Henshaw SD). It is present away from breeding areas from mid-August to early May (to late May in the northern interior).

A. s. nevadensis breeds in grasslands bordering Baldwin L. in the San Bernardino Mtns., and locally through the Owens Valley INY. It bred at Tecopa INY in 1979; it probably also breeds in the Deep Springs Valley INY. A pair (with male singing) in marshy saltgrass near Zzyzx SBE 24 May 1975 indicates possible breeding there.

Subspecies in coastal salt marshes are common but very local permanent residents in *Salicornia* (pickleweed) marshes bordering coastal estuaries. *A. s. beldingi* occurs at Goleta SBA, Sandyland Slough SBA, Santa Clara R. estuary VEN (few), Pt. Mugu VEN, Playa del Rey LA, and at several localities in coastal Orange and San Diego Cos. *A. s. alaudinus* is resident at Morro Bay SLO, and is presumably the form occurring at the Santa Maria R. mouth SLO/SBA and the Santa Ynez R. mouth SBA. While these forms are restricted to the vicinity of coastal salt

350

HLJ80

marshes, foraging birds may range into other tidal wetland habitats (even onto rock jetties). These subspecies have declined in the region due to the dredging of salt marshes and human disturbance. While populations are maintaining themselves in some areas, the subspecies *beldingi* is on the California Rare and Endangered Species list because of the alarming rate of loss of its habitat.

The subspecies *A. s. rostratus* ("Large-billed Sparrow") is now a rare to uncommon post-breeding and winter visitant to the Salton Sea, primarily in salt cedar scrub near the mouths of rivers. It has gone unrecorded in the late 1970s. It occurs from mid-July through the winter (perhaps as late as April); it withdraws to the Colorado R. delta in Mexico to breed. This subspecies was formerly common in winter along the length of the coast in salt marshes and on beaches; its winter range included the Channel Is. Specimen dates ranged from 17 Aug to 8 Mar. It occurred primarily from Santa Barbara south, but it was recorded in the region north to San Luis Obispo Co. The only recent record for District C is 11 Nov 1977 Tijuana R. estuary SD; this subspecies is, however, possibly overlooked. Its decline in the region is undoubtedly due in part to the drying up of marshes at the mouth of the Colorado R. This subspecies is easily separable in the field from the interior and *beldingi/alaudinus* forms, but not from certain subspecies that are resident to the south in Baja California.

SHARP-TAILED SPARROW
Ammodramus caudacuta

Casual winter visitant to coastal marshes; two records of spring vagrants in the interior, and an additional interior record of a probable wintering bird.

This species is possibly regular in winter along the coast. It has been recorded most frequently at Upper Newport Bay ORA, where it frequents cordgrass marsh. This sparrow was first recorded here 17 Oct 1970; subsequently it was recorded each winter from 1972-1973 until at least 1976-1977 (up to three each winter, with a late date of 14 Mar 1977). Other winter records for the region are: 27 Dec 1952 Morro Bay SLO (5); 16 Jan-12 Feb 1944 near Venice LA (2); 2 Nov 1963 Tijuana R. estuary SD; and 12 Nov 1970 Morro Bay.

There are two spring records, both for the interior: 25-26 May 1976 Oasis MNO and 27-29 May 1976 Furnace Creek Ranch INY. One at West Pond near Imperial Dam IMP 29 Mar 1975 had probably wintered locally.

All specimens for the region belong to the brightly-marked interior race *A. c. nelsoni*.

LE CONTE'S SPARROW
Ammodramus leconteii

Three records: 27 Oct-1 Nov 1974 Furnace Creek Ranch INY (two present on 28 Oct); 23-24 Oct 1976 Little L. INY; and 21-24 May 1977 Furnace Creek Ranch.

Freshly-molted fall Grasshopper Sparrows have been mistaken for this species. There are three additional fall records for northern California.

GRASSHOPPER SPARROW
Ammodramus savannarum

Uncommon and very local summer resident on grassy slopes and mesas west of the deserts; noted only very rarely in migration and in winter.

Breeding localities include: vic. San Simeon SLO, Montana de Oro State Park SLO (sporadically), w. of Goleta SBA, nr. Simi Valley VEN, La Jolla Valley, w. Santa Monica Mtns. VEN, vic. Temecula RIV, vic. Dana Pt. and El Toro ORA, vic. Rancho Bernardo SD, and Mission Gorge SD. It breeds sporadically in other areas (perhaps regularly in some areas not listed above); this species has certainly declined as a breeder in recent decades because of development of open hilly areas. It was formerly more widespread through District C east to Beaumont RIV. This sparrow has nested to about 1500m in the San Jacinto Mtns., but it does not breed elsewhere in District M.

Along the coast (including the Channel Is.), it is noted only casually in migration away from breeding areas; records extend from 10 Aug (Year?)

Highland Park LA and 11 Aug 1972 Encino LA to early November, plus three additional May records from the Channel Is.

In the interior it is primarly a very rare fall transient; 13 records from District D extend from 18 Sep 1974 Furnace Creek Ranch INY to 11 Nov 1979 Lanfair Valley SBE (5). The majority of desert records are for Furnace Creek Ranch, but is has also been recorded at Kelso SBE and Lanfair Valley, Big Pine INY, and Deep Springs INY. There are three spring records for District D: 25 Apr 1959 Morongo Valley SBE; 11-23 May 1975 Furnace Creek Ranch; and 25 May 1979 Furnace Creek Ranch.

This species has been recorded three times in District S: 9 Nov 1963 SESS; 11 Nov 1970 SESS; and 12 Dec 1964 SESS. It was also recorded once at nearby Regina IMP (in District D) on 5 Feb 1978. The only record for District R is 4 Apr 1978 near Palo Verde IMP.

The Grasshopper Sparrow is quite rare in the region in winter, but it is undoubtedly overlooked and is probably regular. In addition to the winter records from the interior noted above, there are about 13 winter records for District C; these extend north to San Bernardino SBE and coastal Los Angeles Co. It has been recorded in winter as high as L. Henshaw SD (in District M) 27 Jan 1978.

For breeding, Grasshopper Sparrows require fairly continuous native grassland with occasional taller weedy stems or shrubs for singing perches. They are most often found on hillsides and on coastal mesas. In winter and migration this species is quite secretive and undoubtedly overlooked.

VESPER SPARROW
Pooecetes gramineus

Fairly common winter visitant, primarily in the interior. Also breeds locally in sagebrush habitats.

The Vesper Sparrow is a fairly common but local winter visitant in the interior; it occurs primarily in Districts R and S and very locally in District D north to the Owens Valley, Antelope Valley, and Carrizo Plain. It has lingered into May on the northern deserts. This sparrow is rare along the coast, where it is primarily a fall transient. It is generally rare in winter in District C; it occurs primarily in the interior parts of the district (e.g. Cuyama Valley SLO/SBA where up to 30 were present 10 Mar 1979). It is certainly no longer "common" on the coastal slope in winter, as was stated by Willett (1933). In winter it prefers overgrown weedy fields and the brushy borders of grassland and agricultural areas; it often occurs in areas with a sandy substrate.

This species is an uncommon transient and winter visitant on the Channel Is.; most occur from early September to mid-November and again from late March to late April (with records extending to late May).

The Vesper Sparrow is an uncommon and very local breeder on sagebrush plains, slopes, and valleys where there is a mixture of grassland.

It is found only at higher elevations in the White and Inyo Mtns., and around Baldwin L. in the San Bernardino Mtns. A singing male in sagebrush in the Lockwood Valley VEN 12 Jun 1980 suggests breeding in that part of the region.

LARK SPARROW
Chondestes grammacus

In general, resident in the region, but status complex. Numbers greatest in winter, but breeds in District C, locally in Districts D and M, and has bred in District R.

In winter this sparrow is fairly common to common in District C; the largest numbers are in the interior and northern portions of the district. In winter it is also fairly common in District R and uncommon in District S. It also winters locally on the western edge of the deserts and commonly on the Carrizo Plain SLO. This species is a common winter visitant on some of the larger Channel Is. and an uncommon to fairly common transient on the other islands.

The Lark Sparrow is an uncommon to fairly common breeder through much of its winter range in District C, especially in open oak woodlands mixed with grassland or pastureland in the northern and interior portions of the district. It is locally fairly common in summer in suitable habitat in the lower portions of District M (up to about 2200m in the San Bernardino Mtns.). It has recently nested in District R in orchards around Blythe RIV; it possibly nests in orchards in the Coachella Valley in District S. In District D it nests very locally in the higher valleys (Antelope Valley, Owens Valley, etc.).

This species is primarily a transient through District D (away from the few nesting and wintering localities noted above). Spring transients are noted into late May. In fall migrants are noted by mid-July. The fall passage is largely over by the end of September.

BLACK-THROATED SPARROW
Amphispiza bilineata

Common summer resident in District D; uncommon and local in winter on the deserts. Very rare vagrant to the coast, primarily in fall.

In District D it breeds from the Fish Lake Valley MNO and Deep Springs Valley INY south through Death Valley and the drier fringes of the Owens Valley to the Mohave Desert and locally on the Colorado Desert. On the Colorado Desert it is largely restricted to ocotillo and succulent scrub habitats on canyon slopes; it does not breed on creosote flats. This species breeds west on the deserts to Walker Pass KRN, the Antelope Valley, and the base of the Peninsular Ranges. It breeds up the desert slopes of the San Bernardino Mtns. to nearly 2000m. There is an isolated breeding population west of the deserts in the drier canyons along the northern part of the Santa Barbara/Ventura Co. border (e.g. Ballinger Canyon, Quatal Canyon).

In winter it withdraws from the northernmost parts of its breeding range. It is present in small numbers from the e. Mohave Desert south through the Little San Bernardino Mtns. and the western edge of the Colorado Desert (east base of the Volcan Mtns. SD). This species is more widespread in migration in the interior; there are a few early August records for District S. In District R it is primarily a post-breeding visitant in the riverbottom areas; it remains irregularly in winter and it breeds locally in dry washes adjacent to District R.

In District C this sparrow is a very rare but regular fall vagrant. There are about 15 records, mostly from August to 16 Nov 1971 near Santa Barbara SBA; early records are: 23 Jul 1973 Santa Barbara I. and 6-7 Aug 1922 Pasadena LA. A maximum for the coast was five on Santa Barbara I. 12 Sep 1976. This bird is casual along the coast in winter; there are seven records from late November to 18 Mar 1978 Newport ORA. There are six records of spring vagrants along the coast (four come from the Channel Is.), from 10 Apr 1897 near Pasadena LA to 29 May 1975 Santa Barbara I.; a later record is 12 Jun 1979 Orange ORA.

Black-throated Sparrows breed in arid scrub on desert hillsides, canyons, and washes, especially where dominated by cactus, ocotillo, or other taller, thorny plants. On the northern deserts they breed in flats of *Atriplex* (saltbush) and creosote, especially where interrupted with taller growth (e.g. Joshua Trees).

SAGE SPARROW
Amphispiza belli　　　　　　　　　　　*Map p. 399*

Uncommon to common resident in arid brushlands and desert scrub; there is a withdrawal from the higher northern parts of the range in winter and an influx of Great Basin birds into the region at this season.

The race breeding in the interior, *A. b. canescens*, nests commonly from the western fringes of the Owens Valley and locally elsewhere in the northeastern part of the region (Argus, Panamint, and Grapevine Mtns.), south through the western edge of the Mohave Desert to the desert slopes of the Transverse Ranges (e.g. in the Antelope Valley). It also breeds northwest to the Carrizo Plain SLO, the dry northern interior of Santa Barbara and Ventura Cos., and locally into District M (Mt. Pinos, Baldwin L. in the San Bernardino Mtns., etc.). Farther south, a pair with a juvenile in the New York Mtns. 9 Jul 1977 and one or more nesting pairs with newly-fledged juveniles at Baker SBE 24 May 1980 probably represent *canescens*.

In winter *canescens* withdraws from the higher parts of its breeding range. At this season it is common and widespread from the Death

Valley area south through the Mohave Desert to southeastern California; it occurs on the arid fringes of District S, and in weedy scrub (especially *Suaeda*) along the Colorada R. Birds wintering in the interior are augmented by birds from the Great Basin, *A. b. nevadensis* (indistinguishable in the field from *canescens*). *Nevadensis* occurs commonly through District D; it arrives later and departs earlier than *canescens* (based on specimen evidence). Pale interior birds of both of these races have been collected in the interior of District C in winter (e.g. Riverside RIV). *Nevadensis* has even reached San Clemente I.

The darker coastal subspecies *A. b. belli* is an uncommon to fairly common but local resident in dense, dry chaparral in interior foothills of District C; it occurs locally close to the coast, as in the coastal ridges of the Santa Barbara area and in the w. Santa Monica Mtns. VEN. Centers of abundance include w. Riverside Co. from the Jurupa Mtns. east to the vicinity of Sunnymead and Beaumont, and the vicinity of El Cajon SD. The distribution of this race is rather spotty; it is essentially sedentary. A related race, *A. b. clementae*, is resident on San Clemente I.; its population is small, and habitat destruction by goats has warranted its placement on the California Rare and Endangered Species List.

Sage Sparrows require vegetation of little complexity; birds in the interior breed in low tracts of sagebrush, saltbush, and creosote, and winter in similar (or even more barren) habitats. Nominate *belli* breeds in low, dense chamise (*Adenostoma fasciculatum*) chaparral and in dry coastal sage scrub, often with stands of cactus.

CASSIN'S SPARROW
Aimophila cassinii

Casual late spring visitant; six records.

This species was recorded at the same locality near El Cajon SD 15-30 May 1970, 8-11 May 1976, and 10-12 Jun 1978 (but apparently not present 1971-1975, or in 1977); in each year a singing male was present in a mixture of grassland and coastal sage scrub. The other three regional records are all for the same spring: 2 May 1978 NESS; 8-16 May 1978 Stoddard Valley, s. of Barstow SBE; and 21 May-7 Jun 1978 Lanfair Valley SBE (up to 15 singing males, but no evidence of nesting). The 1978 "invasion" (also pronounced in southern Arizona) followed a winter of heavy rains on the deserts; the resulting lush growth of annuals may have been responsible for the unprecedented numbers of this somewhat opportunistic species.

RUFOUS-CROWNED SPARROW
Aimophila ruficeps   Map p. 399

Fairly common resident in suitable habitat through most of District C (but largely absent from the coast north of Pt. Mugu VEN) and on Santa

Cruz and Anacapa Is. Also breeds very locally on the desert ranges; one record of a vagrant in the northern part of District D.

Preferred habitat consists of slopes with sparse brush intermixed with grassy areas; these slopes are often quite steep and rocky. Coastal sage scrub is the most frequently occupied vegetation type (including California sagebrush, buckwheat, and other shrubs, frequently with taller plants such as yuccas available for singing perches). It does not occur in dense, continuous chaparral. It was recorded once near Mountain Springs IMP (18 Mar 1978) but this species is apparently not resident there, although it breeds in adjacent San Diego Co. It is rather scarce on the lower slopes of the San Bernardino Mtns.

An interior subspecies, *A. r. scottii*, has recently been found summering in the New York and Providence Mtns. in e. San Bernardino Co. It has been recorded there 25 Mar-29 Jul, and 25 Nov 1972 (Providence Mtns.); it is probably resident, but winter coverage is limited. Breeding habitat consists of steep, rocky pinyon slopes with intermixed grasses. A bird seen 8 May 1974 at Scotty's Castle INY was most likely *scottii*, and indicates that at least some movement takes place.

GREEN-TAILED TOWHEE
Pipilo chlorurus

Common summer resident in brushy montane thickets; rare to uncommon transient in the lowlands, and very scarce winter visitant, primarily in the southeastern part of the region.

This species breeds on all of the major ranges west of the deserts from Mt. Pinos south to the Santa Rosa Mtns. Small numbers have also been recorded recently breeding on Cuyamaca Peak SD, and one to two were on Hot Springs Mtn. SD in June 1980. This species breeds on the northern desert ranges from the White Mtns. south through the Coso and Panamint Mtns. Breeding birds arrive by the end of April and the species is common by mid-May. Numbers decrease in September; it is quite rare in District M into October, although migrants have been noted as late as 24 Oct (Piute Mtns.). Breeding habitat consists of tracts of sagebrush or montane chaparral bordered by at least some growth of conifers.

The Green-tailed Towhee is an uncommon spring and fall transient in the lowlands of the interior, primarily in the northern portion of District D, where spring transients are recorded through May. It is a scarcer and earlier spring transient on the southern deserts. It is a rare winter visitant in Districts S and R and in well-vegetated washes and brushy areas in the southern portion of District D; within District R it is most numerous in the southern portions. This towhee is casual in winter on the northern deserts, although it is perhaps more regular than the few records indicate: 31 Jan 1974 Tecopa INY; 7 Jan 1976 New York Mtns.; 27 Feb 1978 Afton Canyon SBE; 29 Dec 1973 Mid Hills SBE; and 23 Feb 1980 Valyermo LA.

On the coast it is a rare but regular fall transient, generally along the immediate coast and, particularly, on the Channel Is. In fall it has been recorded as early as 29 Jul 1974 Santa Barbara SBA. It is casual through the winter in District C, although it is probably regular in the San Diego area. There are scattered winter records north to Los Angeles and San Bernardino Cos., and three from farther north: 3 Jan 1965 Santa Barbara; 26 Dec 1979-17 Feb 1980 Ventura VEN; and 27 Mar 1980 near Oxnard VEN; there are also two winter records for the Channel Is. A few coastal records of spring transients exist in April and early May; there are several April and May records for the Channel Is. (to 31 May).

This species is quite secretive away from its breeding grounds; it is undoubtedly more numerous as a transient than the records indicate.

RUFOUS-SIDED TOWHEE
Pipilo erythrophthalmus   Map p. 400

Common resident throughout District C, in the lower portions of District M, and very locally in riparian brush in the northern portion of District D. Rather rare transient and winter visitant in lowlands of the interior.

This towhee is a common resident throughout District C and in the brushy lower and middle portions of District M (east to Eagle Mtns. RIV). Birds breeding in the interior are primarily restricted to higher elevations (White Mtns. south to the Kingston, Clark, New York, and Providence Mtns.). It also breeds in the Owens Valley in brushy riparian thickets (status here not reflected in the graph for District D).

In winter it largely withdraws from the northern interior (especially the mountains). This species winters sparingly on the deserts from the Mohave Desert south; it is rare in winter in Districts S and R. It is a rare transient through most of District D.

The Rufous-sided Towhee breeds on the larger Channel Is., although it has possibly been extirpated from San Clemente I. It is an uncommon fall transient on the smaller islands.

Rufous-sided Towhees occupy dense, tall brush in well-developed chaparral, riparian thickets, and oak woodland; they are also resident in suburban areas where shrubs are dense enough. They require somewhat denser cover than the Brown Towhee.

BROWN TOWHEE
Pipilo fuscus   Map p. 400

Common resident throughout District C, and in chaparral in the lowest portions of District M. A small, isolated population occurs in the Argus Mtns. INY.

This towhee occurs on the desert slopes of the coastal ranges at such areas as Hesperia SBE, the base of the Volcan Mtns. SD (San Felipe Valley, etc.), and Mountain Springs in extreme sw Imperial Co.

358

Coastal races are almost totally sedentary, with the exception of some limited movement above the breeding range in District M. A pair accompanied by two juveniles 29 Jun 1980 at 2000m on Mt. Palomar SD represented an exceptionally high breeding locality. This species is unrecorded on the Channel Is.

An isolated, relict subspecies, *P. f. eremophilus*, is a scarce, local, and presumably resident bird in streamside thickets in the Argus Mtns. INY. A bird of this race was collected 22 Mar 1919 south of Lone Pine INY; this suggests at least limited movement of this interior race.

Brown Towhees are widespread in brushy areas of the coastal lowlands and foothills; they occupy chaparral, coastal sage scrub, gardens, etc.

ABERT'S TOWHEE
Pipilo aberti   Map p. 399

Common resident along the length of the Colorado R., and fairly common resident in the Imperial and Coachella Valleys. Also resident in District D at Brock Ranch IMP, between the Imperial Valley and the Colorado R.

Abert's Towhees occur almost exclusively in thickets of willow, cottonwood, mesquite, and salt cedar; and also in brush in ranchyards and orchards. They shun the arid desert scrub which borders the valleys in which they occur. This towhee is quite sedentary.

ICTERIDAE:
MEADOWLARKS, BLACKBIRDS, AND ORIOLES

STREAK-BACKED ORIOLE
Icterus pustulatus

Six records: 22 Sep 1962 Tijuana River Valley SD; 13 Oct 1962 Tijuana River Valley; 8 Oct 1963 Tijuana River Valley; 2-5 Jan 1966 Rancho Park, Los Angeles LA; 1 May 1931 L. Murray Dam near La Mesa SD; and (in the interior) 6 Nov-21 Dec 1977 Furnace Creek Ranch INY.

This subtropical species has also been recorded casually in southeastern Arizona.

HOODED ORIOLE
Icterus cucullatus

Common summer resident in District C; fairly common summer resident in the southern interior, breeding uncommonly north to Inyo Co. Rare but regular winter visitant along the coast.

This oriole is a common summer resident in District C, where it occurs mainly from Santa Barbara Co. south. In the interior it also breeds fairly commonly in the southern portion of District D, along the Colorado River, and, uncommonly, in District S. Breeding birds begin arriving in mid-March (exceptionally as early as late February); most have departed by mid-September.

In District D this species breeds in very small numbers north to the northern deserts; it has been recorded north to the Owens Valley INY, Oasis MNO, and the northern part of Death Valley INY. Most of the northernmost records appear to pertain to spring overshoots, but the species has nested at Scotty's Castle INY.

It is a scarce transient on the Channel Is.; it has bred at Avalon, Santa Catalina I.

There are only three late fall and winter records for the interior: 22 Nov 1955 Mecca SESS; late Nov 1977 Blythe RIV (not graphed); and 14 Feb 1978 El Centro IMP. A male near Palm Springs RIV 23 Feb 1955 was probably an early spring arrival.

The Hooded Oriole is a rare but regular winter visitant along the coast in the vicinity of feeders and flowering exotic shrubs. A maximum of eight was recorded in Santa Ana ORA during the winter 1963-1964.

Hooded Orioles are very partial to palms for nesting, and are especially common in suburban areas where palms and exotic shrubs are extensively planted. They also breed in habitats with native fan palms in desert canyons and oases, and in riparian woodlands of cottonwoods, sycamores, etc.

NORTHERN ORIOLE
Icterus galbula

The "Bullock's" race is a common summer resident in suitable woodland habitat throughout District C, in the lower portions of District M, and locally in Districts D, R, and S. Fairly common to common spring transient and uncommon fall transient, remaining rarely to uncommonly in winter in District C. The "Baltimore" race is a rare spring and fall vagrant, also wintering rarely but regularly in District C.

The "Bullock's" Oriole is a common summer resident in District C, the lower canyons of District M, and suitable riparian habitat in District D (mostly the northern portions), District R, and, locally, in District S. Woodlands with broadleafed trees (sycamores, cottonwoods, oaks, etc.) are occupied for breeding; numbers are greatest in woodlands of the coastal and foothill canyons. The first birds generally arrive around 10-15 Mar in the southern part of the region.

In spring this form is a fairly common to common transient throughout the region. It is an uncommon transient in fall, when it occurs primarily along the coast. Breeding birds depart rather early (July), and the fall migration is largely over by early September. Stragglers in the interior have been recorded into late October. Generally it is an uncommon transient on the Channel Is.; it does not breed.

The "Bullock's" Oriole is rare to uncommon in winter along the coast; it is generally restricted at this season to extensive plantings of flowering eucalyptus and other exotic flowering trees and shrubs; it occurs singly or in small flocks. There are also about six winter records for District S (some involving up to three birds), and one for nearby Brock Ranch IMP 11 Feb 1979 (graphed under District S).

The "Baltimore" Oriole is a rare but regular fall vagrant and winter visitant in District C (always outnumbered by "Bullock's") and rare but regular spring vagrant in the interior. Fall records come primarily from the immediate coast and the Channel Is. It has been recorded as early as 22 Aug 1977 Goleta SBA. This form is casual in fall in the interior, where it has occurred 27-30 Nov 1964 SESS (the only record for District S), and at scattered localities in District D.

In winter this form is found primarily around flowering exotics and feeders (areas which attract wintering orioles in general); wintering birds are recorded casually into April. There are several records of late spring vagrants on the coast; the latest is 23 May-26 Jun 1968 Griffith Park, Los Angeles LA.

Spring records for the interior are mainly from late May to early June. Earlier was one in the Saline Valley INY 7 May 1977.

It has summered in District R at Blythe RIV in 1977 (an adult male which nested with a female Bullock's).

Many authorities consider the Baltimore and Bullock's Orioles to be specifically distinct; this view has been fortified by recent data from the Great Plains. Hybrid adult male Baltimore X Bullock's Orioles have been recorded in the region.

ORCHARD ORIOLE
Icterus spurius

Rare but regular vagrant, primarily in fall. Very rare, but probably annual winter visitant.

Along the coast it is a regular fall vagrant; it has been recorded as early as late August and, exceptionally, to 12 Aug 1964 Dana Pt. ORA (an adult male which remained into late November). Most records are for the immediate coast, but a few are for the interior of District C. This species has recently proven to be of annual occurrence along the coast in winter; it is shown as casual on the bar graph to underscore the fall peak in records. At this season it occurs primarily around exotic flowering trees and shrubs (eucalyptus, bottlebrush) and around feeders. There are five coastal records, extending from 27 Mar 1978 Goleta SBA to 29 Apr 1980 Malibu LA, which are believed to pertain to spring vagrants. There are three additional late spring records: 22 May 1980 Tijuana River Valley SD; 7 Jun 1966 Montecito SBA; and 12 Jun 1980 Upper Cuyama R. VEN.

In the interior it is a very rare fall vagrant; there are about a dozen records for District D (mostly the northern portion). Records of fall vagrants extend from 4 Sep 1971 Tollhouse Spring INY to 19 Nov 1972 Furnace Creek Ranch INY. It has also been recorded once in fall in

District S: 9 Sep 1968 SESS. There are four very late fall and winter records for Districts S and R (some or all of which may pertain to wintering birds): 13 Jan 1954 Mecca NESS; 31 Oct-4 Dec 1971 SESS; 18 Nov 1973-30 Jan 1974 SESS; and 20-21 Feb 1974 Imperial Dam IMP. There are six spring records with dates from 21 May 1972 Deep Springs INY to 31 May 1973 Mesquite Springs INY; these are from the deserts from Desert Center RIV north. In spring in District R it has been recorded 23 Apr 1978 Earp SBE and 15 Jun 1969 Imperial Dam.

The Orchard Oriole is unrecorded on the Channel Is.

Most fall records for this species are of females or immature males. In late summer and early fall these birds should be distinguished very carefully from juvenile Hooded Orioles.

SCOTT'S ORIOLE
Icterus parisorum   Map p. 400

Fairly common summer resident in arid woodlands of District D and in the adjacent lower portions of District M; also breeds very locally into the drier interior of District C. Rare and local winter visitant in District D; casual fall, winter, and spring vagrant to District C.

This species breeds in desert woodlands dominated by yucca, pinyon, and juniper, and locally into adjacent riparian and dry oak woodland. It is fairly common on the Mohave Desert south to Joshua Tree National Monument and west to both Walker Pass KRN (just outside the region) and the north slope of the San Gabriel and San Bernardino Mtns. This species is also fairly common south along the desert slopes of the San Jacinto, Santa Rosa, Volcan, and Laguna Mtns. Smaller numbers breed in the northern desert ranges (Grapevine, White, Inyo, Coso, and Panamint Mtns.). It also breeds very locally west to the upper Cuyama Valley region SBA/SLO/VEN. In District C there is also a breeding record for 15 km east of San Diego SD in May 1890. Five birds, including two singing males, were in eucalyptus near Escondido SD 7 Jun 1979. It occasionally ranges into the higher portions of District M after the breeding season (e.g. 4 Aug 1979 summit of Mt. Pinos).

Transients are noted only casually in the interior lowlands, including Districts S and R.

This oriole winters in very small numbers on the western edge of the southern deserts, particularly in wooded canyons (e.g. Palm Springs RIV, Morongo Valley SBE, and Anza-Borrego State Park SD). Groups of up to six birds have been noted in winter in these areas. It has been recorded twice in winter in District S: 22 Dec 1975 SESS and 11 Feb 1967 SESS.

Coastally, the Scott's Oriole is a casual, but perhaps annual, vagrant in fall, winter, and spring; it is probably most regular in spring on the southern coast. In fall it has been recorded exceptionally as early as 24 Jul

1976 Anacapa I. The remaining fall records (about 15) are primarily from early September to early November. There are about 25 winter records for District C, about half of which come from the interior portions of the district. Winter records from the interior coastal areas such as Pauma Valley SD and San Jacinto RIV appear to fit the pattern of wintering birds on the western edge of the deserts. In winter it has been recorded north on the coast to Santa Barbara Co. There is one winter record for the Channel Is.: 5 Dec 1972 Santa Cruz I. There are also three fall records (one cited above) and one spring record for the islands. There are some 25 coastal records from 20 Mar 1972 San Diego to 2 Jun 1901 San Diego; most of these come from San Diego Co. during the period from early April to mid-May. Very late coastal spring records are: 29 May 1914 San Diego and the June record above.

YELLOW-HEADED BLACKBIRD
Xanthocephalus xanthocephalus

Common summer resident in Districts S and R, with some remaining through winter. Fairly common transient and local breeder in District D. Mainly a spring transient along the coast, breeding and wintering very locally.

This species is a common summer resident in marshes and adjacent agricultural areas in Districts S and R. It remains in variable numbers in agricultural fields in these districts in winter: fairly common in District S, somewhat local in District R (e.g. vic. Blythe RIV).

The Yellow-headed Blackbird is a fairly common transient and local breeder in District D; it generally departs in winter. Breeding localities include the Antelope Valley LA/KRN, Oasis MNO, Deep Springs L. INY, and the Owens Valley INY. It nests irregularly (or formerly) up into District M around Big Bear L., San Bernardino Mtns. In winter it is generally only casual in District D, where it has been recorded 29 Dec 1968 China Lake SBE/KRN and 19 Dec 1977 Joshua Tree National Monument SBE/RIV; small numbers do, however, winter in the Antelope Valley.

Throughout District C it is generally an uncommon to fairly common spring transient. It is an uncommon migrant in fall, when most birds are found on the southern coast. It is generally absent from the coast in summer, although it does breed very locally and irregularly (e.g. Irvine ORA, Tijuana River Valley SD). Former breeding localities in District C include: Otay Mesa SD, Goleta SBA, Nigger Slough LA, and San Jacinto L. RIV. A flock of 1000 in San Diego 19 Apr 1884 was an exceptional concentration for the coast. In general it is quite rare in winter along the coast, although it may be locally fairly common (e.g. Pt. Mugu VEN, San Luis Rey River Valley SD).

This species is an occasional transient and visitant on the Channel Is. (April through November).

Yellow-headed Blackbirds breed in dense marshes around lakes or ponds. In winter they are generally found with large mixed flocks of blackbirds around dairylands and agricultural areas.

RED-WINGED BLACKBIRD
Agelaius phoeniceus

Common resident almost throughout. Very widespread breeder throughout District C, but generally restricted to the vicinity of water outside of that district. Transient away from suitable nesting localities in District D. There is some withdrawal from the colder northern deserts and montane valleys in winter.

There is a small breeding colony on Santa Cruz I.; it is otherwise an uncommon transient and winter visitant on the Channel Is.

In winter Red-winged Blackbirds form large flocks which are usually mixed with other blackbird species and which are found in agricultural areas and open fields. Marshes are utilized for roosting. They breed in freshwater marshes and, in District C, other wet, brushy, or weedy areas, riparian borders, pasturelands, etc.

TRICOLORED BLACKBIRD
Agelaius tricolor
Map p. 400

Local resident in District C; generally common where it occurs. It also breeds on the western edge of District D in the Antelope Valley. Casual on the Channel Is. and in the eastern part of the region.

This species breeds in District C from San Diego Co. north locally through all of the coastal counties, including the interior portions of the district. It winters primarily in the vicinity of breeding localities; there is only slight dispersal at this season. In the Antelope Valley numbers are greatly reduced in late summer and early fall. On the deserts away from the Antelope Valley, small numbers have been found in recent winters at L. Tami near Yermo SBE.

The Tricolored Blackbird is casual in the eastern part of the region; records are: 31 May 1969 Panamint Springs INY (ad. male); 25-26 May 1974 Furnace Creek Ranch INY (ad. male); 7 Jun 1975 Furnace Creek Ranch (ad. male); 13 May 1978 Kelso SBE (male and female); and in District S, 12 Mar 1978 near Finney L. SESS (ad. male) and 3 Mar 1980 near Calexico IMP. Published records of large flocks at NESS lack convincing details and should be disregarded.

It is a casual spring and fall visitant to the Channel Is. with six records.

Tricolored Blackbirds breed in dense colonies in extensive reed beds. Like other blackbirds, they congregate (in either mixed-species flocks or pure flocks) in agricultural areas outside of the breeding season. Even in the breeding season most foraging takes place in agricultural areas or on open lawns (golf courses, cemeteries, etc.). Care should be taken in identifying this species out of range; females are very similar to females of some races of the Red-winged Blackbird.

WESTERN MEADOWLARK
Sturnella neglecta

Common resident in grasslands and fields throughout the region; some winter influx into the region.

While the Western Meadowlark is generally resident, in winter there is some withdrawal from the coldest areas, including more or less complete withdrawal from montane grasslands. It is more numerous and widespread in the coastal lowlands and in desert agricultural areas in winter. It is resident on all the Channel Is.

Western Meadowlarks inhabit a variety of open habitats, including agricultural fields (especially in winter), grasslands, weedy lots (even in semi-urban areas in winter), and montane pasturelands.

The Eastern Meadowlark (of the southwest breeding race *S. magna lilianae*) has recently been collected on the Arizona side of the Colorado R. Although it is currently unrecorded in California, it should be watched for in agricultural areas of the southeastern part of the region in winter.

GREAT-TAILED GRACKLE
Quiscalus mexicanus

Fairly common to locally common resident in District R; uncommon but spreading resident in District S (mainly SESS). Small numbers resident very locally in District D; casual visitant through the remainder of District D and to District C.

This species is resident along the length of the Colorado R., the greatest numbers occur in the vicinity of Imperial and Laguna Dams IMP and L. Havasu SBE. This grackle has been rapidly increasing, even in the last few years. It is also an uncommon but increasing resident at the south end of the Salton Sea; in recent years it has nested at the mouth of the Alamo R. and at Ramer L., foraging around the shore of the Salton Sea, in agricultural areas, and around cattle pens south to the vicinity of El Centro IMP. A few have been recorded recently at NESS.

In District D it has nested recently at Furnace Creek Ranch INY (one pair in 1977, and up to 30 birds by fall 1979). A pair was feeding young at Olancha INY 20 Aug 1980. A few have also been noted recently at Baker SBE. It is a casual visitant elsewhere in District D (Yucca Valley SBE, Desert Center RIV north to Stovepipe Wells, Mesquite Springs, and Panamint Springs INY). In future years it will undoubtedly colonize additional agricultural areas and oases on the deserts.

This species is casual in District C. The six records are: 16 Feb-29 Mar 1968 San Pedro LA; 5-6 Feb 1977 Sweetwater Res. SD; Aug 1978-22 Nov 1979 vic. San Pedro (not graphed); 12 Sep-early Nov 1978 Jalama Beach SBA; 12 May-Jun 1979 and again 6 May through summer 1980 L. Cachuma SBA (not graphed); and 2-7 Jul 1979 Gaviota SBA.

The Great-tailed Grackle was unrecorded in California until 6 Jun 1964 when a female was taken at West Pond, near Imperial Dam IMP. Another was found at SESS 18 Jun 1964. At Imperial Dam nesting was suspected in 1968 and documented in Jun 1969. In the 1970s this species continued a dramatic increase in the region, part of a widespread expansion in the southwest in response to human habitation and agriculture. In the deserts it now occurs in park-like areas where groves of trees are mixed with open lawns, or agricultural areas. It is often found in the vicinity of marshes, which are utilized for roosting and nesting.

COMMON GRACKLE
Quiscalus quiscula

Casual vagrant, with most records for spring. Recorded 11 times as follows: 20 Nov 1969 El Cajon SD; 21-26 May 1975 Furnace Creek Ranch INY; 30 Apr 1976 Morongo Valley SBE; 9 Feb-26 Mar 1977 Carlsbad SD; 28 May 1977 Scotty's Castle INY; 30 May-8 Jun 1977 Deep Springs INY; 22 May 1979 Scotty's Castle; 9 Jun 1979 near Blythe RIV; 7 Oct 1979 Furnace Creek Ranch; 21 May 1980 Deep Springs; and 24-26 May 1980 Furnace Creek Ranch.

All California birds appear to be of the "Bronzed" subspecies, *Q. q. versicolor.*

RUSTY BLACKBIRD
Euphagus carolinus

Rare but regular late fall vagrant, primarily in the northern interior. Also a casual late fall and winter visitant along the coast and (especially) on the Channel Is. Casual in spring.

Fall vagrants in the interior have been recorded as early as 25 Oct 1975 Death Valley INY and as late as 15 Dec 1977 Furnace Creek Ranch INY; most records are from Kelso SBE north, but there is one record farther south in fall: 27 Nov 1964 Borrego Springs SD. There are no certain winter records for the deserts, but there are six early spring records as follows: 26 Feb 1959 Imperial NWR IMP (perhaps wintering; the only record for District R); 25-26 Mar 1976 Kelso; 28 Mar 1975 Morongo Valley SBE; 10 Apr 1980 Tecopa INY; 16 Apr 1975 Big Pine INY; and 27-28 Apr 1976 Kelso. It is unrecorded in Districts S and M.

Along the coast it has been recorded 12 times, all since 1974, in Santa Barbara and Ventura Cos.; all of these records are for all and winter except 12 Apr 1977 Goleta SBA. South of there it has been recorded seven times in late fall (four in Los Angeles Co., one in Orange Co., and two in coastal San Diego Co.). There are also nine late fall and winter records (seven since 1974) on the Channel Is., some involving more than one individual (e.g. six on Santa Catalina I., 2-4 Jan 1976).

Rusty Blackbirds are partial to the vicinity of freshwater, and are often found at ponds and flooded areas at desert oases and on coastal plains. They are often, but not always, in association with Brewer's Blackbirds. A favored locality in late fall is Furnace Creek Ranch.

BREWER'S BLACKBIRD
Euphagus cyanocephalus

Common to abundant resident throughout, although largely only a winter visitant in Districts S and R.

This blackbird adapts very well to human modification of the landscape; it is an abundant urban bird, and is common around human dwellings, ranches, and agricultural fields through much of the region. In District M it breeds commonly around human settlements and around wet meadows and lakeshores, but in winter it is largely confined to the vicinity of towns. Small numbers breed in District S in the Coachella Valley RIV (not graphed). This species avoids arid scrublands, and is thus rather local as a breeder in District D. It is a fairly common visitant to the Channel Is.; it winters on the larger islands.

BRONZED COWBIRD
Molothrus aeneus

Uncommon summer resident along the Colorado R.; casual elsewhere in the region.

Birds arrive in District R around 10 Apr and have generally departed by late July or early August. This species is seen most consistently around Laguna and Imperial Dams IMP; more erratically, it is found in the vicinity of Earp and Parker Dam SBE, Blythe and Lost L. RIV, and Bard and Winterhaven IMP. Although it is a relatively recent colonist in much of the southwest, this species has spread only slightly in the region since the first California record (29 May 1951 Whipple Point, L. Havasu SBE).

It has been recorded casually on the deserts away from the Colorado R.: 22 Apr 1956 Westmorland SESS; 13 Jul 1968 Mecca NESS; 10 May 1976 Brock Ranch IMP; and 25 May 1977 Kelso SBE. It has also been recorded in summer from 1973 to 1976 at Jacumba SD, with extreme dates 3 May 1976 and 17 Jul 1974; a juvenile was observed there 13 Jul 1974 (this record not graphed).

There is one record for the coastal slope: 12 Jun 1963 and 9 Apr-30 May 1964 Whittier LA (probably summered both years).

Along the Colorado R. Bronzed Cowbirds are found primarily in park-like settings (ranchyards, residential areas); for breeding they mainly parasitize Hooded and Northern Orioles.

BROWN-HEADED COWBIRD
Molothrus ater

Fairly common to common summer resident in woodlands throughout. Common in winter, but less widespread; the greatest numbers winter in agricultural areas.

This species is a common summer resident throughout District C, and in riparian groves and other woodlands through Districts D and R. In District M it also breeds fairly commonly to commonly in woodlands, foraging in open areas.

The Brown-headed Cowbird winters commonly in agricultural portions of Districts S and R, and very locally in District D (e.g. Antelope Valley LA/KRN); it most often occurs with mixed blackbird flocks. Very small numbers winter elsewhere on the deserts north to Death Valley and the Owens Valley, but the species generally departs the colder areas at this season. It is fairly common to locally common in winter in District C, but it is much less widespread at this season than in summer; flocks are found with other blackbirds around lawns and agricultural areas.

It is a common transient throughout, including the Channel Is.; this cowbird is often encountered at sea during migration (especially in fall).

Brown-headed Cowbirds have increased greatly in range and numbers since the early part of this century. The species must have been a very sparse resident (or perhaps absent) on the coastal slope, as specimens were unknown from that part of the region until about 1915. It was, however, well established by the early 1930s (Willett 1933), and the detrimental effects of its parasitism of the broods of many species of smaller passerines was evident by then. The cowbird has been a major factor in the decline of many passerines nesting in riparian habitats (notably Willow Flycatcher and Bell's Vireo, but also species such as Warbling Vireo and Yellow Warbler). The effects of its parasitism have been most severe in lowland riparian habitats.

BOBOLINK
Dolichonyx oryzivorus

Primarily a rare to uncommon fall transient along the coast and very rare fall transient through the interior. Rare spring transient through the northern deserts; casual in spring along the coast.

In some falls over 100 birds may be recorded in District C (exceptionally over 200, fall 1979). It occurs mainly along the immediate coast and on the Channel Is.; favored spots are around the Tijuana River Valley SD and in Goleta SBA. The fall passage is mainly 10 Sep-15 Oct, with stragglers to early November; extreme dates are 24-31 Aug 1979 Goleta and 11-17 Nov 1978 Carson LA.

This species is a very rare fall transient in the interior; there are about 20 records extending from 2 Sep 1973 Kelso SBE to 4 Nov 1972 Furnace

Creek Ranch INY (exceptionally to 15 Nov 1979 Furnace Creek Ranch). All records are for the northern deserts (Kelso north) except for one at NESS 28 Oct 1977. An unseasonal record of an adult male at Niland Boat Ramp IMP 31 Jul 1965 is hard to categorize. It is unrecorded in District R.

In spring the Bobolink is a rare but regular transient at the northern desert oases; it has been recorded south to Morongo Valley SBE. It is most regular at Furnace Creek Ranch. Spring records in the interior extend from 13 May 1978 Lanfair Valley SBE to 9 Jun 1973 Furnace Creek Ranch and, exceptionally, 28 Jun 1977 Saline Valley INY. Along the coast (including the Channel Is.) there are about ten records of spring vagrants; most of these have dates from 29 May 1978 near San Simeon SLO to 25 Jun 1977 Arcadia LA and the majority are from the Channel Is. Later records are: 24 Jul 1973 Santa Barbara I. and 25-26 Jul 1976 Tijuana River Valley (ad. male).

In fall Bobolinks occupy weedy fields, agricultural croplands (corn, alfalfa, etc.), and marshy ditches; they occur primarily on coastal plains. Flocks may sometimes number up to 50 birds.

FRINGILLIDAE: FINCHES

PINE SISKIN
Carduelis pinus

Fairly common throughout the year in District M, but with some seasonal fluctuations in numbers there. Erratic winter visitant to the lowlands.

This species breeds from Mt. Pinos south through the Transverse Ranges to the San Jacinto Mtns. It was also recorded 19 Jul 1966 Mt. Palomar SD, but it is not known to breed there. It has been recorded into late May on most of the mountain ranges of the e. Mohave Desert, but there is no evidence of nesting on any of these ranges. It is to be looked for in summer in pine woodlands at the northern extreme of District C (e.g. vic. Cambria SLO); it breeds just north of the region in s. Monterey Co.

The Pine Siskin is an erratic winter visitant to the coastal lowlands; it is rare some years and even common others. Within District C it is scarcest on the southern coast and on the Channel Is., where it is primarily an erratic fall transient. During flight years this bird is also found in numbers on the southern deserts (including Districts S and R), but it is scarcer than on the coast and it is absent some years (the bar graph primarily reflects status in District C). It is primarily a transient through the northern deserts; flocks may occasionally winter, for example in the Antelope Valley LA. In the lowlands it has been recorded from early October (to 9 Sep 1976 Deep Springs INY) to late April; stragglers occur to early May in District C (to 1 Jun on the Channel Is.) and flocks occasionally linger into early June at the northern desert oases.

In District M it is sporadically common in winter; at this season most of the birds have probably originated outside of the region.

Pine Siskins nest in coniferous forests at the higher altitudes. Wintering birds occur around planted conifers and, especially, fruiting deciduous trees (alders, sycamores, sweet gums, etc.). Flocks may also occur in weedy fields.

AMERICAN GOLDFINCH
Carduelis tristis

Fairly common resident in District C. Transient and winter visitant in Districts D, S, and R, with the largest numbers in the northernmost parts of District D.

This species is common in lowland willow groves throughout District C. During the winter it occurs in flocks in weedy areas and around deciduous trees locally throughout the district. It is a very rare transient on the Channel Is.

The American Goldfinch is a transient and winter visitant in Districts D, S, and R. It is fairly common to, locally, even common during fall, winter, and spring around weedy fields, roadsides, and deciduous trees on the extreme northern deserts (Owens Valley, flanks of the White Mtns.). It is primarily an uncommon transient elsewhere on the deserts (and probably through District M). This goldfinch is regular in winter in small numbers in District S (e.g. vic. Niland SESS) and in District R. Transients have been recorded on the northern deserts to the end of May.

LESSER GOLDFINCH
Carduelis psaltria

Common resident in brushy areas, weedy fields, woodlands, and riparian groves throughout the coastal lowlands and locally through the lower portions of District M (including the desert ranges). Common, but rather local summer resident on the deserts, wintering in the southern portions.

In winter there is much withdrawal from District M and the northern interior. This species is an uncommon resident along the Colorado R., it breeds locally in taller riparian groves (more widespread in winter). It is primarily a winter visitant in District S, but small numbers do remain to breed. In District D the largest numbers breed in riparian areas and around ranchyards (e.g. Owens Valley, Morongo Valley, etc.).

The Lesser Goldfinch breeds on the larger Channel Is.; it is a fairly common visitant to the smaller islands, mostly in fall.

LAWRENCE'S GOLDFINCH
Carduelis lawrencei

Status complex. Primarily a summer resident in the region, but erratic even at that season. Occasionally common.

This species is a rather common but local summer resident along the western edge of District D from the Antelope Valley LA and the vicinity of Morongo Valley SBE south through the Anza-Borrego Desert; it also ranges into the adjacent arid slopes and valleys of District M. It is a fairly common summer resident in District C, where it occurs primarily in the more arid inland valleys and foothills. This species is generally quite scarce as a breeder on the immediate coast. It may arrive as early as late February; most depart by late September.

The Lawrence's Goldfinch remains erratically in winter in the southern coastal lowlands; it is rare or almost absent some years, but uncommon to locally common others, with large concentrations noted as follows: 700 in Tijuana River Valley SD winter 1963-1964; 500 there in winter 1968-1969; and, exceptional for so far north, 25 in Morro Bay SLO 14 Dec 1963. Most winter concentrations have been from Los Angeles Co. south. There is one winter record for the Channel Is., where it is primarily an uncommon spring and fall transient: 19 Dec 1927 Santa Catalina I. (4).

In the southern portions of District D and in District S it is primarily a rare spring transient (March-April) and casual winter visitant. Many were present at Brock Ranch IMP 24 Mar 1973 and one pair constructed a nest. This species is an irregular winter visitant in District R; it may almost be common some years (e.g. 1977-1978), and has remained to nest once: 11 Jun 1978 n. of Blythe RIV (pair with juveniles).

This species is a rare spring and fall visitant on the northern deserts. There are ten records for the e. Mohave Desert, mostly in spring, and even fewer records north of there. Fall dates on the northern deserts are mainly from late August through October; earlier records are: 2 Aug 1959 Panamint Mtns. INY (several), and 30 Jul 1976 New York Mtns. SBE.

Lawrence's Goldfinches breed around riparian thickets and oases within arid woodlands (arid oak savanna, pinyon-juniper, chaparral, open coniferous forest).

ROSY FINCH
Leucosticte arctoa

Uncommon resident in the White (and possibly Inyo) Mtns., frequenting talus slopes, rocky cliffs, and snowbanks well above timberline. Erratic late fall visitant at lower elevations in these mountains.

Our breeding race is *L. a. dawsoni* ("Gray-crowned Rosy Finch," in part). This race also breeds just outside of the region in the high Sierra Nevada west of the Owens Valley, and has wandered somewhat lower on these slopes in late fall and winter.

"Gray-crowned" birds are erratic late fall and winter visitants to the lower slopes of the White and Inyo Mtns., especially around rocky substrates and even roadsides when snow cover is great; favored localities are Westgard Pass INY and Gilbert Pass INY. A few are probably present at these lower elevations most falls, with small numbers remaining through the winter after large fall flights. The largest recorded concentrations are 10,000+ at Westgard Pass 19 Nov 1947 and 1000+ there 11 Nov 1972. One at Panamint Springs INY 3 Nov 1953 was exceptionally low. There is only one record south of Inyo Co.: 12 Nov 1972 summit of Mt. Pinos VEN (during one of the largest fall invasions on record).

Most or all birds comprising the late fall flocks in areas such as Westgard Pass appear to originate outside of the region. These races include *littoralis*, *wallowa*, and *tephrocotis*. The "Black Rosy Finch," *L. a. atrata*, has been recorded four times with flocks of "Gray-crowns" as follows: 19 Nov 1949 Deep Springs Valley INY; 11-18 Nov 1972 Westgard Pass (4+); 20 Nov 1972 Gilbert Pass; and 28 Nov 1975 Westgard Pass. It is possibly more regular than the few records indicate.

PURPLE FINCH
Carpodacus purpureus   Map p. 400

Fairly common resident in oak and oak-conifer woodlands in District M and the northern portions of District C. Somewhat erratic winter visitant to the lowlands; occasionally fairly common in the coastal lowlands, but always rare on the deserts.

This species breeds in the major ranges west of the deserts; the largest numbers occur in wooded canyons on the coastal slopes and in coniferous forests with a mixture of oaks (i.e. below about 2200m). It breeds south through the mountains of San Diego Co. In District C it breeds in oak woodlands in San Luis Obispo and Santa Barbara Cos., and southeast in small numbers to the Santa Monica Mtns. LA/VEN and the Santa Ana Mtns. ORA. It also breeds in oak woodlands in canyons of the foothills of the Transverse Ranges.

The Purple Finch is an uncommon to fairly common winter visitant in the coastal lowlands, primarily from Los Angeles Co. north. It is occasionally quite rare, especially on the southern coast, where it is uncommon even in flight years. This species winters regularly on the larger, northern Channel Is.; it is a rare transient on the other islands.

In the interior it is a rare fall transient through the northern deserts and a rare and erratic winter visitant on the southern deserts (including Districts S and R). The earliest interior record is 17 Sep 1975 Furnace Creek Ranch INY. Winter concentrations on the deserts are correlated with large influxes on the coast, e.g. up to 15 near Niland SESS 28 Nov 1970 and up to five at Bard IMP 7 Jan 1973. The only spring record for the deserts is: 11 Apr 1917 Death Valley (2).

While Purple Finches generally breed at lower elevations than the Cassin's Finch and require more broad-leafed vegetation than that species, there is considerable overlap in breeding distribution. Of the two, in winter only the Purple Finch normally occurs in the coastal lowlands, where it occurs in oak woodlands and tall chaparral, and around deciduous shade trees.

CASSIN'S FINCH
Carpodacus cassinii   Map p. 400

Common resident in District M. Rare transient in the interior lowlands, and casual winter visitant in District C.

This species breeds in the higher mountains from the Piutes and the Mt. Pinos area south through the San Gabriel and San Bernardino Mtns. to the San Jacinto and Santa Rosa Mtns. It occurs primarily in open coniferous forest above 2000m; unlike the Purple Finch, the largest numbers occur at higher elevations (to timberline) and in more arid forests (above the pinyon-juniper zone). Records for the Kingston Mtns. (21 Jun 1977) and New York Mtns. (28 Jun 1977) suggest possible breeding on the higher ranges of the Mohave Desert, but it is otherwise restricted in the desert ranges to the White and Inyo Mtns. and, at least on the Nevada side, the Grapevine Mtns.

The Cassin's Finch is generally a rare transient in the interior lowlands; it has been recorded primarily on the northern deserts (where it may be uncommon to fairly common in spring) from early October through November (a few into December) and again from mid-April through May and even into early June. In mid-winter, there is a record of four at Furnace Creek Ranch INY 25 Dec 1970. South of San Bernardino Co., it has been recorded only at Brock Ranch IMP 17 Feb 1975, 2 Apr 1971 (5), and 22 May 1971. It is unrecorded in Districts S and R. Birds also regularly move down the desert slopes of the coastal mountain ranges in fall and winter (e.g. Yucca Valley SBE on the western edge of District D). There is also a small winter movement into the desert mountains which lie outside of the breeding range, and to Figueroa Mtn. SBA and the Laguna Mtns. SD.

This species is a casual winter visitant to the coastal lowlands; it is frequently reported on the coast without details, and we suspect many reports pertain to Purple Finches. It is erratic in its appearance; up to 15 were on the Palos Verdes Peninsula LA during winter 1970-1971, with two during Nov 1970 on Pt. Loma SD. During Nov 1972, one or two were on the Palos Verdes Peninsula, six were in Montecito SBA, and "numbers" were in San Bernardino SBE. Scattered records for other winters come primarily from the base of the Transverse Ranges. Within District M, there is considerable fall and winter movement into the Yellow Pine forests on the lower border of the district.

One record for the Channel Is.: 1 May 1929 San Nicolas I.

HOUSE FINCH
Carpodacus mexicanus

Abundant resident in lowlands throughout, especially in the coastal lowlands and around towns and ranches in the interior. Also resident in smaller numbers in District M, in open forests and around settlements. Uncommon only in the highest mountains and away from water in District D (although it is resident in desert woodlands). Resident on all of the Channel Is., although it does not breed annually on Santa Barbara I.

The House Finch is perhaps the most abundant and widespread native passerine in the lower portions of the region. It is quite adaptable, and fares well even in urban centers.

RED CROSSBILL
Loxia curvirostra

Irregular visitant, also breeding erratically in montane forests (and exceptionally in planted conifers along the coast). The largest numbers are generally present in fall and winter, but non-breeding visitors may occur at any time during the year.

This species probably breeds most regularly in the White Mtns.; it has also been recorded nesting in the Mt. Pinos region, and is believed to nest in the San Gabriel, San Bernardino, and San Jacinto Mtns. Flocks have been noted in late spring in the other desert ranges, e.g. 25 May 1938 Providence Mtns. (up to 20), and 23 May 1977 New York Mtns. (7); these records likely pertain to birds breeding outside the region. Even in the mountain ranges where breeding has been documented, non-breeding representatives of various extralimital subspecies have been collected in mid-summer. Flocks occur erratically through the winter in District M, including the desert ranges; these flocks involve several subspecies. In the Laguna Mtns. SD it has been recorded to mid-May, but it is unrecorded through the summer.

The Red Crossbill is a rare and erratic winter visitant to the coastal lowlands; it is absent most winters, but in some years flocks are widespread. At this season it occurs mainly around plantings of introduced conifers. It has exceptionally remained to breed in the coastal lowlands after large winter invasions. During the winter 1966-1967 up to 150 birds were on Pt. Loma SD, and numbers were also on the Palos Verdes Peninsula LA; on 28 Mar 1967 an active nest was found on the Palos Verdes Peninsula, and birds were suspected of nesting that spring at Pt. Loma. Mid-summer and very early fall records for District C are: 31 Aug-3 Sep 1908 Valle Vista RIV (2 on 31 Aug) and 15 Jul 1974 Monterey Park LA (3). Flocks have been noted in spring and occasionally summer on Santa Cruz I. (e.g. "hundreds" 27 Mar-3 Apr 1920).

There are very few records for the desert lowlands. It has been recorded on the northern deserts as follows: 4 Nov 1973 Furnace Creek Ranch INY; 7-8 Sep and 20 and 30 Nov 1976 Furnace Creek Ranch (2); and fall

1976 Oasis MNO (small numbers; not graphed). It has also been recorded at Yucca Valley SBE 3 Apr-31 May 1980 (up to 10) and three times at nearby Morongo Valley SBE: 1 Sep 1963 (2); 24 Feb 1973 (3); and 24 Feb 1977. There are only two records from farther south on the deserts: 28 Nov 1950 SESS (2) and 27 Jan 1973 Brock Ranch IMP (2).

The movements of this opportunistic species seem to defy prediction; they are somewhat better understood when the component subspecies involved are considered individually, but these races are certainly not identifiable in the field. Our visitants come from widely scattered areas — the Pacific Northwest, the Rocky Mountains, and even the mountains of western Mexico; their appearance fits no simple seasonal pattern. When Red Crossbills do reach the region they are closely tied to conifer seed crops (e.g. of the White Fir and Jeffrey Pine in our highest mountains). As noted above, introduced plantings of conifers are utilized in addition to our native species.

EVENING GROSBEAK
Coccothraustes vespertinus

An irregular transient and winter visitant throughout, generally quite rare. Occasionally noted in fairly large numbers, but more often only small flocks or scattered individuals occur, with none reported some years.

The largest numbers have been recorded during flight years in the northern interior and then primarily during migration (May, October, and early November). The spring passage appears to be largely through the eastern part of the region; stragglers are noted into early June in the northern interior.

West of the deserts, flights bring birds into District M south through the mountains of San Diego Co. Smaller numbers are erratically noted in District C, primarily from Santa Barbara Co. south to Los Angeles Co., and along the foothills of the Transverse Ranges. It has been recorded as early as 29 Aug 1975 Mt. Pinos (10). Late spring records west of the deserts include: 4 May 1978 Temple City LA; 8 May 1902 Cahuenga Pass, Los Angeles LA; and 31 May 1930 Mt. Pinos (2). It has been recorded once in District M in mid-summer: 27 Jul 1976 upper Arrastre Ck., San Bernardino Mtns. It is unrecorded on the Channel Is.

This species is casual in the lowlands of the southern interior: 7 Nov 1970 Bard IMP; 10 Nov 1963 Thousand Palms Oasis RIV; Oct-Nov 1977 n. of Blythe RIV (10-15); and 16 May 1964 Yaqui Well SD. It was also recorded 30 Apr 1978 at Jacumba SD.

When found in the region, Evening Grosbeaks are generally around conifers or catkin-bearing deciduous trees. Their appearances are quite sporadic; recent flight years have been 1954-1955 (e.g. up to 100 at Big Bear L. SBE), 1963-1964, 1972-1973 (large numbers widespread throughout the region), and 1977-1978.

INTRODUCED AND EXOTIC SPECIES

A steadily-increasing diversity of non-native bird species exists in a wild or semi-wild state in southern California. The mild climate, extensive exotic plantings, and large human population of the region have made it a target for the purposeful introduction of exotic species as well as a popular site for avicultural activities (and the inevitable escapes and releases which go along with them).

Introduced and exotic species are treated together in the following section; bar graphs are not included (most species are largely or completely sedentary). Five species are numerous and widespread in non-urban, unmanaged habitats: Chukar, Rock Dove, Spotted Dove, European Starling, and House Sparrow. These species can reasonably be assumed to be of considerable ecological importance in the communities they inhabit, in terms of impact on food resources, nesting sites, predator populations, etc. Other species, because of low population levels, poor breeding success, and/or restriction to artificial or highly-managed habitats (e.g. urban centers or hunting clubs) are certainly not integral parts of natural communities, and are considered only briefly.

It is pointless to include a list of all bird species which have been observed, as escapees, in a free-flying state in southern California; this lengthy list would have little value. We have included, however, a list of species whose status in southern California as escapees or genuinely wild vagrants is uncertain as part of the Supplemental List (p. 380).

Much remains to be learned about populations of exotic birds in the region, their degree of successful establishment, and their impact on native species and ecosystems. In addition, much need be learned of the kinds and numbers of birds which are kept and bred in captivity in and around the region. Only with this information can we confidently judge the validity of unusual records which may pertain either to escapees or natural vagrants.

COMMON TURKEY
Meleagris gallopavo

Small numbers are resident in oak and oak Digger Pine woodlands in Santa Barbara and especially San Luis Obispo Cos., on Santa Catalina I., and very locally in foothills elsewhere west of the deserts. Breeds.

CHUKAR
Alectoris chukar

Fairly common but somewhat local resident in arid, rocky canyons and slopes in the northern part of District D, and very locally elsewhere on the deserts. The largest numbers occur in Kern, San Bernardino, and Inyo Cos. Often seen, sometimes in large numbers, at watering holes such as Scotty's Castle, Tollhouse Spring, and Deep Springs INY, and Ft. Piute SBE. Also a fairly common resident on San Clemente and San Nicolas Is. Quite successfully established.

RING-NECKED PHEASANT
Phasianus colchicus

Stocked at numerous hunting clubs and adjacent agricultural and grass-land areas on the coastal slope. Formerly widespread, but open habitats have diminished due to urbanization. Now generally restricted to a few hunting club areas, around marshes and grainfields. Stocked into the Imperial Valley, but now scarce there.

COMMON PEAFOWL
Pavo cristata

Feral populations breed around parks, large estates, and park-like residential areas. Small, semi-wild populations roam the Palos Verdes Peninsula LA and the San Gabriel Valley LA in the vicinity of the Los Angeles County Arboretum, the Huntington Library, etc. Very small local breeding populations occur elsewhere on the coastal slope.

ROCK DOVE
Columba livia

Abundant resident in areas of human habitation throughout the region, although it does not breed on most of the Channel Is. Nests on buildings, seacliffs, and (rarely) natural cliffs in the interior.

SPOTTED DOVE
Streptopelia chinensis

Common in, and virtually restricted to, urban, suburban, and rural portions of District C, from the vicinity of Santa Barbara SBA south to nw San Diego Co. and east to the edge of District D as in the Beaumont/Banning area of Riverside Co. Outlying populations penetrate District D locally, as at Morongo Valley SBE, Thousand Palms RIV, and the Antelope Valley LA (rare). Occurs locally in District S along the northwestern shore of the Salton Sea in Riverside Co. Has been noted as high as 1500m near Mountain Home, San Bernardino Mtns. SBE. Also breeds just outside the region in and around Bakersfield KRN. Strays have been noted east to Desert Center RIV and south to Calipatria IMP.

RINGED TURTLE DOVE
Streptopelia risoria

A few small populations exist in parks around central Los Angeles (Olvera Street, Pershing Square, MacArthur Park, etc.). Small populations and frequent escapees are found elsewhere in District C from Santa Barbara SBA to San Diego SD.

YELLOW-HEADED PARROT
Amazona ochrocephala

Local populations breed in and around West Los Angeles and the w. San Gabriel Valley LA. Escapees are often noted through the remainder of District C. Fruits and nuts from exotic plantings are used for food; cavities in tree trunks and limbs and in dead palm frond clusters are used for nesting. Most often seen while flying to feeding or roosting areas at dawn and dusk.

LILAC-CROWNED PARROT
Amazona finschi

Small numbers resident in the greater Los Angeles area, with nesting documented for the San Gabriel Valley LA.

RED-CROWNED PARROT
Amazona viridigenalis

Small numbers resident in the greater Los Angeles area, with nesting documented for the San Gabriel Valley LA. Also called the Green-cheeked Parrot.

CANARY-WINGED PARAKEET
Brotogeris versicolorus

Local resident on the Palos Verdes Peninsula LA, as at Pt. Fermin. Breeds. Escapees or very small local populations occur elsewhere on the coastal slope.

ROSE-RINGED PARAKEET
Psittacula krameri

Small numbers occur at various suburban localities on the coastal slope, e.g. vic. Pt. Dume LA. Suspected of breeding. Also called Ring-necked Parakeet.

EUROPEAN STARLING
Sturnus vulgaris

Abundant resident at lower elevations throughout, although local in District D (where generally restricted to ranchyards, agricultural areas, and riparian oases). Fairly widespread, but generally uncommon resident in District M (to about 2500m); generally restricted to the vicinity of human habitation in District M in winter. Transient through the Channel Is., breeding locally. Has recently penetrated Joshua Tree woodlands on the higher deserts. Largely withdraws from the northern portions of District D in winter, except in the vicinity of towns and agricultural areas.

The starling has undoubtedly been responsible for local declines in populations of cavity-nesting birds in the region. This species colonized the region from the east and north in the late 1940s, with breeding not documented until the late 1950s. The largest increase took place during the 1960s, with most of the spreading in the region completed by the early 1970s.

HOUSE SPARROW
Passer domesticus

Abundant resident in and near areas of human habitation at lower elevations throughout. Occurs locally in District M, around larger settlements such as Big Bear L., San Bernardino Mtns. SBE. Breeds on some of the Channel Is., and has been noted as a rare transient on Santa Barbara I. (indicating some dispersal or seasonal movement in the region.)

Many additional species are frequently reported as escapees in the region, but are certainly not wild vigrants. Some of these species (and others unmentioned here) have undoubtedly nested successfully in the region, but population recruitment through breeding is probably insignificant. Examples of such frequent escapees are: American Flamingo *(Phoenicopterus ruber)*, Mute Swan *(Cygnus olor)*, Common Shelduck *(Tadorna tadorna)*, Ruddy Shelduck *(T. ferruginea)*, Budgerigar *(Melopsittacus undulatus)*, Red-whiskered Bulbul *(Pycnonotus jocosus)*, Blue-gray Tanager *(Thraupis virens)*, European Goldfinch *(Carduelis carduelis)*, and Red Bishop *(Euplectes orix)*.

SUPPLEMENTAL LIST

AMERICAN ANHINGA
Anhinga anhinga

Two records of this species are possibly valid: 9 and 12 Feb 1913 at "Potholes," above Laguna Dam on the California side of the Colorado R. IMP (with two reported on the latter date); and 4 Feb 1977 through at least fall 1980 Sweetwater Res. SD (female).

For details on the Colorado R. record see Brooks, *Condor* 15: 182, 1913, Dawson *Condor* 18: 24, 1916, and Dawson *Birds of California* p. 1936, 1924. Although we feel that this record may be correct, little written documentation is available to support the sight record (which is still circulating through CBRC). There is no question that the Sweetwater Res. record pertains to an American Anhinga, but we are suspicious of the origin of the bird (see *AB* 31: 373, 1977); its lengthy stay casts doubt as to its validity as a wild vagrant.

Two adults were found over the Hollywood Res. LA 21 Feb 1971, but a nearby bird collection had lost two American Anhingas shortly before the sighting. There is an additional record of this species in northern California: an adult at L. Merced, San Francisco 2 June-16 Jul 1939 (with what was probably the same individual at nearby Searsville L. 28 and 30 May 1939); for details see Bolander *Gull* 21: 70, 77, 81, 1939, and Stephens *Gull* 21: 70, 1939. This record was dismissed at the time as pertaining to an escapee, and the CBRC recently reached the same conclusion.

This species does occur on the coast of western Mexico north regularly to central Sinaloa. Farther north it has been recorded once at Alamos, Sonora (November), and once at Tucson AZ (12 Sep 1893). We would prefer to see a fully substantiated interior record (e.g. Lower Colorado R. or Salton Sea) prior to acceptance on the main list.

FALCATED TEAL
Anas falcata

An adult male was present on Newport Bay ORA during Jan and Feb 1969. Although certainly correctly identified, the bird was quite likely an escapee. This species does occur somewhat regularly as a wild stray to the w. Aleutians in Alaska, but no clear pattern of vagrancy to the remainder of the west coast of North America exists.

AMERICAN BLACK DUCK
Anas rubripes

One was seen near Niland SESS 11 Nov 1978 (*AB* 33: 213, 1979). Although there is no doubt concerning the identification of this bird, we feel that the record may pertain to an escapee or released bird. We would await a clearer pattern of records from the southwest prior to acceptance on the main list. There is a specimen from the Sacramento Valley of northern California (Willows, Glenn Co., 1 Feb 1911) which was thought at the time to be a probable escapee (see Grinnell and Miller 1944, p. 560).

Recent sight records of American Black Ducks in the Tijuana River Valley SD (Aug 1980) and at Newport Bay ORA (winter 1979-1980) almost certainly pertain to escapees; both birds associated with domestic ducks.

AMERICAN BLACK VULTURE
Coragyps atratus

One was observed 3 km north of Parker Dam SBE 5 Sep 1977 (*AB* 32: 257, 1978). If correctly identified, this would almost certainly be a genuine stray (this species is common only 150-200 km east of the Colorado R.); however, the substantiating details are perhaps too weak to support inclusion of this species on the main list. Some doubt exists as to origin in the other California sighting, a bird over Chico, Butte Co., northern California 13 Apr 1972 (*AB* 26: 803, 1972).

SWALLOW-TAILED KITE
Elanoides forficatus

One was reported near San Diego SD 7 Sep 1972, but supporting details are sketchy (rejected by CBRC). This striking species has been recorded northwest to Big Bend National Park, TX, and Winkleman, AZ.

CRESTED CARACARA
Polyborus plancus

One reported in Grinnell and Miller (1944) as occurring near Ft. Yuma on the Colorado R. during the winter of 1853 lacks substantiating details. This species has been recorded in extreme northern Baja California and "not far" east of Yuma AZ; it is likely to eventually turn up in the southeastern part of the region. Several coastal reports have been dismissed as likely pertaining to escapees.

BLACK-TAILED GULL
Larus crassirostris

An adult was collected on San Diego Bay SD 26-28 Nov 1954 (Monroe, *Auk* 72: 208, 1955). As the possibility of ship-assisted passage to California seems strong, we await a clearer pattern of vagrancy to the west coast of North America before accepting this species on the main list. The CBRC did not accept this record for the state list.

KITTLITZ'S MURRELET
Brachyramphus brevirostris

A juvenile was picked up alive on the beach at La Jolla SD 16 Aug 1969; the bird subsequently died and is now a specimen at the San Diego Natural History Museum (Devillers, *California Birds* 3: 33-38, 1972).

Although there is no doubt concerning the identification of this individual, its age raises doubt as to how it reached the region. All other records of northern alcids in California waters in middle and late summer (e.g. Horned Puffin and Thick-billed Murre) have been of adults. The August date is exceedingly early for a juvenile northern alcid to reach southern California, and the possibility of assisted passage caused the CBRC to reject this record.

RUDDY GROUND-DOVE
Columbina talpacoti

A male was observed near Fillmore VEN 24-26 Nov 1978 (Webster *et al.* 1980). This species occurs in northwestern Mexico north to north-central Sinaloa; the lack of records between there and California makes us suspicious of the origin of this individual. The record has not been submitted to the CBRC.

GREEN VIOLETEAR
Colibri thalassimus

A male was carefully studied and photographed near Iris Meadow on Mt. Pinos KRN 31 Jul-1 Aug 1977 (Webster *et al.* 1980); the description and photos clearly show it to be of the northern, nominate race which occurs north in western Mexico to Jalisco. The many individuals of this species which have been imported in captivity to the United States are of more southerly subspecies, originating in South America. Vagrants of the northern race have been recorded in southern Texas; studies of nominate *thalassinus* in Mexico show it to be at least partially migratory. However, until there is a connecting pattern of records from southeastern Arizona (no records there currently), we feel that a cautious approach is warranted. This species was not accepted for the state list by the CBRC.

MAGNIFICENT (RIVOLI'S) HUMMINGBIRD
Eugenes fulgens

Grinnell and Miller (1944) cite a record of a bird said to have been collected in San Gorgonio Pass RIV/SBE 15 Jul 1889, but mention doubt as to the correctness of the locality. This species occurs commonly north to the mountains of southeastern Arizona, rarely to north-central Arizona (summer), and as a stray in late summer and early fall to the mountains of southern Colorado, southern Utah, and (once) southern Nevada. Its appearance in the mountains of southern California is thus anticipated.

GREEN KINGFISHER
Chloroceryle americana

Grinnell and Miller (1944) cite two records: fall 1865 ("at several points on the Colorado River between Ft. Mohave and Ft. Yuma"), and at Poway Valley SD. While the latter record was thought to pertain to a misidentification, the Colorado R. sightings (by Coues) were probably correct but lack supporting details; the lower Colorado R. was drastically different physically in the nineteenth century and may well have supported this species. Green Kingfishers have occurred irregularly in recent years in southeastern Arizona, but there are no records for the western part of that state.

EASTERN WOOD-PEWEE
Contopus virens

A calling bird was studied carefully at Big Sycamore Canyon, Pt. Mugu VEN 18-19 Oct 1974. Although accepted by the CBRC, the record leaves us with some doubt because of the extreme similarity between the Eastern and Western Wood-Pewees; we feel that only a specimen will suffice for certain identification of a non-singing bird. It appears to the authors that many of the calls of the two species overlap, and field identification should be based only on full songs.

Another record of this species from northern California (15 Jun 1975 Southeastern Farallon I.) pertains to a silent bird captured and photographed; it was also accepted by the CBRC, but we regard the record as tentative for the reasons outlined above.

FORK-TAILED FLYCATCHER
Tyrannus savana

A specimen (subsequently lost) was purportedly obtained in Santa Monica LA in "late summer, 1883" (Monroe and Barron *AB* 34: 842-845, 1980). This neotropical species is a regular vagrant north to the eastern United States, but no other records exist west of Texas. With no specimen or details, it is difficult to assess the validity of the record.

GRAY SILKY-FLYCATCHER
Ptilogonys cinereus

One was observed and photographed with migrant flycatchers in Ventura VEN 9 Apr 1976 (Webster *et al.* 1980). This species occurs regularly in western Mexico north to sw Chihuahua and n. Sinoloa, and shows some migratory (or altitudinal) movement within its range. There is a recent sight record for Arizona (*AB* 34: 920, 1980), but until a clearer pattern of intermediate records emerges, this species is best kept off the main list. Its status in captivity is uncertain.

YELLOW GROSBEAK
Pheucticus chrysopeplus

An adult male was observed at Solano Beach SD 22 Jun 1978. Although this species is said to be commonly kept in captivity in Mexico and even southern California, the date of this record closely matches the pattern of vagrancy to southern Arizona (records northwest to Prescott); for this reason, we feel that the above record may be valid. Small numbers of this species summer as far north as central Sonora; it is migratory in the northern portion of its range.

RUSTIC BUNTING
Emberiza rustica

One was observed with White-crowned Sparrows 18 Nov 1965 northeast of Upland SBE (*AFN* 20:461, 1966). we feel that the bird was probably correctly identified (the observer was familiar with this species from Korea), but have received no written details; the record has not been considered by the CBRC. This species does occur as a regular stray to the w. Aleutians in Alaska, and its appearance elsewhere on the west coast of North America is probably not unlikely.

WHITE-COLLARED SEEDEATER
Sporophila torqueola

An adult male of the west Mexican *torqueola* group was observed in the Tijuana River Valley SD 19 Sep 1977. This species occurs north in western Mexico to n. Sinaloa (there are no records from Sonora or Arizona); its status in captivity is uncertain.

ADDITIONAL SPECIES RECORDED FROM NORTHERN CALIFORNIA

The following list briefly describes the status of the 34 species which have been recorded in California only outside of the southern California region (through November 1980). Information is mainly derived from McCaskie *et al* (1979). All unusual species have been accepted by the CBRC unless otherwise indicated.

WANDERING ALBATROSS *Diomedea exulans* One record: 11-12 Jul 1967 Sea Ranch, Sonoma Co.

STREAKED SHEARWATER *Calonectris leucomelas* Three October records for Monterey Bay.

GREATER SHEARWATER *Puffinus gravis* One record: 24 Feb 1979 Monterey Bay.

RED-FOOTED BOOBY *Sula sula* Two records for Southeast Farallon I. in fall 1975.

GYRFALCON *Falco rusticolus* One record: 23 Oct 1948 near Tule Lake, Siskiyou Co.

RUFFED GROUSE *Bonasa umbellus* Rare to uncommon resident in extreme northwestern California.

SHARP-TAILED GROUSE *Tympanuchus phasianellus* Formerly resident in grasslands of northeastern California; now extirpated.

MONGOLIAN PLOVER *Charadrius mongolus* One record: 13-18 Sep 1980 Moss Landing, Monterey Co.; what was possibly the same individual was seen nearby on 3 Oct 1980.

NORTHERN DOTTEREL *Charadrius morinellus* One record: 12-20 Sep 1974 Southeast Farallon I.

JACK SNIPE *Lymnocryptes minimus* One record: 20 Nov 1938 near Gridley, Butte Co.

LESSER BLACK-BACKED GULL *Larus fuscus* One record: 14 Jan 1978 Seaside, Monterey Co.

THICK-BILLED MURRE *Uria lomvia* Casual fall and winter visitant to inshore waters; nearly all records are for Monterey Bay.

CRESTED AUKLET *Aethia cristatella* One record: 16-17 Jul 1979 near Bolinas, Marin Co.

BLACK-BILLED CUCKOO *Coccyzus erythropthalmus* Four fall records for the coast (Monterey, Marin, and Humboldt Cos.).

SNOWY OWL *Nyctea scandiaca* Very rare visitant during invasion winters, primarily on the northern coast.

GREAT GRAY OWL *Strix nebulosa* Rare and local resident in the northern and central Sierra Nevada.

BLUE-THROATED HUMMINGBIRD *Lampornis clemenciae* One record: a female near Three Rivers, Tulare Co., from late Dec 1977 through

27 May 1978; the bird nested, raising hybrid offspring with *Calypte sp.*
BLACK-BACKED THREE-TOED WOODPECKER *Picoides arcticus*
Uncommon and local resident in high mountain forests south to Tulare Co.

PILEATED WOODPECKER *Dryocopus pileatus* Local and uncommon resident in coastal and interior coast range forests from Santa Cruz Co. north, and in the Sierra Nevada from Greenhorn Mtn. KRN (just outside our region) north.

YELLOW-BELLIED FLYCATCHER *Empidonax flaviventris* One record: a bird measured and photographed on Southeast Farallon I. 16 Sep 1976.

COMMON SKYLARK *Alauda arvensis* One record: a bird was present at Pt. Reyes, Marin Co. during winter 1978-1979, fall 1979 (it may have wintered locally), and again in winter 1980-1981.

GRAY JAY *Perisoreus canadensis* Uncommon and local resident in coast range forests south to Mendocino Co., and in the Warner Mtns., Modoc Co.

BLACK-CAPPED CHICKADEE *Parus articapillus* Uncommon and local resident in Del Norte, Siskiyou, and Humboldt Cos.

SEDGE WREN *Cistothorus platensis* One record: 4-8 Nov 1980 Bolinas Lagoon, Marin Co. We anticipate more records of this highly migratory (but secretive) species. The record has not yet been accepted by the CBRC.

NORTHERN WHEATEAR *Oenanthe oenanthe* Two records: 11 Jun 1971 Southeast Farallon I., and 15 Sep 1977 Shelter Cove, Humboldt Co.

GRAY-CHEEKED THRUSH *Catharus minimus* Six fall records and two late spring records for Southeast Farallon I. and adjacent Marin Co.

DUSKY WARBLER *Phylloscopus fuscatus* One record: 27 Sep 1980 Southeast Farallon I. (not yet accepted by CBRC).

YELLOW WAGTAIL *Motacilla flava* One record: Pt. Reyes, Marin Co. 17 Sep 1978 (not yet accepted by CBRC).

GOLDEN-CHEEKED WARBLER *Dendroica chrysoparia* One record: 9 Sep 1971 Southeast Farallon I.

FIELD SPARROW *Spizella pusilla* One record: 17 Jun-9 Jul 1969 Southeast Farallon I.

BAIRD'S SPARROW *Ammodramus bairdii* One record: 28 Sep 1969 Southeast Farallon I.

COMMON REDPOLL *Carduelis flammea* Two winter records for the northeastern part of the state (one involving many birds) and an anomalous late May record for Humboldt Co.

PINE GROSBEAK *Pinicola enucleator* Uncommon resident in the higher portions of the Sierra Nevada.

WHITE-WINGED CROSSBILL *Loxia leucoptera* One record: a flock of twelve at Mosquito Lake, Trinity Co., 1 Sep 1978.

ADDENDUM: RECENT RECORDS

The following recent records (to March 1981) supplement the information in the main text; these records are not graphed.

RED-NECKED GREBE One at the Santa Maria R. mouth SBA/SLO on 12 Oct 1980 establishes the earliest record for the region.

LAYSAN ALBATROSS One was off Santa Rosa I. 15 Nov. 1980.

WILSON'S STORM-PETREL One was 10 km w. of San Diego SD 3 Sep 1980.

FORK-TAILED STORM-PETREL One was 80 km w. of Morro Bay SLO 13 Sep 1980.

BLUE-FOOTED BOOBY A minor incursion occurred in fall 1980, with up to three at NESS 12 Sep-23 Oct.

AMERICAN WHITE PELICAN Two hundred were at San Jacinto L. RIV during winter 1980-1981.

LITTLE BLUE HERON One at Tinnemaha Res. INY 19 Sep 1980 establishes the first fall record for District D.

REDDISH EGRET Away from San Diego Co., one was at Long Beach LA 26 Sep 1980, with possibly the same bird at Seal Beach ORA after 8 Nov 1980.

WOOD STORK Four additional records away from Districts S and R are: 24 Aug-8 Sep 1980 and 28 Dec 1980 (2) Oceanside SD; 16-26 Sep 1980 El Monte LA; and 15 Oct 1980 San Jacinto L. RIV.

GREATER WHITE-FRONTED GOOSE A flock of up to 750 at San Jacinto L. in Feb 1981 confirms that this locality is a regular migration stopover.

TUFTED DUCK One was at Pt. Mugu VEN Feb-Mar 1981; one was at Lopez L., e. of Arroyo Grande SLO Feb 1981.

GREATER SCAUP One at Pt. Mugu VEN 27 Sep 1980 establishes the earliest record for the region.

OLDSQUAW One at Little L. INY 26 Oct 1980 establishes an additional record for District D.

MERLIN The first record of the *richardsonii* race in the north coastal area was a bird in the Cuyama Valley SBA 21 Feb 1981.

SANDHILL CRANE A flock of 210 near Santa Maria SBA 4-5 Jan 1981 undoubtedly represented birds moving from the Carrizo Plain due to dry conditions.

BLACK-BELLIED PLOVER Seventy-two juveniles near Lancaster LA 20 Sep 1980 represented a maximum count for that part of the region.

LESSER GOLDEN PLOVER About 12 juveniles were near Lancaster LA 20 Sep-25 Oct 1980, suggesting a regular passage through the area.

PIPING PLOVER One was at Morro Bay SLO 1 Oct-15 Dec 1980.

HUDSONIAN GODWIT A dead bird was found at NESS 11 Oct 1980.

SEMIPALMATED SANDPIPER A juvenile at the Santa Maria R. mouth SBA 19 Oct 1980 was exceptionally late.

RUFF An additional record for District D was of a juvenile near Lancaster LA 21-26 Oct 1980; one at SESS 27 Dec 1980-6 Jan 1981 was the first for District S and represents the only interior winter record.

PARASITIC JAEGER An adult near Lancaster LA 20-21 Sep 1980 establishes the first interior record away from Districts S and R.

LONG-TAILED JAEGER An adult and immature were at NESS 20 Sep 1980 (with two immatures present on 23 Sep 1980).

SOUTH POLAR SKUA Eight off Morro Bay SLO 13 Sep 1980 help confirm the fall pattern off the north coast.

LAUGHING GULL One at SESS 7 Dec 1980-8 Feb 1981 establishes another winter record for District S; additional coastal records are for San Diego SD 3-13 Feb 1981 and for Laguna L. near Los Osos SLO 13 Mar 1981.

LITTLE GULL An adult was near the mouth of the Santa Ana R. ORA 22 Nov-21 Dec 1980 and an immature was there 24 Jan 1981.

BLACK-HEADED GULL An immature was at Pt. Mugu VEN Dec 1980; what was possibly the same bird was at Redondo Beach LA 1 Jan-Mar 1981. One was near the mouth of the Santa Ana R. ORA 21 Nov 1980-25 Feb 1981.

HEERMANN'S GULL One of the few interior winter records was of one at SESS 27 Dec 1980-15 Feb 1981.

YELLOW-FOOTED GULL Up to two were at Otay SD in District C 13-28 Feb 1981.

BLACK-LEGGED KITTIWAKE Two were at NESS 28 Nov 1980 (with one present to 6 Jan 1981); one was at Lake Henshaw SD 15 Jan 1981; additional sightings along the Colorado R. indicate a unique interior invasion in the southwest during winter 1980-1981.

COMMON TERN An exceptional concentration was 1000+ at NESS 20-23 Sep 1980.

LEAST TERN A late immature was near San Pedro LA 1-5 Oct 1980.

BLACK SKIMMER Additional winter records for District S are 26 Dec 1980 NESS (2) and 27 Dec 1980-Feb 1981 SESS.

MARBLED MURRELET One was at Hermosa Beach LA 5 Oct 1980, and one was w. of Gaviota SBA 17 Apr 1977.

XANTUS' MURRELET Additional records of nominate *hypoleuca* are 12 Sep 1974 San Nicolas I. and 1 Nov 1980 off Morro Bay SLO (2).

WHIP-POOR-WILL A calling bird of the *arizonae* race was in Pacific Palisades LA 6 Mar-1 Apr 1980 and again 3 Dec 1980 through at least Feb 1981; this represents the first winter record of this race north of Mexico.

BLACK-CHINNED HUMMINGBIRD The San Diego SD bird returned for its second winter 20 Dec 1980-18 Jan 1981; another was in Long Beach LA 15-25 Dec 1980.

OLIVE-SIDED FLYCATCHER The wintering bird in Griffith Park, Los Angeles LA returned in winter 1980-1981; a specimen was obtained at Camp Baldy LA 12 Dec 1952.

ACADIAN FLYCATCHER One seen at Pt. Loma SD 27 Sep 1980 would constitute the first record for California; this record is circulating through the CBRC.

AMERICAN DIPPER One along Cold Creek in the Santa Monica Mtns. LA 25 Oct 1980 was well away from breeding areas.

GOLDEN-CROWNED KINGLET One on San Clemente I. 11 Sep 1980 was exceptionally early.

RED-THROATED PIPIT Birds were at Goleta SBA 24 Sep 1980, at the Santa Clara R. estuary VEN 28 Sep 1980, and near Santa Maria SBA 18-31 Oct 1980.

BELL'S VIREO One at Goleta SBA 22 Jan-8 Mar 1981 establishes the first winter record away from the extreme southern part of the region.

SOLITARY VIREO Birds apparently of the eastern nominate *solitarius* race were at Carpinteria SBA 22 Sep 1980 and on Pt. Loma SD 23 Sep 1980.

HUTTON'S VIREO An additional record for District D was of one near Lancaster LA 20 Dec 1980.

BLUE-WINGED WARBLER One was on Pt. Loma SD 22 Oct 1980.

GOLDEN-WINGED WARBLER One was at Thousand Palms Oasis RIV 3 Oct 1980.

CAPE MAY WARBLER One was near Malibu LA 21 Dec 1980.

BLACK-THROATED BLUE WARBLER One near Lake Fulmor in the San Jacinto Mtns. 26-27 Jan 1981 was exceptional for the date and locality.

GRACE'S WARBLER The bird in Montecito near Santa Barbara SBA returned for its second winter 4 Nov 1980-8 Mar 1981.

BLACKPOLL WARBLER One at L. Henshaw SD 7 Nov 1980 was a late interior record on the border of District M.

WORM-EATING WARBLER One in Santa Barbara SBA 3 Jan 1981 establishes the first winter record for the region.

KENTUCKY WARBLER One was at Cambria SLO 14 Sep 1980 and one was at Goleta SBA 14 Oct 1980.

CONNECTICUT WARBLER One was at Furnace Creek Ranch INY 20 Sep 1980, and up to two were on Pt. Loma SD 4-12 Oct 1980.

MOURNING WARBLER An immature female was at Carpinteria SBA 20-23 Sep 1980.

SHARP-TAILED SPARROW One was at Pt. Mugu VEN 25 Oct 1980, and at least three were at the Tijuana R. estuary SD after 22 Nov 1980.

BREEDING RANGE MAPS

HLJ80

The sixty maps that follow show the approximate breeding ranges of sixty-six selected species in the southern California region. Maps are provided primarily for species whose breeding ranges cannot be described easily in the text account. Thus, for example, most montane species, whose distributions can be described by a simple listing of mountain ranges, are not mapped. Also not mapped are very local species, and those restricted to coastal or wetland habitats.

Further details for the species mapped here should be sought in the species accounts. Localities of sporadic breeding are generally not mapped, but are noted in the accounts. In several cases, closely related species have been mapped together to emphasize areas of sympatry or near-sympatry. Sub-species have been noted on the maps of only three species: Black-tailed Gnatcatcher, Solitary Vireo, and Sage Sparrow. This does not, of course, imply that all other species mapped are mono-typic.

WHITE-TAILED KITE

NORTHERN HARRIER

RED-SHOULDERED HAWK

GAMBEL'S QUAIL
CALIFORNIA QUAIL

MOUNTAIN QUAIL

BAND-TAILED PIGEON

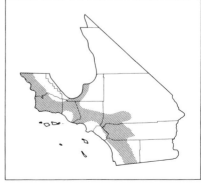

391

WHITE-WINGED DOVE

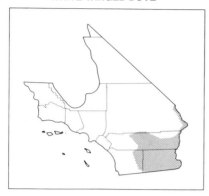

COMMON GROUND-DOVE

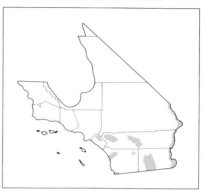

COMMON SCREECH-OWL

NORTHERN PYGMY-OWL

SPOTTED OWL

BLACK-CHINNED HUMMINGBIRD

ACORN WOODPECKER

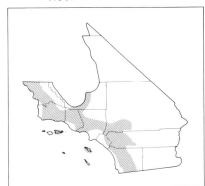

LADDER-BACKED WOODPECKER
NUTTALL'S WOODPECKER

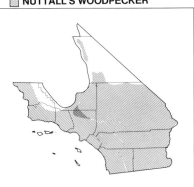

DOWNY WOODPECKER

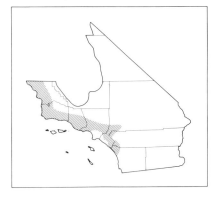

HAIRY WOODPECKER

OLIVE-SIDED FLYCATCHER

WESTERN WOOD-PEWEE

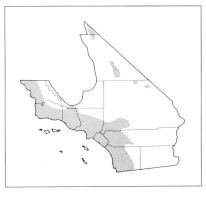

WESTERN FLYCATCHER

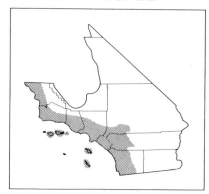

CASSIN'S KINGBIRD

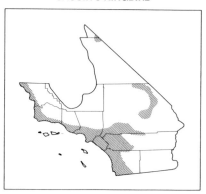

VIOLET-GREEN SWALLOW

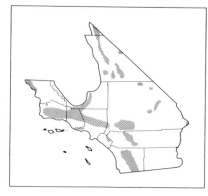

BARN SWALLOW

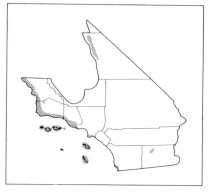

STELLER'S JAY

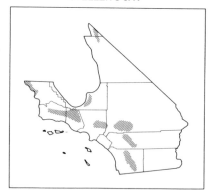

SCRUB JAY

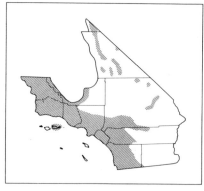

BLACK-BILLED MAGPIE
YELLOW-BILLED MAGPIE

COMMON CROW

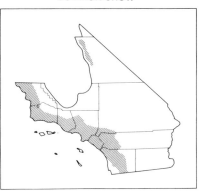

MOUNTAIN CHICKADEE
CHESTNUT-BACKED CHICKADEE

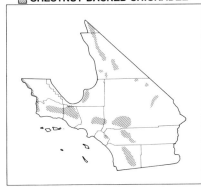

PLAIN TITMOUSE

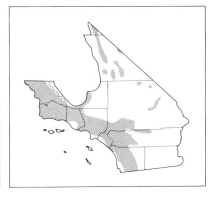

VERDIN

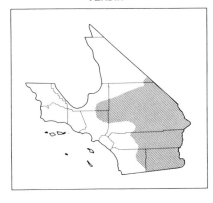

BUSHTIT

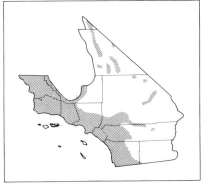

WHITE-BREASTED NUTHATCH

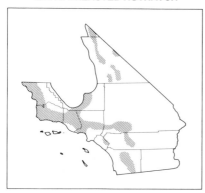

CACTUS WREN

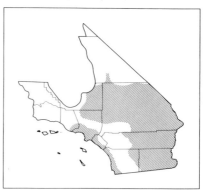

BEWICK'S WREN

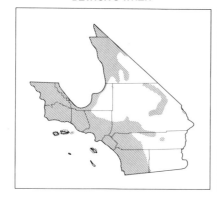

HOUSE WREN

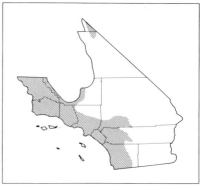

BENDIRE'S THRASHER

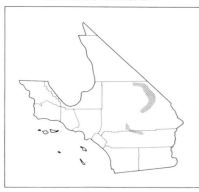

CALIFORNIA THRASHER
CRISSAL THRASHER

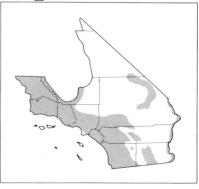

LE CONTE'S THRASHER

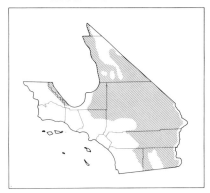

WESTERN BLUEBIRD

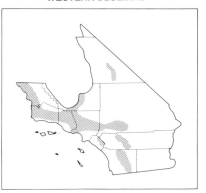

SWAINSON'S THRUSH

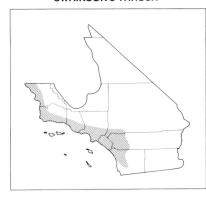

BLACK-TAILED GNATCATCHER

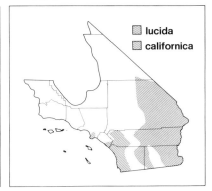

lucida
californica

WRENTIT

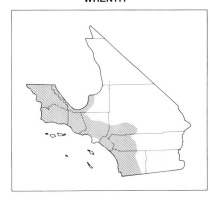

SOLITARY VIREO

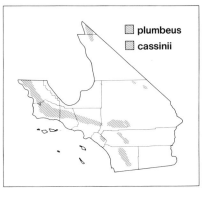

plumbeus
cassinii

HUTTON'S VIREO

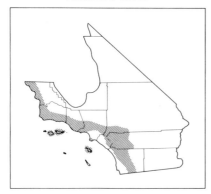

WARBLING VIREO

ORANGE-CROWNED WARBLER

YELLOW WARBLER

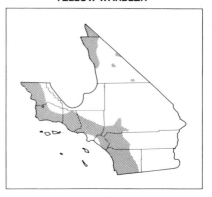

BLACK-HEADED GROSBEAK

BLUE GROSBEAK

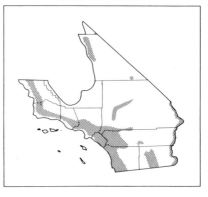

398

SONG SPARROW

DARK-EYED ("Oregon") JUNCO

BREWER'S SPARROW

BLACK-CHINNED SPARROW

SAGE SPARROW

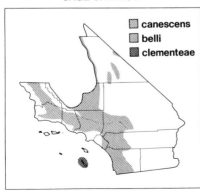

canescens
belli
clementeae

RUFOUS-CROWNED SPARROW

RUFOUS-SIDED TOWHEE

BROWN TOWHEE
ABERT'S TOWHEE

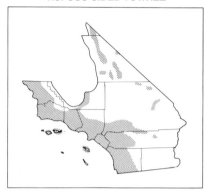

SCOTT'S ORIOLE

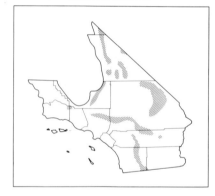

TRICOLORED BLACKBIRD

PURPLE FINCH

CASSIN'S FINCH

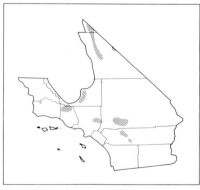

LITERATURE CITED

American Birding Association. 1975. A.B.A. Checklist: Birds of continental United States and Canada. American Birding Association, Austin, TX.

American Ornithologists' Union. 1957. Check-list of North American birds. Fifth Ed. American Ornithologists' Union, Baltimore, MD.

—— 1973. Thirty-second supplement to the American Ornithologists' Union Check-list of North American birds. *Auk* 90: 411-419.

—— 1976. Thirty-third supplement to the American Ornithologists' Union Check-list of North American birds. *Auk* 93: 875 -879.

Cogswell, H.L. 1977. Water birds of California. University of California Press, Berkeley, Los Angeles, London.

Grinnell, J. 1915. A distributional list of the birds of California. Pacific Coast Avifauna No. 11.

Grinnell, J. and A.H. Miller. 1944. The distribution of the birds of California. Pacific Coast Avifauna No. 27, 608 p.

Jones, H.L. 1975. Studies of avian turnover, dispersal and colonization of the California Channel Islands. Ph.D. dissertation, University of California at Los Angeles.

Lane, J. 1979. Birders' guide to southern California. L & P Press, Denver, CO.

Mayr, E. and G.W. Cottrell, eds. 1979. Check-list of birds of the world, Volume 1. Second Edition. Museum of Comparative Zoology, Cambridge, MA.

McCaskie, G., P. DeBenedictis, R. Erickson, and J. Morlan. 1979. Birds of northern California: An annotated field list. Second Edition. Golden Gate Audubon Society, Berkeley, CA.

Metcalf, T.N. 1967. Birds of the Santa Barbara region. Santa Barbara Museum of Natural History, Occas. Papers No. 8, Santa Barbara, CA. (revised 1972)

Miller, A.H. 1951. An analysis of the distribution of the birds of California. Univ. Calif. Publ. Zool. 50(6): 531-644.

Morony, J.J., Jr., W.J. Bock, and J. Farrand, Jr. 1975. Reference list of the birds of the world. American Museum of Natural History, New York, NY.

Palmer, R.S., ed. 1976. Handbook of North American birds, Volume 2: Waterfowl (Part 1). Yale University Press, New Haven and London.

Pyle, R.L. 1953. Annotated field list: Birds of southern California. Los Angeles Audubon Society, Los Angeles, CA (revised 1961 by A. Small)

Remsen, J.V., Jr. 1979. Species of special concern in California. California Dept. of Fish and Game Wildlife Mgmt. Branch Admin. Rep. No. 78.

Small, A. 1974. The birds of California. Winchester Press, New York, NY.

Traylor, M.A., Jr., ed. 1979. Check-list of birds of the world, Volume 8. Museum of Comparative Zoology, Cambridge, MA.

Webster, R., P. Lehman, and L. Bevier. 1980. The birds of Santa Barbara and Ventura Counties, California. Santa Barbara Museum of Natural History Occas. Paper No. 10, Santa Barbara, CA.

Willett, G. 1912. Birds of the Pacific slope of southern California. Pacific Coast Avifauna No. 7.

———— 1933. Revised list of the birds of southwestern California. Pacific Coast Avifauna No. 21.

INDEX

403

404

405

408